·50
/23

HEALTH CARE AS SOCIAL HISTORY

HEALTH CARE
AS SOCIAL HISTORY
The Glasgow Case

Edited by
OLIVE CHECKLAND
and
MARGARET LAMB

ABERDEEN UNIVERSITY PRESS

First published 1982
Aberdeen University Press
A member of the Pergamon Group

British Library Cataloguing in Publication Data
Health care as social history
1. Public health—Glasgow (Strathclyde
Region)
History—Social aspects
I. Checkland, Olive II. Lamb, Margaret
614′.0941′443   RA490.G/

ISBN 0 08 028444 2

PRINTED IN GREAT BRITAIN
THE UNIVERSITY PRESS
ABERDEEN

To
the doctors and nurses
of
Glasgow
past and present

Contents

One. Local government and the health environment

Olive Checkland

Two. The Medical Profession

Margaret Lamb

Three. Poor Law hospitals 1845–1914

Rona Gaffney

Four. Care and treatment of the mentally ill

Frank Rice

Five. Surgeons and surgery

David Hamilton and Margaret Lamb

Six. Tuberculosis

Carolyn Pennington

Seven. Medical radiology: its practical application 1895–1914

Christopher Smith

Eight. Maternal and Child Welfare

Olive Checkland

Nine. Women as doctors and nurses

Rona Gaffney

Notes   191

Appendices

Bibliography   248

Index   270

Tables

Appendix I

Figures

Plates

Maps

Permission to use the following photographs is gratefully acknowledged.

(*a*) Glasgow District Council for plates 13, 15 and 16;
(*b*) The Greater Glasgow Health Board for plates 4, 5 and 14, and Maps 1 and 2;
(*c*) Dr Peter Mackenzie for plate 2 and help with plates 15 and 16;
(*d*) Strathclyde Regional Archives for plate 12.

Permission from Cambridge University Press to use tables 27, 28 & 29 is gratefully acknowledged.

Preface

The notoriety which Glasgow has gained over the past years is nowhere more evident than in the field of health and health care. Experts have come to Glasgow to be shocked. They have rarely been disappointed. Notwithstanding the continuous unfavourable publicity which Glasgow conditions have provoked it is by no means easy for interested parties to discover for themselves the longer-run sequence of events or the response in Glasgow to deteriorating conditions in the city. It is our object to present in this book appraisals of some basic aspects of health care. Indeed we would hope to open up the discussion of the health responses of a particular city, namely Glasgow, seen both in terms of itself and as comprising an important element in the health picture of Britain as a whole. In effect such a study should also be an important aspect of urban history encompassing as it does the health environment from which no contemporary citizen can escape.

The essays are mainly concerned with the period 1830–1900. This is because it is the nineteenth century which generated most problems and which has attracted most scholars. But though the developments after 1900 are only lightly touched upon, much relevant information is provided in the appendices and bibliography and is referred to in the penultimate essay on source materials: it is hoped that these pointers to what is available in the wide range of surviving material will encourage other scholars to close up the gap to the present. In the meantime the work of the National Health Service is described.

Chapter One discusses the problems of implementing health policy as they confronted local government, its politicians and officials down to 1900. Meanwhile the medical profession was busily consolidating its position and emerging as a body which, although anxious to give service for humanitarian reasons, was also determined to establish its own high professional standing by qualifications which ensured strict control of entry. The challenge made to the all-male profession by women is another theme which Rona Gaffney has developed.

A clear account of the Poor Law hospitals is also given by Dr Gaffney which shows how minimal these responses were and how grudging the health care given. Frank Rice has examined the problem of mental illness in the community and shows how difficult it was to run a hospital such as the Glasgow Asylum for Lunatics according to contemporary principles and how easy it was to slip back into the old disciplinary procedures. Carolyn Pennington develops the theme of Tuberculosis and demonstrates how, once fever had been quelled, the Medical Officer of Health was able to turn his attention to TB, a dangerous and killing disease.

David Hamilton and Christopher Smith have explored two aspects of technical advance in nineteenth-century Glasgow. The remarkable expansion of surgery which followed the adoption of antiseptic and aseptic methods, encompassed the development of a wide range of techniques hitherto regarded as all but impossible. Inquiries into the nature and uses of X-rays reveal the development of a new mode of exploration.

The discussion of maternal and child welfare approaches the difficult problem of nutrition. It could be argued that had nutritional standards been adequate and the people well fed the health problems of Glasgow citizens would have been far less onerous than they were. This is a controversial subject into which further research is much needed.

The immediate past is represented by Dr Scott Wilson's account of the relationship between health and environment under the regime of the National Health Service since 1948. Derek Dow has given us a valuable insight into the resource material available in the West of Scotland through the farsightedness of the Greater Glasgow Health Board in setting up a comprehensive archive which should encourage students into the field of medical history. Sydney Checkland provides a view of the problems of urban health in general, and in the particular context of Glasgow and its regional setting.

It is appropriate at the outset to give a general indication of Glasgow's health performance between the 1830s and the present. The overall picture is reflected in the course of the crude death rate (Table 27 in Appendix I). This stood in the early 1820s at about 25 per 1000, had reached 32 by the mid 1830s, moving to its peak at just under 40 in the later 1840s. It then fell quite dramatically to under 30 in the 1850s (some of the 'improvement' being due to a throwing out of the boundary of the city to double its acreage). The trend was then steadily downward, reaching 14.4 by 1931. Thereafter, however, progress was very hesitant (see Table 31). Meanwhile the overall population of the city had increased from 147,043 living on 1,864 acres in 1831 to 1,089,767 people living on 39,725 acres in 1951. Within these overall death rate figures there were startling differences as between the different parts of the city. In 1880–1–2 the extremes were represented by Blythswood with 16.1 per thousand, and Bridgegate and Wynds with 38.3. Nevertheless the story is one of remarkable improvement. It is less impressive, however, if the gains in the more recent years are compared with cities in other developed countries. Similarly Glasgow performed badly in terms of infant mortality as shown in Table 30, Appendix I. In Blythswood the rate was high at 52.9, but in Bridgegate and Wynds it was 138.7.

As to morbidity, here too there was progress, as reflected in the subduing if not conquering of a range of diseases (Tables 28 and 29). Smallpox, typhus and typhoid represented the greatest achievements by 1939, with tuberculosis, one of the greatest curses of the working classes, continuously reduced. Respiratory diseases, however, rose to peaks in the last decade of the nineteenth century and again between 1911–20. Diarrhoea seems to have followed a fairly constant course. Each of these diseases has its own syndrome of incidence, preventive measures and therapies, their respective relationships to dirt, diet and medical science varying greatly. The links between each of these diseases and the efforts made to control and cure them is highly complex. A great range of correlations between relevant factors and incidence can be produced, often with more than one circumstance yielding a high correlation with the incidence of the disease, and hence with a claim to causality.

These data as to mortality and morbidity are of course crude, and subject to difficulties of interpretation and error. But they are the first approximation indicators from which health history must start.

The editors would like to thank the contributors for their co-operation and good humour throughout. We are indebted to our respective spouses for their interest and support. We are grateful to Brenda White who has responded to our many queries with kindly efficiency; and to Colin MacLean of the Aberdeen University Press for his guidance. Mrs Aileen Forbes Ballantyne has prepared the index which was financed by the GGHB. Finally we express our thanks to Isabel Burnside whose help and enthusiasm has never flagged.

The University, Glasgow   E.O.A.C.
May 1981   M.M.L.

Abbreviations

AR Annual Reports
ARMOHG Annual Reports of the Medical Officer of Health, Glasgow

BA British Association for the Advancement of Science, Reports of
BIHM Bulletin of Institutes of the History of Medicine
BMA British Medical Association
BMJ British Medical Journal
BWTA British Women's Temperance Association

CM Master of Surgery
COS Charity Organisation Society
CUS Commission for visiting the Universities of Scotland

DPH Diploma in Public Health

EHR Edinburgh Hospital Reports
EMJ Edinburgh Medical Journal

FFPSG Fellow of the Faculty of Physicians and Surgeons of Glasgow
FPSG Faculty of Physicians and Surgeons of Glasgow
FRCPEd Fellow of Royal College of Physicians of Edinburgh
FRCSEd Fellow of the Royal College of Surgeons of Edinburgh

GAL Glasgow Asylum for Lunatics
GBLC General Board of Commissioners in Lunacy for Scotland
GC Gartnavel Collection
GGHB Greater Glasgow Health Board
GH Glasgow Herald
GHR Glasgow Hospital Reports
GMH Glasgow Maternity Hospital
GMJ Glasgow Medical Journal
GP General Practitioner
GRI Glasgow Royal Infirmary
GUA Glasgow University Archives
GUL Glasgow University Library
GWI Glasgow Western Infirmary

HC House of Commons
HL House of Lords

JRSI Journal of the Royal Sanitary Institute
JRSS Journal of the Royal Statistical Society

LGB Local Government Board
LFPSG Licentiate of the Faculty of Physicians and Surgeons of Glasgow
LRCPEd Licentiate of the Royal College of Physicians of Edinburgh
LRCSEd Licentiate of the Royal College of Surgeons of Edinburgh
LSA London Society of Apothecaries

MB Bachelor of Medicine
MD Doctor of Medicine
MFPSG Member of the Faculty of Physicians and Surgeons of Glasgow
MH Medical History
ML Mitchell Library, Glasgow
MOH Medical Officer of Health

NHS National Health Service

PMO Parochial Medical Officer
PSG Proceedings of the Philosophical Society of Glasgow

RC Royal Commission
RCLAS Report of RC on Lunatic Asylums in Scotland, 1857
RCPEd Royal College of Physicians of Edinburgh
RCPL Royal College of Physicians of London
RCSEd Royal College of Surgeons of Edinburgh
RCSE Royal College of Surgeons of England
RCPSG Royal College of Physicians and Surgeons of Glasgow (from 1962)
RG Registrar General
RPSG Royal Philosophical Society of Glasgow
RSI Royal Sanitary Institute

SC Select Committee
SJ Sanitary Journal
SLC Scottish Lunacy Commission
SMJ Scottish Medical Journal
SRA Strathclyde Regional Archives

TB Tuberculosis

VD Venereal Disease
VIG Victorian Infirmary, Glasgow

WRHB Western Regional Health Board

The Contributors

Editors

Olive Checkland
 Research Fellow in Scottish History, the University of Glasgow
Margaret Lamb
 Department of Economic History, the University of Glasgow

Contributors

Professor S. G. Checkland, Department of Economic History, the University of Glasgow.

Dr Derek Dow, Archivist, to the Greater Glasgow Health Board.

Dr Rona Gaffney, of the Department of Modern History, the University of Glasgow.

Mr David Hamilton, Department of Surgery, the Western Infirmary, Glasgow.

Dr Carolyn Pennington, formerly Wellcome Research Fellow, the Department of Economic History, the University of Glasgow.

Dr Frank Rice, Department of Business and General Studies, North East Surrey College of Technology.

Dr Christopher Smith, Senior Physicist, West of Scotland Health Boards, Department of Clinical Physics and Bio-engineering.

Dr T. Scott Wilson, Community Medicine Specialist, the Greater Glasgow Health Board.

Chapter One

OLIVE CHECKLAND

Local government and the health environment

1. 'Fever by Act of God'

Before 1 January 1855, when the Registration (Scotland) Act came into force, there were few facts available on the health of the people of Glasgow. Previous efforts to give a statistical basis to what were recognised as deteriorating conditions had been painstaking and careful. Several observers, including James Cleland, Alexander Watt and Charles R. Baird had collected and collated figures on Glasgow. This statistical evidence, although valuable, was inevitably piecemeal and idiosyncratic.

Others might have argued that pages of figures were unnecessary: the evidence before their eyes was a constant reminder of the misery of many short Glasgow lives. There were many shocking reports from a variety of specialist sources.[1]

One extended quotation will perhaps suffice to illustrate all which the various enquirers found:

> It is in those frightful abodes of human wretchedness which lay along the High Street, Saltmarket, and Briggate, and constitute the bulk of that district known as the 'Wynds and Closes of Glasgow', that all sanitary evils exist in perfection. They consist of ranges of narrow closes, only some four or five feet in width, and of great length. The houses are so lofty that the direct light of the sky never reaches a large proportion of the dwellings. The ordinary atmospheric ventilation is impossible. The cleansing, until lately, was most inefficient, and, from structural causes, will always, under existing arrangements, be difficult and expensive. There are large square midden-steads, some of them actually under the houses, and all of them in the immediate vicinity of the windows and doors of human dwellings. These receptacles hold the entire filth and offal of large masses of people and households, until country farmers can be bargained with for their removal. There is no drainage in these neighbourhoods, except in a few cases; and from the want of any means of flushing, the sewers, where they do exist, are extended cesspools polluting the air. So little is house drainage in use, that on one occasion I saw the entire surface of a back yard covered for several inches with green putrid water, although there was a sewer in the close within a few feet into which it might have been drained away. The water supply is also very defective; such a thing as a household supply is unknown, and I have been informed that, from the state of the law, the water companies find it impossible to recover rates, and that, had the cholera not appeared, it was in contemplation to have cut off the entire supply from this class of property.
>
> The interior of the houses is in perfect keeping with their exterior. The

approaches are generally in a state of filthiness beyond belief. The common stairs and passages are often the receptacles of the most disgusting nuisances. The houses themselves are dark, and without the means of ventilation. The walls dilapidated and filthy, are in many cases ruinous. There are no domestic conveniences even in the loftiest tenements, where they are most needed, except a kind of wooden sink placed outside some stair windows, and communicating by a square wooden pipe with the surface of the close or court beneath. Down this contrivance, where it does exist, is poured the entire filth of the household or flat to which it belongs, and the solid refuse not unfrequently takes the same direction till the tube becomes obstructed.

Another matter connected with these districts, and their peculiar liability to epidemic disease, is the great and continually increasing overcrowding that prevails. I have been credibly informed, that for years a population of many thousands has been annually added to Glasgow by immigration without a single house being built to receive them. The great proportion come from Ireland. Every cabin in that wretched country that is razed to the ground sends one or more families to find house-room in the cities of England and Scotland, and of this element of disease Glasgow obtains its full share.

The overcrowding and wretchedness of late years has brought typhus with it, a disease that not long ago was almost as rare in the large Cities of Scotland as ague now is; and wherever typhus has prevailed, there cholera now prevails, or has done so recently.[2]

These areas of Glasgow could not be ignored for they, and their impoverished inmates, were believed to be the source of the fever epidemics which periodically swept the city. It became in everyone's interest to adopt an active policy of improvement. However, such a policy proved virtually impossible to implement as every scrap of building, from the vermin-infested attics to the earth-floored cellars, belonged to somebody, eager to protect his rights. Even if property appeared ownerless no-one had power to act and override the unknown owner. Such rights also applied to all the entire 'filth and offal' deposited on every close, wynd or courtyard adjacent to the packed sites. For such excreta was also an asset, its sale to country farmers being negotiated from time to time by jealous owners.

Even in 1832, it was with the greatest difficulty that bags of rags sent to Edinburgh from the districts affected with cholera could be dealt with by the authorities and it was only after protracted litigation and in consideration of the state of alarm for cholera, which then prevailed in the country, that the court of session decided in favour of the Board of Health, reserving the right of the proprietor of the rags to damages for his pecuniary loss. In ordinary times, the process by which a nuisance was removed was both tedious and costly.[3]

What could the local authority have done to alter such arrangements? Any intervention could be readily stopped by owners appealing to a court of law. An examination of old statutes did not help, for although burghs had had power to remove nuisances, these had long fallen into abeyance and their resuscitation would be resisted step by step. In any case few officers were employed by the burgh and their duties did not include 'scavenging'.

In spite of appalling conditions there was no lack of tenants for every corner. The men, women and children who found refuge in the slums of Glasgow often came from turf cabins in Ireland and black houses in the Highlands of Scotland. From such a past Glasgow was the land of opportunity and for many so it proved to be; they used the wynds and closes as temporary accommodation and moved to better houses and better jobs as circumstances permitted. Others, worn and debilitated by previous sufferings, could neither adapt to the quicker pace of life in Victorian Glasgow nor recover sufficiently ever to raise themselves from the trough into which they had fallen. It was therefore no easy matter to make any changes, especially as there were strong reasons for retaining the *status quo*.

There was a point of view strongly held and nationally promulgated that fever epidemics were Acts of God, a form of divine retribution brought down upon the heads of sinful people. The preamble to the Cholera Acts of 1832[4] states that 'Whereas it has pleased Almighty God to visit the United Kingdom with the Disease called the Cholera, or spasmodic or Indian Cholera: and whereas with a view to prevent, as far as possible, by the Divine Blessing, the spreading of the said Disease, it may be necessary that Rules and Regulations should from time to time be established within Cities, Towns and Districts'. In 1853 the Scottish Presbyteries demanded of the central government in London that the country should adopt a national day of prayer to mitigate the effect of disease. Palmerston's brusque reply that 'When man has done his utmost for his own safety then it is time to invoke the blessing of Heaven to give effect to his exertions'[5] (19 October 1853) is a reminder that by the mid-century at least some were not prepared to leave matters entirely in God's hands. W. T. Gairdner, the first part-time Medical Officer of Health in Glasgow, in his lectures on *Public Health* published in 1862 remarked that 'I look upon epidemic diseases as the awful facts of God's providence', although he went on to state 'God's providence giving the seal of authority . . . to a certain amount of interference with private concerns'. Although allowing God's supremacy Gairdner nevertheless argued that public authority was required to intervene on matters pertaining to public health.

Perhaps the fatalistic attitudes of the pious remained potent because there were no positive answers proffered by anyone else. Both the medical profession and the sanitary experts were in disagreement as to the best way of proceeding.

There were two major schools of thought; proponents of either the *miasma theory* or the *contagion theory*. Edwin Chadwick believed that the rotting masses of rubbish and excreta which accumulated everywhere caused noxious gases and that these poisoned both the atmosphere and the people breathing it, with various fevers. This was the miasma theory. Those who supported the contagion theory believed that fevers passed by actual contact between persons, their clothes and other effects. Scottish-trained doctors pinned their faith to the contagion theory although also accepting the miasma theory as a contributory factor. English-trained doctors, strongly supported by Edwin Chadwick as an influential sanitarian, emphasized the importance of miasma and tended to dismiss the contagion theory. Scots doctors resented and resisted the English view.

During any fever epidemic local authorities did attempt to utilise old powers. In 1848 when cholera was raging the Dean of Guild Court in Glasgow ordered the repair or demolition of buildings 'insecure, ruinous, or in any other way dangerous to the safety of the inhabitants'. This was perhaps a beginning, although only those properties which were actually falling down could be dealt with. The *Glasgow Herald* played an active part in reporting the proceedings of the Dean of Guild Court. Indeed the *Herald* challenged the wisdom of building new 'wynds' being laid out in 1851 at Blythswood and Milton, and demanded an Act to control such building.[6]

By this time Glasgow, like other Scottish burghs, had passed several Police Acts (in 1800, 1807, 1821, 1830 and 1837). The police were the only enforcement officers available to the civic authorities. Behind the Police Acts there was perhaps the older more shadowy continental theory of Medical Police (or Polity) by which the state maintained the people's health in the interests of all. Robert Cowan was appointed by the Crown to a new Chair of Medical Jurisprudence and Medical Police at the University of Glasgow in 1839. (Edinburgh had had a similar chair for some time.) There seems to be no doubt that Cowan was an advocate of the ideas of Medical Police. He had already published *Vital Statistics of Glasgow* in 1838 in which he wrote

> Before the Municipal Bill of Glasgow is presented to the Legislature, a well-digested system of medical police should be drawn up and incorporated with the other necessary enactments. Power should be vested in the police to enforce the daily removal of filth of every description. Public water closets should be established, and every measure calculated to promote the general health rigidly enforced (p. 13).

Unfortunately Cowan died in 1841.

It is difficult to judge whether Cowan's ideas, as expressed in *Vital Statistics of Glasgow* would have been an adequate base for the expansion of public health measures in Glasgow. Medical students at Glasgow and Edinburgh continued to have lectures on Cleanliness, (personal and domestic), Ventilation, Purity of Air and Supply of Good Water as well as Abatement of Nuisances but in course of time Medical Jurisprudence came to dominate the syllabus.

The early Glasgow Police Acts remained effective only on paper, for not until 1843 was the first Inspector of Cleansing appointed, and until 1868 he had no department to back him up. The putative duties of the inspector were 'to make regulations for watering, sweeping and cleansing closes, thoroughfares and areas, for the purpose of disinfection and otherwise promoting the health of the inhabitants therein'; for the cleansing of common stairs by tenants; for regulating the emptying of middens and privies 'according to their dimensions and the local circumstances as regards the health and comfort of the persons in the neighbourhood'; the licensing of common lodging-houses, 'prevent overcrowding and secure the reporting of fever by the keepers'; and 'for carrying out disinfection by the Magistrates through the Police'.[7]

When fever was rampant the civic response was never adequate. The only permanent hospital was the Royal Infirmary (opened 1794) which offered general philanthropic health provision for the poor, but was quickly swamped once a fever epidemic started. While sickness raged a fever hospital always had to be found and there was much frenzied activity collecting funds, searching for a site, and gathering staff. Once the epidemic was on the wane, no provision was made for the future, for as Russell remarked 'the hospitals were pulled down, the doctors, nurses and fumigators who had not been buried were paid off'.

2. Loch Katrine's water: a triumph of foresight

By the mid 1850s there was sufficient support for the Loch Katrine water scheme to be undertaken, whereby the pure water of a large highland loch was piped the fifty-odd miles into the city. The immense engineering works were successfully completed in 1859 and a large and steady source of pure and unadulterated water was available in the city. The triumph of the venture confounded the critics. It is hard to understand the strength of the opposition to the Loch Katrine scheme for previously the inadequate water supply had come from two private water companies which drew inadequate and frequently impure supplies from small local reservoirs and from the Clyde.

Once the water was flowing it became another major task to bring the new supply to the houses or at least to stand-pipes in courts and closes. This job continued for many years. It was helped by the clearing away of old housing stock which occurred when railways were built and was less of a problem when new houses were erected.

3. The River Clyde: an open sewer?

The response to the problem of sewage disposal in nineteenth-century Glasgow was not solved as expeditiously or as effectively as that of supplying pure water. The earliest common or public sewers had been built along the main arteries of city streets, including parts of the Trongate and High Street as early as 1816, but the only eventual outlet for the system was the River Clyde. With the growth of population in the nineteenth century the problem became acute although until the 1860s and 1870s few houses were actually in possession of water closets, earth closets often being preferred. The medical profession did not give a strong coherent lead: opinions were divided.[8] The cleansing of the city was effected from 1868 by a municipal department and this involved clearing away middens and all waste matter as a 'gigantic manure business'. The foulness of the river became an embarrassment although getting any plan of action proved to be extremely difficult. There was a wide range of heroic projects advocated by amateur engineers to carry the sewage away to the sea by special devices constructed in the Clyde or to pump it up on to agricultural land. In 1858 the city authorities themselves considered a scheme to deodorise the sewage so that it would be less of a nuisance when pumped into the river. Sir Joseph Bazalgette (in 1867) and Sir John Hawkshaw (in 1873) were brought in as well-known authorities, to advise. Both advocated expensive schemes of pumping the sewage away from the city to outfall either on the Ayrshire coast or lower down the Clyde. These schemes were strongly opposed and were in any case considered to be excessively costly.

The resolution of this matter depended in the end on the project to construct the underground railway. In 1888 the company which planned to build the subway presented a bill to Parliament for this purpose which was strongly opposed by Glasgow Corporation because of expected difficulties with sewers. In order to gain the corporation's approval the railway company agreed to undertake a major re-modelling of the sewage system at their expense. Having found a method of financing the sewerage project at no expense to the rate-payers the city authorities accepted the railway scheme and re-organised their sewer system. It cost the subway company over £200,000 to 'buy off' the corporation. Large scale systems of sewage purification were later introduced,[9] by providing sewerage treatment stations at Dalmarnock, Dalmuir and Shieldhall.

4. John Ure's achievement

In terms of Public Health 1856 was eventful, for both the Nuisance Removal (Scotland) Act was passed and John Ure was elected to the City Council. Ure became a member of the 'Committee on Nuisances' set up under the Act and very soon (on the elevation of Peter Clouston to the Lord Provostship) its chairman. From this time therefore Glasgow had an entrepreneurial enthusiast determined to push through effective public health measures.

Once in the chair of the 'Committee on Nuisances' Ure was tireless. He led small groups on visits to towns in England and Ireland to examine their 'sanitary organizations'. On their return a special committee was set up which made fifteen recommendations.[10] The bulk of the powers incorporated in the Glasgow Police Act of 1862 came from these. (The 1862

Glasgow Police Act was later replaced by another Act in 1866, an Amending Act of 1890 and the Corporation Order (Confirmation) Act of 1904.)

By the Act, the Board of Police were given wide powers and '*shall* from time to time appoint and may at pleasure revoke the appointment of the following special officers: namely, A Master of Works, One or more medical officers for the whole city or for districts of the city, One or more surveyors, And may also appoint and at pleasure revoke the appointment of the following special officers: namely An Inspector of Fires, One or more Inspectors of Nuisances, One or more Inspectors of Common Lodging Houses, One or more Surgeons, An Inspector of Sewers, An Inspector of Cleansing, An Inspector of Lighting.'

But as the Police Act was also careful to state, these posts could either be amalgamated or taken on, among other duties, by police officers empowered by the chief constable. As with earlier legislation, the power was vested in the Police Board.

The Glasgow Police Act of 1862, although it had within it the seeds of innovation, was more of a continuum than a sharp break with earlier legislation. It did however list a possible inspectorate for environmental problems although no appointments were made. It also authorised John Ure to search for a Medical Officer of Health.

There were no obvious candidates for this job. In Glasgow, district Surgeons had been part-time and usually of junior status. Aware that there was no tradition of distinction in public medicine Ure was anxious to secure the services of a doctor who would bring prestige to the new and challenging post. In the course of his search Ure came across the writings of W. T. Gairdner on *Public Health in relation to air and water.* Gairdner had delivered these lectures in Edinburgh in 1861 'to an audience partly composed of students of medicine and partly of persons otherwise interested in the subject of Public Health'. It seemed that Professor Gairdner would be an excellent choice.

5. 1863: the first Medical Officer of Health*

In January 1863 Dr William Tennant Gairdner (1824–1907) became the first part-time Medical Officer of Health for the city of Glasgow. Gairdner had just moved to Glasgow on being appointed to the Chair of the Practice of Physic in the University. For nearly ten years he held conjointly the post of Medical Officer of Health and his University chair.

As Gairdner's post was part-time, five District Surgeons of Police were also appointed as his assistants. They were Drs MacGill, Dunlop, Renfrew, Young and Johnston. Their main functions were associated with policing although they helped Dr Gairdner collect as much information as they could and prepared reports on conditions in their various districts.

* I am grateful to Mrs Brenda White for the use of her as yet unpublished material.

In March 1863 'a special non-medical inspector' was appointed in Glasgow and he created a rudimentary sanitary service. The first 'office' was established in the Central Police Building (where the sanitary inspector already had a desk within the office of the Surgeon of Police). After the Glasgow Police Act (9th) was passed in 1866 (later added to by the Public Health (Scotland) Act of 1867) it was possible for Glasgow 'to develop a permanent sanitary department and commence the daily routine of the sanitary function, undisturbed by a perpetually impending dissolution.'[11]

As Medical Officer for the city Gairdner saw his first task to be the collection of information on the people's state of health. It seemed clear enough to him that without a statistical base he could do little to work out any policy. He proposed to divide the city into manageable units and to use these as a base for his enquiries. After various schemes had been tried the city was divided into 24 sanitary districts and these remained until 1903 when the extension of the city's boundaries caused a re-organisation.[12] In some quarters Gairdner's plans were resented and certainly aroused anxiety and later hostility in the city. They seemed to be an invasion of privacy. Landlords and property owners feared what his enquiries might reveal. The police regarded the whole exercise as frivolous and dangerous and an encroachment on their preserves. The Police Board, a powerful arm of the corporation, representing many powerful voices in the city, became alarmed at all Gairdner's activities.

There was one part of his programme for sanitary improvement which did arouse enthusiasm even from his critics: for he was deeply interested in the extension of *voluntary* schemes for 'sanitary visitation'. In the summer of 1866 when a cholera epidemic threatened Glasgow, Gairdner, through the churches, organised large numbers of volunteers to visit the homes of the working people and to encourage cleanliness of persons and of homes. Gairdner's commitment to the Sanitary Visitation Movement as an aid to 'cleanliness, ventilation, free space in the home, decency, external comfort' was part of his 'public health' response to the evangelical Christianity of the day.[13]

In the field of hospital provision Gairdner was also successful. The Kennedy Street Hospital was opened in 1865 as a permanent fever hospital and the young James Burn Russell was appointed as medical superintendent (see Section 6 below). In October 1870 the Corporation bought Belvidere House and its estate where the first buildings there were opened, also for fever, in December 1870.

But although his evangelical enthusiasm delighted the citizens of Glasgow his secular enquiries did not. By 1869 there was considerable friction between Gairdner and some of the city's officials. The Dean of Guild (Mr William Macewan) was particularly critical and his unfriendliness seemed to be conveyed to the members of the Police Board.

By 1872 a hostile Police Board decided, as it had the right to do under the terms of the 1862 Police Act, to rescind the appointments of Gairdner and the five District Surgeons.

It was an embarrassing debacle, particularly wounding for Gairdner himself. When the Police Board in an attempt to soften the affront, offered him a consultancy at £100 a year, he declined,[14] although not until Dr Russell had been 'unanimously appointed Medical Officer'.

The sorry end to Gairdner's career as part-time Medical Officer of Health must raise questions.[15] The Police Board must have felt threatened by the establishment by Gairdner of a Public Health department. Perhaps Gairdner, from a well-connected Ayrshire family, failed to use tact and persuasion in handling local officials.

Once the break had come Gairdner must have reflected that his University Chair was his important life's work. In fact the University had moved to Gilmorehill in 1870, the Western Infirmary was due to open in 1874 and thereafter his home, university and hospital wards would be almost adjacent to one another. Gairdner must have recognised that professional distinction must come from his university achievements rather than from anything which he could have done, on a part-time basis, for Public Health.

6. 1872–1898 James Burn Russell: a great Medical Officer of Health

In November 1872 James Burn Russell (1837–1904) became the first full-time Medical Officer of Health for the city of Glasgow, a post he held with distinction until 1898. Russell, a man of flair and vision,[16] created the public health service in Glasgow and welded it into an efficient and effective department. He engaged himself for more than a quarter of a century with the health problems of the city. All the difficulties were exacerbated by the extraordinary growth of the population of Glasgow: a rough estimate suggests that during Russell's term the population increased by nearly 200,000 souls. Most of the newcomers were Highlanders or Irish driven by dearth at home to risk the unknown hazards of life in an industrial city. Any urban authority at any period would have had difficulty in coping with so large and unrelenting an influx, but Victorian Glasgow was particularly unprepared. Health provision was minimal, and indeed as far as the ordinary citizen was concerned could scarcely be said to have existed.

All this Russell knew, for he stood in the great medical tradition of service to his community and especially service to the poor. His humanitarianism combined with his personal drive and enthusiasm ensured that he would pursue a policy of positive action. The question really was where should he begin?

During his career in Glasgow Russell seemed to have three major preoccupations. His first priority was to protect the inhabitants from the various fevers which beset them. Much of Russell's career was given over to this task. He began by trying to categorise and distinguish the various infectious diseases. Then he was driven on from infections to examine housing, for as he saw it the prevalence of fever seemed to be in a direct relationship to overcrowding. Finally any enquiry was useless without figures to back it; Russell therefore continually gathered information, enabling him to indicate the dangers to public health and to urge his recommendations with strong statistical support.

Russell had been a distinguished student in the University of Glasgow. He began his studies in the autumn of 1854 and graduated Bachelor of Arts in 1858. Thereafter (as was the Scottish tradition) he proceeded to medical studies graduating in 1862 as MD, CM. His commitment to public medicine was confirmed by his early appointment (after periods as house surgeon at the Royal Infirmary and the City Poorhouse) as the first Medical Superintendent at the Parliamentary Road (also known as Kennedy Street) Fever Hospital in 1865. He was thus the first medical man of evident promise in the west of Scotland to opt for service in the cause of public health.

Russell continued to battle against fevers throughout his career. But the emphasis changed. He became more of an environmentalist, increasingly involved with housing which was often so bad as to be a health hazard. In some Glasgow homes he found much to disturb him. Glasgow's site crowded into the Clyde valley, hemmed in by hills. The area of the city is relatively small. This is perhaps one reason for the prevalence of tenement building. Within the tenements house units were very small; standard 'houses' could be 'a room', 'a room and kitchen', 'two rooms and kitchen'. Russell quickly identified inadequate housing as a cause of fever, general poor health and high mortality.

If Russell spent his days grappling with the health problems of the poorer people of Glasgow he often spent his evenings lecturing, explaining and exhorting.[17] He thus created an attitude of concern which must have ensured him a sympathetic public response as well as encouraging councillors and baillies to respond positively to his plans for extending social welfare.

Perhaps the most influential paper he ever gave was 'Life in one Room' (delivered at Park Parish Literary Institute, Glasgow, 27 February 1888). In it he gave eloquent testimony to the many problems, including those of health which result from living confined in a small place. Other lectures relating to housing space, included 'The House', 'The House in relation to Public Health', 'Uninhabitable Houses', 'Common Lodging Houses'. Russell's concern for housing standards led him to support the 'ticketed' house scheme.

Many Glasgow tenements and larger older houses were rather like rabbit warrens with 'houses', home to individual families, taking up a very small cubic area. The concept of 'ticketed' houses enabled the authorities in Glasgow to decide on a minimum space for adults and children, measure the 'house' of each family and nail to the door a ticket which stated the number of adults and children legally entitled to live there. To ensure that the rules were kept, nightly inspections were organised by sanitary and police officials. It was a rough system which must have been resented, although the legends of the supernumerary lodger, dashing from close to close always in advance of the inspectorate must have had some substance.

Consequent upon his involvement with housing Russell pursued his enquiries into mortality. He understood the importance of working out actual figures to back his arguments and it was not difficult to show how death rates varied between good and bad housing areas.

Russell's achievement in Glasgow was impressive. He brought to the post of Medical Officer of Health qualities of dedication and determination. He used the authority vested in him with skill. He lectured widely and often, creating a climate of opinion which he could use as a base for further advances. Glasgow was fortunate in having so distinguished a man as its first full-time medical officer of Health.[18]

7. Municipal initiative: Belvidere Hospital[19]

The city corporation of Glasgow had no enthusiasm for the permanent fever hospital but by the 1860s the short-term expediencies into which it was forced whenever a fever epidemic occurred, and the presssure exerted by Ure and Gairdner, caused action to be taken. In April 1865 the Parliamentary Road Hospital was opened. It was also known as Kennedy Street Fever Hospital and was 'a substantial pavilion hospital, partly brick, partly wood' which 'was erected and opened with 136 beds on April 25, 1865'.[20]

The matter of civic responsibility was complicated by the fact that the Poor Law Authorities were already in the field (see Chapter Three below). They were responsible for the pauper sick who alone were entitled to hospital treatment: but many were stricken with fever who were not paupers. Despite many bitter definitional problems about who were paupers and who were not it became clear that the municipal authority had to shoulder a bigger burden. After a great deal of controversy the Corporation resolved (23 April 1881) that 'all classes of citizens suffering from infectious disease should be treated in hospital without any charge being made therefore'. Russell, writing in 1881 (perhaps after April 23?) commented, 'Hospitals not only bear an important part in the prevention of infectious diseases, but indirectly also in the education of local authorities. They give concrete expression to the costliness of slums and nuisances.'[21]

Within little more than five years of its reluctant but permanent commitment to the fever hospital Glasgow Corporation, dissatisfied with the crowded site of the Kennedy Street Hospital bought (in October 1870) for £17,000 Belvidere House and its 33 acre estate 'on the banks of the Clyde some 2½ miles east of the Royal Exchange'. As fever was once again rampant the matter became urgent. The speed at which building was undertaken was quite astonishing, 'the contractor entered the stubble field on 22nd November 1870 and on the 19th of the following month one pavilion was occupied'.[22] Once established Belvidere proved of tremendous use. Over the years the corporation gradually built up the hospital complex and channelled successively all the cases of infectious diseases there.

It was a notable success story. The smallpox hospital was completed in 1877 and the permanent fever hospital of 390 beds in 1887. Great care was taken in the design of the hospital. There were 'rounded window ledges' to avoid collecting dust, floors of 'waxed Dantzig oak' and double glazing, so that the temperature could be kept steady. Glasgow corporation received high praise for its efforts. The hospital was described as 'the largest fever hospital out of London and the finest in the three kingdoms'.

It is important to note, perhaps because of the scope and opportunities offered to doctors, that Belvidere attracted distinguished medical and surgical staff. William Macewen (later Sir William), became the first resident and did excellent work there. Macewen's brother-in-law James W. Allan became medical superintendent in 1875. In 1900 John Brownlee took over and established with his young assistants a strong tradition of laboratory research.

TABLE 1

Patients treated at Glasgow Fever Hospital 1865–1894

	Treated	Died
Parliamentary Road	16 786	1 807
Belvidere (Fever)	56 320	6 195
Belvidere (Smallpox)	1 179	71
	74 285	8 073

Source: J. B. Russell, Public Health and Administration in Glasgow (Glasgow 1905), p. 71.

TABLE 2

The principal diseases from which these patients suffered

	Treated	Died
Scarlet fever	22 982	2 080
Typhus	11 255	1 417
Enteric Fever	8 846	1 268
Measles	8 356	717
Relapsing fever	4 901	102
Smallpox	4 232	620
Whooping cough	3 210	618
Erysipelas	1 447	120
Diphtheria	617	261
Cholera	21	13

Source: J. B. Russell, Public Health and Administration in Glasgow (Glasgow 1905), p. 71.

In the course of time diagnosis of fevers became more careful and more accurate. Russell analysed the numbers of patients and the fevers from which they suffered.

Because of strong leadership from Russell, Macewen and Allan proper steps were taken to organise an efficient and well trained body of nurses. Almost the first step was to build a large nurses' home and ensure that every nurse had a room of her own. This was a great attraction, for many girls who pined for a useful life and were eager to be properly trained to undertake nursing service, could not leave home unless they had somewhere respectable to live. A Mrs Sinclair was appointed matron and she trained her nurses with care. The resultant group of women brought dedication and distinction to the hospital.

Glasgow corporation were therefore fortunate to launch so successful a project and attract to its service so keen a body of men and women. As a result of fine traditions quickly established Belvidere avoided the stigma of the Poor Law Hospitals and became (although not as prestigious as the voluntary hospitals) a highly regarded part of the health services of the city.

Over the years although they remained a threat to the health of its citizens many fevers virtually disappeared. Plague appeared in 1900 and 1901 and caused eight deaths, otherwise typhus and enteric fever were the main killers, although on a much smaller scale than in earlier years.

Although it remained a fever hospital 'acute primary pneumonia' cases came to be admitted in large numbers. By the 1920s and 1930s these cases usually numbered more than 1000 a year. Scarlet fever, diphtheria, poliomyelitis were all treated at Belvidere.

Belvidere was handed over to the National Health Service in 1948 after almost eighty years of service to the community. It was subsequently modernised and refurbished and so continues to serve the population as a general hospital in the east end of Glasgow.

8. A new century: new objectives

Throughout the nineteenth century, Glasgow was a thriving city with a firm and prosperous core of heavy industry. Later in the twentieth century, because of the failure of the original industrial base, the expansionist image of the city has been replaced by one of contraction. Both periods have presented problems of health care to those responsible. In the time of expansion there were never enough facilities to satisfy the demand. During a phase of contraction there probably are more nearly enough houses, hospital beds, nurses and doctors but the position is not necessarily better because they are of the wrong sort or in the wrong place.

During the earlier expansionist years all Glasgow's problems were exacerbated by the stream of incomers from Ireland and the Highlands of Scotland. The low standards and poor health of many of these people were a constant source of concern. Many of them were ill-fed and ill-housed which made them vulnerable to a wide variety of diseases, particularly fevers.

Society did provide a safety net in the form of the Poor Law which was supposed to succour these in need. There was in those days no concept of the refugee maintained at public expense and then finally resettled. Newcomers lodged with relatives or friends and fended for themselves unless they could squeeze some help from poor relief.

From 1845 the Scottish Poor Law was organised on a secular basis and gradually provided more aid but the basic rules still held. One of the most damaging stipulated that relief should be withheld from a man and his dependents whilst he was still able-bodied; others concerning 'settlement' could deny aid to those who had not lived in an area for very long.

By the end of the nineteenth century some were beginning to question the deal which had been forced upon the working class. The franchise Acts of 1867 and 1884 had extended the vote to most adult males. Had the working class thereafter moved in unison (as Marxian class interests would have suggested) much might have been achieved, but despite the activities of the Fabian society and other socialist groups small advantage was taken at this time of the political power available.

Even before Victoria died in January 1901 new questions were being asked about the people's health. The onset of the Boer War had resulted in vigorous recruiting campaigns. Medical inspection of volunteers who rushed to join the colours revealed serious physical deficiencies and army medical officers found themselves rejecting substantial numbers of men. The newspapers were indignant and the matter became a *cause célèbre* overnight.

In 1903 the government set up an Interdepartmental Committee on Physical Deterioration to consider the causes of poor health. Special note was taken of the Report of the Royal Commission on Physical Training (Scotland) (appointed 1902) which had recommended games and physical education in schools but also suggested school medical inspections and school meals for children.

But the machinery to aid the poor was the Poor Law and it was to a Royal Commission on the Poor Laws and Relief of Distress that the government turned in 1905 to try to discover the real state of affairs. The Commission consisted of eighteen people; four of these Beatrice Webb, George Lansbury, H. Russell Wakefield and Francis Chandler, were socialists or at least had radical views. As a result they produced a minority report (in 1909) which recommended that

The Scottish Poor Law be abolished, and in its stead, an entirely different method of provision for those needing public aid be inaugurated, so as to get rid of pauperism, both the name and the thing.[23]

9. 1909–1948

From 1909, when the demand to abolish the Poor Law was first made, to 1948 there was an increasing pressure on government to provide more adequately for those in need. Lloyd George's role in effecting change cannot be overlooked. He had already introduced (from 1 January 1908) the old age pension which provided 5s. a week for those over seventy. This removed at a stroke thousands of the old from the stigma of poor relief and was but a foretaste of the National Insurance schemes and Widows' pensions providing state guaranteed succour.

In Glasgow there was an increasingly strong voice from the left demanding better support for under-privileged classes. Housing remained a top priority for those involved with social injustice. Glasgow started to build council houses in the 1920s and after 1933 when the Labour party took political control over the city, a policy of positive discrimination in favour of council house building, to the exclusion of the private builder, was undertaken. The city fathers made every endeavour to satisfy the social needs of the people who had elected them.

The hospital system remained structured as before, the Voluntary hospitals (especially those teaching hospitals attached to the University) remaining most prestigious. The Municipal hospitals were also highly regarded concentrating as they did on infectious diseases and laboratory services, while the Poor Law hospitals were performing well although often in poorer areas of the city and therefore less able to attract the very best staff.

During the war Glasgow and the Clyde suffered serious bombing and much damage was done. Late in 1942 William Beveridge's *Report on Social Insurance and Allied Services* was published. In this *Report* although dismissed as Utopian by many, Beveridge touched the imagination of a people weary with war and eager to embrace the concept of 'a free national health service, policies of full employment, family allowances for second and further children, and abolition of poverty by a comprehensive system of social insurance, with benefits paid at subsistence level and as a statutory right'.[24] On the strength of the euphoria created by the Beveridge *Report* a Labour government came into power in July 1945 pledged to introduce ambitious social security measures. It was left to Aneurin Bevan the Minister of Health from 1945 to implement the National Health Service in 1948.

Chapter Two

MARGARET LAMB

The Medical Profession

1. A century of advancement

The explosive activities and developments of the nineteenth century pro-foundly affected the medical profession and medical services. Urbanisation, the concentration of large numbers of people both in living accommodation and in factories, produced social and medical problems which were conse-quently reflected in the structure and nature of the provision of health care and the personnel involved. The State became increasingly involved in medical matters: in education and qualification, in health on a community scale ('public health'), and in legislation in various fields, which necessarily included some reference to medicine (the Poor Law, Factory Acts, Regis-tration Acts, etc.).

Apart from this, scientific advance brought about marked changes in techniques, affected standards of care and caused increasing expectations from 'consumers'. Results included more effective treatment, the growth of specialisation, an extension of hospital provision and convalescent schemes. These processes were marked by independent activity on the part of practi-tioners and charitable agencies and by 'self-help' on the part of the con-sumer through the medium of Friendly Societies. The range of oppor-tunities for medically qualified people widened considerably and with it the prospects for greater financial security—the possibility of a regular income as a 'paid agent' increased, to be supplemented in most cases by whatever general practice came the way of the doctor. With the enlarged range of medical appointments came the opening-up of the profession itself, as women successfully challenged a hitherto male monopoly.

TABLE 3

Doctor/patient ratios in nineteenth-century Glasgow

Year	1801	1811	1821	1831	1841	1851	1861	1871	1881	1891	1901
Population '000s	77	100	147	202	255	329	395	478	511	566	740
Medical men	41	67	132	201	231	240	222	236	280	403	558
Potential patients in '000s per doctor	1.9	1.6	1.1	1.0	1.1	1.4	1.8	2.0	1.8	1.4	1.3

Note: Recommended figures (Ministry of Health) at the present time (1981) are:
1 GP per 2200 of the population
If hospital consultants are taken together with GPs, the ratio becomes:
1 per 1200 of the population. (GGHB Memo.)
Source: Post Office Directories; Medical Directories.

2. The power structure

As is evident from Table 3, there was an increase of roughly an order of magnitude in the population of Glasgow during the nineteenth century: the numerical strength of the medical profession more than kept pace with this expansion and provided a higher doctor/patient ratio at the end of the period. It is virtually impossible to determine the proportion of the population which used available medical services at any particular period; but since doctors are necessarily engaged in earning a living, the question can be posed: 'What differences, if any, were there in the pattern of medical work at the beginning of the nineteenth century and at its end, bearing in mind the comparative figures?'

Several factors come under consideration but probably the most important lies outside the area of 'primary care'—that is, a great proportion of doctors, by the end of the nineteenth century, held medical appointments of various kinds which directly or indirectly provided a stable element of income. The amounts involved, varied widely as did the commitments of time and energy, but they were a source of financial stability amid the uncertainties of competitive general medical practice.

The fact that there were these opportunities is a reflection of the burgeoning prosperity of Glasgow during the last three decades of the century. Increasing numbers of skilled workers and a steady upward social movement created a more dependable demand for medical care and one which was more financially rewarding. Concomitantly, the status of the medical practitioner rose, for despite the position of Glasgow's medical Corporation[1] in the life of the city, the average member of the profession in the mid-nineteenth century was conscious of a low estimate of his worth in the strongly commercial atmosphere of Glasgow. He was ruffled by the submission of his scientific knowledge and noble purpose to the scrutiny of a practical mercantile eye and aware of a restricted social milieu in which to take his place:

> . . . the social status of the profession is . . . immeasurably below the proper standard. Probably the same is true of the legal profession, at least to some extent. The only learned body of any weight in the councils of Glasgow is the clerical.[2]

However, economic advance and social change mitigated the effects of existing professional structure in the lower ranks: they were offered more even chances of improving their position. At its apex, power was reinforced and the pattern became more obviously allied to those established earlier in London and Edinburgh.

Three factors which were to have lasting effects upon the make-up of the medical profession in Glasgow were particularly significant at the end of the eighteenth century, and contributed to the growth of a hierarchy.

Glasgow doctors were perforce members of the Faculty of Physicians and Surgeons of Glasgow: membership was both a medical qualification and a badge of community. The opening of the city's first large voluntary general hospital, the Royal Infirmary (1794), provided these men with the opportunity of influencing its running—officially, as part of the Board of Management and individually as its obvious medical staff. Although no specific requirement was laid down, 'use and wont' assured that the physicians and surgeons appointed to the Infirmary continued to be Members (after 1850, Fellows) of the Faculty.

Secondly, the introduction by the Faculty of the grade of 'Town Licentiate' established a precedent (1811) in the city,[3] and produced a bipartite class system of medical practitioners. It was, however, flexible enough to allow of upward mobility when good fortune followed the Licentiate's efforts to establish himself in general practice.

TABLE 4

Towards a medical élite

	1800	1810	1820	1830	1840	1851	1861	1871	1881	1891	1901
Total practitioners	41	67	132	201	231	240	222	236	280	403	558
Faculty Members or Fellows	36	44	75	82	73	60	57	78	94	106	114
% Faculty	88	65	57	41	31	25	25	33	39	26	20

Sources: Post Office Directories. Duncan, A., *Memorials of the Faculty of Physicians and Surgeons of Glasgow.*

Thirdly, from the mid-eighteenth century the development of the embryonic medical school in Glasgow reinforced the value of Faculty membership: the University professoriate was originally drawn from the resident medical men and for more than fifty years the custom continued that senior teachers should be of high standing in the Faculty too.[4] Similarly, as extramural, free-lance teaching expanded to meet student demand, the entry of Licentiates into the field was barred by the requirements of the medical licensing bodies.[5]

So, the Faculty dominated the medical scene and Members were in a position to increase their own status and economic rewards as their energies and inclinations dictated. By mid-century, they were aware of a threat—the number of medical men who were university graduates and the growing prestige of the MD degree. More frequently, application for membership of Faculty was not a first medical qualification, the essential starting point for a medical career, but indicated a step up the ladder for the man of ambition and means.[6] As a corollary, some well-established Members took the MD in mid-career and by 1860 the degree was almost a *sine qua non* for entry to the higher echelon of the power structure. By the erection of judicious barriers[7] the Faculty maintained and strengthened its distinct identity in Glasgow's increasing medical force.

3. Medical practice

The nature of medical practice involved a direct relationship between doctor and patient in consultation for the purposes of diagnosis of a medical problem and subsequent advice and treatment. The doctor, if called, visited patients in their homes; alternatively, he received patients in his home, or in 'rooms' in separate premises, or at his 'shop'; the latter quite literally was a trading establishment where the general practitioner (in the widest sense) dispensed the medicines he prescribed, cutting out the pharmacist middleman and guaranteeing some financial gain from his professional activities. This was regarded as a completely acceptable arrangement by the Glasgow profession at the beginning of the nineteenth century—only 'pure' physicians eschewed dispensing and they were rarities. Doctors were 'on their own'—the partnerships of the eighteenth century, which were normally of the teacher-pupil, then senior-junior type, had almost disappeared—and becoming established was no easy matter, particularly if financial support from family or 'independent means' were not available. Harry Rainy, son of a clergyman, had a net income of £7 for his first year in practice:[8] but he had 'connections' and abilities and prospered. He later (1841) became Professor of Medical Jurisprudence. The 'shop', therefore, was often an economic necessity. Successful practice allowed of its abandonment, in fact almost demanded it as time went on; increasingly, the dispensing practitioners belonged to the non-Faculty majority of medical men. The Faculty's use of the trading element of general practice as a bar to Fellowship was a real one; for example, John Dougall, an active and respected member of the profession and a practitioner of long standing had to refuse election to Fellowship in 1872 because he could not afford to dispose of his 'shop'.[9]

For those who had the means, medical treatment was carried out at home until late in the nineteenth century, when facilities for 'paying patients' enabled surgical procedures in particular to be carried out under more suitable conditions in private nursing homes or, more rarely, in the general hospitals. Infirmaries and hospitals were primarily for the low-income sick whose living conditions hampered proper treatment.

In 1800, doctors lived and worked amongst their patients. As the population increased, without a proportionate increase in the appropriate kind of housing accommodation, overcrowding of the older parts of the city resulted; although working, at least on the fringe of these areas, may have been necessary, the development of lands to the west of historic Glasgow provided more attractive living conditions for the more affluent. By mid-century, Faculty Members almost formed a colony in the Blythswood area, and none of them was to be found on the south side of the Clyde. In Trongate, Gallowgate and Saltmarket were found the 'shops' of the humbler members of the profession, usually non-graduates, the Licentiates of the medical Corporations.

This trend continued, although not quite so obviously, and the medical élite later followed the migration, westwards again, of the University Medical School and Anderson's College; a minor establishment appeared south of the Clyde, consolidated by the development of the Victoria Infirmary in the later years of the century.

General practice was, for long, the custom in Glasgow and primary care the accepted responsibility of members of the profession. This did not preclude at any time consultations between doctors over difficult cases,[10] but purely consulting practice was not established in Glasgow until the 1860s, with the advent of W. T. Gairdner. He, as Professor of Medicine in the University, did not set up in practice, as his predecessor had been wont to do, but was much in demand as a consultant. He was continuing an Edinburgh 'form' which had been long established there and which was the legitimate aim of ambitious medical men.[11]

The previously-quoted writer in the Glasgow Medical Journal (see note 2) rather bitterly posed the question in 1861, 'Now, what is the ordinary result of a professional man's career in Glasgow?' and replied as follows:

> Ten years of wasting inaction, or of miserable servitude behind a counter, followed by, say, twenty or thirty years of badly-remunerated toil and worry, to end either in an old age with restricted comforts or in leaving those who have been accustomed to better things to struggle through their race on a wretched pittance. Supposing a practitioner to be busily engaged every day of his life and paid at the usual rate, it would hardly be possible for him to keep up the position of a gentleman and at the same time suitably educate and provide for his family. But we are not always busy and, even when we are, how much of our work is there for which there is no pecuniary return. We say unhesitatingly that we never knew of a practitioner in Glasgow who had no public appointment and no private means who was able to leave his family in anything like affluent circumstances: and there are few, even of those who have held appointments, who have been able to do so.

The range of 'public appointments' was considerable even in 1861: not all of them were salaried but the potential advertisment inherent in any connection of an official kind was beneficial to private practice. Subsequently, an increasing proportion of the city's medical manpower took advantage of widening opportunities to lessen their dependence upon the vagaries of general practice.

TABLE 5

Medical 'opportunities'

	1800	1825	1851	1861	1871	1881	1891	1901
Total medical force			240	222	236	280	403	558
No. of doctors having any kind of medical appoint-ment			71	101	127	171	267	361
%			29.5	45	53	61	66	65

Source: Post Office Directories; Medical Directories.

4. Opportunities for doctors

(a) Hospitals

Though their origins may be different, it is possible to group together the appointments and attachments which involved doctors. The following tables give some idea of numerical strengths and will be set in context by appropriate comment.

The Glasgow Royal Infirmary provided concentrated medical experience for a very small number of doctors at any one time over roughly fifty years. From the beginning, appointments were of limited tenure and were part-time so that the work was shared around the Faculty Members—though they monopolised the system as against the rest of the Glasgow medical corps, they were careful to see that there was a degree of freedom for themselves within it. Indeed, they influenced changes of regulation to their advantage. So, when the two posts of physician to the Glasgow Royal Infirmary did become the preserve of the two or so 'pure' physicians of the city, Faculty pressure caused the Board of Management to concede that a well-established general practitioner, provided that he held the MD degree, could adequately fill the vacancy.[12] It happened, therefore, that some doctors served in both capacities during their working lives: the Glasgow

TABLE 6

Hospital appointments for doctors: full and part-time

	1801	1825	1851	1861	1871	1881	1891	1901
CHARITABLE								
(a) General								
No. of hospitals	1	1	1	1	1	2	3	3
No. of appointments	6	6	13	13	24	24	34	44
(including Hospital						21	34	38
Dispensaries)							7	21
(b) 'Special' Lunacy	0	1	1	1	1	1	1	1
No. of appointments		2	2	4	4	4	4	4
Others	0	2	3	3	4	5	12	10
No. of appointments		3	10	18	22	27	72	98
POOR LAW								
No. of Institutions			3	3	3	3	3	2
No. of appointments			4	4	7	6	6	5
LUNACY						1	1	2
No. of appointments						1		7
MUNICIPAL								
No. of Institutions	1	1			2	1	1	2
No. of appointments	1	1			3	5	7	10
TOTAL Hospitals	2	5	8	8	11	13	21	20
TOTAL Appointments	7	12	29	39	60	88	164	227

Note: The Glasgow University Lying-in Hospital is not included above—it was the preserve of
   the Professor of Midwifery (see page 32).
Source: Various, including directories and Annual Reports.

practitioners probably had wider experience of hospital problems than any
other group in the country.

Pressure upon accommodation led to additional building over the
years—a 'Fever House', wards and a 'Dispensary' (out-patient department)—and extra appointments were necessary. At the lowest level these
were more appropriately filled by younger men—there was an annual
output of a dozen or so who, as advanced students or as new graduates, had
served as Resident assistants. A career structure evolved from mid-century
and as tenure of posts lengthened, the old division between medicine and

surgery began to re-emerge: the hospital doctors who had been accustomed to carry out these duties alongside general practice gradually withdrew from primary patient care and the hitherto slow growth of consulting practice in Glasgow was given impetus.

The opening of the Western Infirmary (1874) staffed on the general pattern of the Glasgow Royal Infirmary provided an immediate widening of the field of opportunity. The Victoria Infirmary made a modest beginning: in a very real sense, it was the result of local community effort and it was staffed by the general practitioners of the area.[13] They were a close-knit group, as were the Fellows of the Faculty on the north side of the river, but without their powers or pretensions. The Victoria also showed refreshing initiative in appointing a woman doctor to a clinical post by the end of the century.[14]

Remuneration for hospital service even at senior level was modest and, though it was described as a 'salary' in 1810, it could only be regarded as an honorarium, at £50, in 1875. At this time, because the new Glasgow Western Infirmary siphoned off large numbers of clinical students, the Glasgow Royal Infirmary increased the salaries paid to senior physicians and surgeons to 100 guineas per annum.[15] Clinical teaching was remunerative to some degree but the fees paid by students for 'hospital tickets' were regarded as much a contribution to institutional finances as a reward for the educational work of the staff.

The nineteenth century saw the creation of the medical administrator—in the hospital setting he had the title of Medical Superintendent and, in Glasgow, he first appeared at the Glasgow Royal Infirmary in 1838. This appointment had been preceded by years of acrimonious discussion, as the Managers, concerned with the efficient running of an institution dependent upon philanthropic financing, eventually over-rode the objections of the medical staff, who feared interference in the exercise of their professional judgment by another professional, whose purposes were not necessarily in line with their own. They reluctantly accepted that a constant experienced medical presence was in the best interests of the patients and that someone who understood their problems could prove a valuable buffer and ally in issues affecting Management and Clinical staff.

The Superintendent appointments were novel in that they were resident, full-time and fully salaried: the figures vary, but £250 to £500 per annum would seem to be the range before 1900. In return for security, the doctor gave up a considerable degree of freedom. He was the 'middleman' between two power groups and the opportunity for the exercise of independent judgment as a medical man would be negligible. In the early years, the Glasgow Superintendents were not, perhaps for this reason, drawn from the ranks of the established profession; there was no rivalry evident when appointments needed to be made.

The innovative nature of the post is reflected in the changing personnel during the ten years or so following the first appointment. By mid-century, it was established that the incumbent be a graduate: subsequently, it is apparent that this kind of post was taken up by young men, who were

experienced in the work of various kinds of medical institutions at junior
level but probably had little knowledge of general practice. It developed as a
'career' avenue in medicine, with some movement from one Glasgow
institution to another; or as a period of experience in a varied medical life
(see Table 7).

TABLE 7

Medical Superintendents in Voluntary general hospitals

		From	Hospital	To
Qualifications			*Glasgow Royal Infirmary*	
			1841 Mr Martin	
FRCSEd.	1843			
MD	1850		1851 Dr J. Steele	
MD	1850	Assistant Physician, Royal Asylum	1861 Dr J. McGhie	
LFPS	1857	Medical Superinten-dent, Barony	1871	
MD	1862	Poorhouse	— Dr M. Thomas	
			1901	
MB, CM	1889	Surgeon to Barlinnie Prison	1911 Dr M. Thom	
FPSG DPH	1890			
			Glasgow Western Infirmary	
LRCPEd. LFPSG	1871	Physician Superin-tendent, Kennedy Street Fever Hospital	1875 Dr Lilly	MO and Vaccinator, 4th District, Stoneham Union, Southampton
MB, CM	1874	Paisley Infirmary	1881 Dr J. Alexander	Dispensary Physician
MD	1877			Glasgow Western Infirmary and private practice
MB, CM	1852	Superintendent, Chalmers Hospital, Banff	1891 Dr A. W. Russell	General practice and Samaritan Hospital
MB, CM	1884	Medical Superin-tendent, Victoria Infirmary	1901 Dr D. J. Mackintosh	
			Victoria Infirmary	
MB, CM	1884	Senior Assistant Physi-cian, Belvidere	1891 Dr D. J. Mackintosh	Glasgow Western Infirmary
MB, CM	1890	Clinical Assistant, London Throat and Ear Hospital	1901 Dr D. O. MacGregor	

Source: Post Office Directories; Medical Directories (mainly census years).

It was not long after the establishment of the new general hospital in 1794 that groups of poor people for whom special facilities would be advantageous were identified: mainly as a result of philanthropic endeavour, the first decade of the nineteenth century in Glasgow saw moves to found special hospitals, for the care of women in childbirth and those suffering from venereal disease and for the care of lunatics. The last two materialised as the Lock Hospital and the Glasgow Asylum for Lunatics (just in advance of legislation acknowledging the particular needs of the mentally ill). Support was not forthcoming at this time for a public Lying-in Hospital.[16]

Medical entrepreneurs were not encouraged by their professional colleagues—the Faculty tended to be against 'specialists' who openly set themselves apart from the generality of Glasgow practitioners. Private consultation amongst colleagues did take place, but that was a different ethical matter. So, the individuals who did so in the earlier years of the century were motivated certainly by interest but also by particular circumstance: in the case of the obstetrician, Towers (Lying-in Hospital, 1792), by his University teaching post, and in that of Mackenzie and Monteath (Eye Infirmary, 1824) by their standing in the medical community, Mackenzie's own fairly affluent private circumstances, and his obvious expertise in a field which was newly recognised as productive of medical advance in an otherwise static period.[17]

TABLE 8

Medical staff in Specialist hospitals

		1825	1851	1861	1871	1881	1891	1901
Specialist hospitals	Number	2	3	3	4	5	12	10
	Appointments		3	10	18	22	27	72	98
Asylums	Number	1	1	1	1	1	1	1
	Appointments		2	2	4	4	4	4	4

Source: Post Office Directories; Medical Directories.

The Glasgow Lying-in Hospital which was eventually set up in 1834 completed Glasgow's hospital services until the seventies; it was a public institution and its constitution expressly provided for representation on its management of the non-Faculty members of the profession. This was the first concession to the 'ordinary' and numerous general practitioners of the city and an admission that they should have a part to play in the organisation of medical services.

TABLE 9

Medical Officers in Poor Law hospitals

Qualifications	From		City Poorhouse (Town's Hospital—1733)	To
Qualifications MFPSG MD			1841 Dr Auchincloss (non-resident)	
MD	1838	House Surgeon at Glasgow Asylum for Lunatics	1851 Dr J. Crawford	Private practice and Professor of Medical Jurisprudence, Andersonian University
MD	1855	Assistant Physician, Glasgow Asylum for Lunatics	1861 1871 1881 Dr A. Robertson	Physician, Glasgow Royal Infirmary
MB CM	1877	MOH, Kilmaurs	1891 Dr G. Buchan	Parochial Medical Officer, Shotts and Bothwell parishes
			Barony Poorhouse— Barnhill 1849	
FFPSG	1828		1851 Mr W. Lyon (non-resident)	
MD	1829		1855 Dr M. Mather	General practice
LFPSG	1857	House Surgeon, Greenock Infirmary	1861 Mr M. Thomas	Medical Superintendent, Glasgow Royal Infirmary (1867)
LRCSEd. LRCPEd.	1863	Visiting Physician, Tranent Lunatic Asylum and Stiell's Hospital	1871 Mr A. J. MacGregor	
MB CM	1873		1881 Dr W. Core	Medical Superintendent, Stobhill Hospital
MD	1876		1901	
			Govan Poorhouse	
LFPSG	1829		1851 J. Muir	
LFPSG	1832	Medical Superintendent, Immigration Hospital, Montreal	1861 W. Liddell (non-resident)	
			1871 W. Liddell— resident	
			1881 W. Liddell at Merryflats (1873)	
LRCSEd. 1862 LRCPEd. 1869		Parochial Medical Officer, Barony	1891 W. Riddell Watson	Govan District Asylum, Hawkhead, Paisley
MB CM	1892		1901 W. J. Richard	

Source: Post Office Directories; Medical Directories (mainly census years).

From the seventies until 1900 and following a trend throughout the provincial cities of Britain as well as in London, the number of specialist hospitals doubled, arising, with the exception of the Sick Children's Hospital, from personal initiatives by doctors pursuing particular interests. The earlier ones provided a target for much bitter criticism from the *Glasgow Examiner*, the short-lived journal of the non-Faculty general practitioners: they themselves could not think of such self-indulgence and self-advertisement and feared for their own livelihood if patients were to be attracted from the generalist to the specialist. Nevertheless, these institutions, dependent upon public subscription survived; they obviously fulfilled a public need.

At the same time, they provided experience for the younger members of the profession; since a career biased towards hospital work was emerging from the eighties on, with the voluntary hospital as the highest goal, movement from one 'junior' position to another in the 'specialist' hospitals became common. Although the senior appointments were in the hands of the élite Faculty Fellows, the enterprise of some widened the field of opportunity for a greater number.

Tenure of appointment was in practice almost unlimited at this level (i.e., Physician, Assistant Physician and for Surgeons too) and new seniors were often chosen from those who had had previous experience in the speciality.

These smaller institutions did not offer administrative or full-time medical posts—even the long-established Eye Infirmary was run without a Medical Superintendent until 1922. The Glasgow Asylum for Lunatics, on the other hand, had already created the resident post of 'Physician Superintendent' about ten years after the Royal Infirmary's first Medical Superintendent was appointed, but he combined two roles as his designation implies.[18] It is curious that the Glasgow profession fought shy of this particular position; many of the young men served as House Surgeons or Assistants but they showed little ambition for the more senior post which, through the later nineteenth century, was filled by 'incomers' to the city (see Table 10). Perversely, J. G. Fleming served as 'non-resident Surgeon' for over twenty years.

Remuneration was reasonable and a new building at Gartnavel presumably provided more than adequate working conditions at the time. The first Physician Superintendent was paid £400 per annum (though 'fees received from patients' were included in that sum) and was provided with board and lodging: the Surgeon's salary was £30 per annum.

Only a small number of doctors was involved in the running of the Poor Law Hospitals (see Chapter 3): following the Poor Law (Scotland) Act of 1845, the four parishes of Glasgow appointed Medical Officers, to be based in whatever accommodation the parish was able to provide for its destitute and sick poor. At some periods, Assistants were appointed, and each parish appointed a number of parochial district surgeons to give 'outdoor' medical relief (see below).

It would appear that, in the early days, the Poor Law medical service counted some of the city's professional élite as its officers but, by 1861, when the pattern was established and a clearer idea of the work involved was apparent, they had quietly withdrawn. The field was left to younger men of little general practical experience or to those without the highest medical qualifications. To this extent, the Poor Law hospital doctors may be said to be seeking some kind of security, either because of an already proven lack of success, or the daunting prospect of becoming established in general practice.

TABLE 10

Physician Superintendents in Glasgow Asylum for Lunatics

	From	Glasgow Asylum for Lunatics	To
Qualifications			
CM	1827	1841 Dr W. Hutcheson	General Practice,
MD	1838		Troon
LFPSG	1833 Medical Superintendent,	1851 ⎫	
MD	1844 Dundee Lunatic	1861 ⎬ Dr A. Mackintosh	Honorary Consulting
	Asylum	1871 ⎭	Physician, Royal Asylum for Lunatics
MD	1857 Medical Superintendent,	1881 ⎫	
LRCS Ed.	Glamorgan County	1891 ⎬ Dr D. Yellowlees	
	Asylum	1901 ⎭	

Source: Various, including directories, AR GAL.

The Poor Law institutions had perforce to deal with the mentally ill, who were segregated from the other inmates; the size of the problem prompted the Barony Parochial Board to build a separate unit for lunatics at Woodilee in 1875. Govan Parish was obliged to build an asylum along with its Poorhouse in 1873, at Merryflats, but there was no special medical officer appointed for the former. It is fairly clear that mental illness as a 'speciality' emerged during the second half of the century and that the senior resident officers had chosen to follow this particular line early in their careers and tended to follow it more closely than their counterparts in other hospitals. This is not to infer that it was regarded as a bye-way in medicine—as began to happen in the nineteenth century and to an even greater degree today, special teaching or training in a particular field followed by examination and certification confer status on the diplomate and respectability upon the subject.

Lunacy as a branch of medicine had attained to this by the end of the century.[19]

The salaries paid varied somewhat from parish to parish and a new appointment was sometimes used as an opportunity to economise for a few years—until, perhaps, the Medical Officer had proved his worth. In general, remuneration compared not too unfavourably with that of Medical

Superintendent in the charitable institutions: the extent of the range was only £80 by 1896, and City parish appears to have paid the most generously in the later years of the century (£500 per annum).

TABLE 11

Medical Officers in Poor Law lunatic asylums

		Woodilee (1875)	
MD 1863	Medical Superintendent, Argyll and Bute District Asylum	1881 Dr J. Rutherford	Crichton Royal Asylum, Dumfries
MD 1864	Assistant Physician, Glasgow Royal Asylum for Lunatics	1891 1901 Dr R. Blair	

		Gartloch (1895)
MB CM 1888 Certificate Med. Psychol. Association	Assistant Physician, Glasgow Royal Asylum for Lunatics	1901 Dr L. R. Oswald

Source: Various, including directories (mainly census years).

From Table 9 it can be seen that, though long tenure could and did occur, the Poor Law hospital service was not necessarily a dead-end:[20] indeed, its officers, by eventually rehabilitating themselves amongst the élite, may have helped to improve the status of the appointments so that, by the end of the century, good medical graduates were in these resident posts.

The evolution of a career structure can be detected both in general medicine and in the field of lunacy—roughly a parallel of the emerging structure in the voluntary general hospitals, but at not so prestigious a level and each structure in its early stages providing an avenue into the other. Talent, connections perhaps, and ambition, providing the unquantifiable elements in the eventual point of arrival.

The Town's Hospital could be regarded as a municipal enterprise, though it originally catered for the homeless destitute and was not primarily a medical institution. But the destitute inevitably are in need of medical care and this was provided by the members of the Faculty of Physicians and Surgeons from 1733 until the Hospital became the Poorhouse for City parish under the provisions of the Poor Law of 1845. Perhaps this time-honoured connection with service to the poor in the City of Glasgow explains the initial involvement of prominent members of the profession with the parochial hospitals.

Temporary hospitals to cope with floods of patients during the fever epidemics of the first half of the nineteenth century and financed municipally or parochially were staffed by the profession on an ad hoc basis, and were often regarded as a particular form of service by professionals to the community in times of emergency (but not necessarily on a voluntary basis). This term soon became a misnomer for the continuing large numbers of fever patients and the pressure upon hospital accommodation; so, during a period of active concern by the City Fathers for the massive problems resulting from explosive population growth, the decision to take powers under the 1862 Police Act to alleviate the situation fitted into the pattern. A

TABLE 12

Physician Superintendents in Municipal fever hospitals

	From	Kennedy Street Fever Hospital	To
Qualifications			
MD CM 1862	Assistant Medical Officer Town's Hospital	1865: Dr J. B. Russell	Belvidere
		1870 1880 } A succession of short-term appointments, e.g.,	
		Dr Gavin Tennant	Dispensary Physician GW1
		Dr Samson Gemmell	Extra Physician GW1
		Dr J. H. Lilly	Medical Superintendent GW1

	From	Belvidere	To
Qualifications			
MD CM 1862	Physician Super-intendent, Kennedy Street Fever Hospital	1871: Dr J. B. Russell	Medical Officer of Health, Glasgow
MB CM 1869	Resident Surgeon, Fort William Hospital	1881 1891 } Dr J. W. Allan	Dispensary Physician GR1 and private practice
MB CM 1894 DPH 1898:	Medical Officer of Health, Guernsey	1901: Dr J. Brownlee	

Source: Post Office Directories; Medical Directories (mainly census years).

hospital financed by the Town Council and managed by it through the recently-created Medical Officer of Health had an in-built prestige; it was of local inspiration and execution (much as had been the Town's Hospital of the eighteenth century) and not imposed by remote legislators in London, as were the Poor Law institutions. The clientele would conceivably be more mixed, since fever was no respecter of the class divisions in society. The building itself, working conditions and rates of pay were not subject to the philosophy of 'the absolute minimum'. From the point of view of the medical staff, the Fever Hospital, though perhaps a potentially more hazardous place of work, provided a useful, respectable and very acceptable experience for both senior and junior staff.

The original Fever Hospital was sited in Parliamentary Road and came into operation in 1865, but it was quickly recognised that further accommodation would be required. The Corporation, with strong backing from the Medical Officer of Health (Dr Gairdner) and the Physician Superintendent (Dr Russell), carefully planned a purpose-built hospital at Belvidere, which took in its first patients at the close of 1870. This institution was enlarged over the next decade, whilst the original fever hospital was used increasingly for cases of smallpox and childhood infections, and eventually closed in 1878.[21] It was held 'in reserve' until 1890; the more vigilant concern for the health of the community which had developed steadily as a result of the Public Health (Scotland) Act of 1867, prompted municipal action on accommodation for infectious diseases, and the Parliamentary Road Hospital was opened again for cases of measles and whooping cough. Nevertheless, the important municipal hospital, and the more prestigious, remained Belvidere, until, as a result of boundary changes in 1891 and the further increase in the city authority's responsibilities for health, a second major hospital at Ruchill was built and opened in 1900: municipal service was providing further opportunities for medical men.[22]

(b) Dispensaries

TABLE 13

Medical appointments in Dispensaries

	1801	1825	1851	1861	1871	1881	1891	1901
No. of dispensaries	1	4	2	2	6	4	4	3
No. of appointments	1	4	2	8	7 + 3C	22 + 2C	23 + 11C and S	25 + 16C and S
Total	1	4	2	8	10	24	34	41

C = Consulting staff
S = 'Special' staff

Source: Various, including directories.

These 'doctors' shops' writ large are difficult to trace in Glasgow in the early nineteenth century.[23] Their purpose, as developed in Edinburgh, was to serve the sick poor; in Glasgow, it is conceivable that the needs of these people were considered to be adequately covered by the Town's Hospital with its indoor and outdoor services (see below, Section (e)), by the fact that the Faculty of Physician and Surgeons published a standard sliding scale of charges which varied according to income, and that, in the last resort, doctors regarded free treatment of the poor as part of their professional duties. So, a Dispensary recorded in 1800 is a 'subscription' dispensary, and it was no longer in operation in 1820.[24]

The University Lying-in Dispensary of 1834 may well have been prompted by the death of the Lying-in Hospital's principal financial supporter, Professor John Towers, in 1832,[25] and the simultaneous moves to found the publicly-supported Glasgow Lying-in Hospital. The Dispensary, besides being a cheaper alternative form of service to the poor, would provide a clinical teaching base for Professor Cumin of Midwifery. The Dispensary continued and developed at the expense of the attached Hospital, in accordance with the philosophy of John Pagan (appointed to the Chair of Midwifery in 1840), who disagreed with the principle of hospital confinements on the grounds that puerperal fever and sepsis flourished in lying-in wards. He advocated domiciliary care, which continued to be provided by the Dispensary until its incorporation into the Western Infirmary following the University's move to Gilmorehill.[26]

Apart from the GRI Dispensary which was organised at this time, four others[27] set up by 1838 were short-lived. The Gorbals Dispensary was perhaps the most successful, since reference is made to it by doctors who had worked there (in the Medical Directory 1852, e.g., James Rowand, LFPS,—late Surgeon, Gorbals Dispensary).

The sudden increase in numbers of Dispensaries between 1861 and 1871 reflects the fashion for 'specialism' and particularly the entrepreneurial activity of McCall Anderson, who ran both the Skin and Ear Dispensaries himself. The later reduction in numbers was not due to failure but to success and rationalisation. McCall Anderson's Ear Dispensary was able to attract charitable funds and convert itself into a Hospital and Dispensary; and the functions of the Western Public Dispensary were taken over by the Western Infirmary and Anderson's College Dispensary.[28] General dispensaries gradually absorbed the 'specials', but specialist doctors were attached to them and continued to exercise and develop their particular skills.

The attitude of the Glasgow doctors towards Dispensaries was voiced from time to time in the Glasgow Medical Journal—they were not regarded as an unmitigated benefit to the community. As could be expected, the comments involved accusations of self-interest and self-aggrandisement at the expense of less affluent colleagues (mis-management), professional arrogance, complaints of and abuse of the dispensary services; and assertions that provision for the sick and needy was already made, without the need for new special facilities. However, as one member of the profession admitted '. . . the competition for appointments was the reason why they were honorary with no accompanying honorarium. Generally speaking, however, such applicants—and among these he included himself —expected that some good would result from the holding of such appointments, either in the direction of experience or in some way or other not at the time, perhaps, well-defined'.[29]

Some attempt at remedying the abuse of such medical charities, in conjunction with the Charity Organisation Society, was made in 1887, but came to nothing: they continued to be exploited by professionals and public alike.

TABLE 14

Educational appointments for medical men

	1800	1826-45	1851	1861	1871	1881	1891	1901
University of Glasgow	2P 3L	4P + 1L to 7P	7P 1L	7P 1L	7P 4pA 1L	9P 3pA 3L 3 Dem.	9P 8pA 2L 3D	18pA 1 Dem 4 + 1L
Anderson's University (later Anderson's College Medical School 1876).	2P	2P to 7P	7P	7P	8P	7P 2pA 4L	7P 3pA 3L 4D	8p 5L
College St. School	3	4						
Portland St. School		5P to 6P						
St Mungo's College						'GRI School' 12L	21	12P 12pA 8L
Queen Margaret College							8	11L
Western Medical School						4	5	7L
Totals:	10	16 to 24	15	15	20	47	73	96

Note: P = Professor. pA = Assistant to Professor. L = Lecturer. D = Demonstrator.
Source: Various, including directories, Annual Reports, GUA

(c) *Educational appointments*

Features of the organised medical teaching of Glasgow through the nine-
teenth century are the constant presence of the University Faculty of
Medicine and the ebb and flow around it of extra-mural 'schools'—(see
Table 14).

University medical teaching had been sporadic and uninspired[30] until
William Cullen revitalised attitudes and attracted students to Glasgow.
Before becoming part of the University establishment as Lecturer and then
Professor of Medicine (1751) he first gave lecture courses on Medicine,
Chemistry, etc., as an independent teacher and set an example which other
enthusiasts followed.[31] By the end of the eighteenth century, the pressure of
demand for teaching from students and from the medical profession for
facilities had produced a more active University Medical Faculty, with a
supplementary staff of three Lecturers.

Competition (or opportunity) had appeared in 1796, with the establishment of Anderson's Institution[32] and the appointment of a professor of
Surgery. John Burns, the nominee, was already established as a popular
lecturer in Anatomy in his own rooms in College Street and there he
continued, with various assistants, until proper facilities for medical
teaching were eventually provided by the Anderson Trustees in 1828, and
some modest expansion was possible.[33]

This was timeous too and perhaps prompted by the awakening of the
Glasgow doctors to post-war opportunities. The interest of the State in
trained medical manpower, provoked partly by the demands of the long war
years was reflected in the institution of Regius Medical Chairs in Scottish
Universities to augment existing provision of medical teaching:[34] This was
paralleled by the definition of curricula and the stricter regulation of
teachers and examinations by Universities and medical licensing bodies.
Glasgow's Faculty of Physicians and Surgeons, which had hitherto
examined the knowledge and skills of those non-graduates who were to
practise predominantly in the West of Scotland now sought to exploit the
demand for medical qualifications by revision of criteria and standards for
the granting of a Faculty Licence, so as to put it 'on the same footing' as
diplomas of the other medical Corporations. In so doing, the non-
University teaching in Glasgow was effectively confined to the Members of
Faculty (or to the Fellows of other Royal Colleges) who might live in the
city; Glasgow University did not even countenance their courses until past
the mid-century (1875) and provided very few internal appointments. Thus
medical teaching was the preserve of the élite of the Glasgow profession.[35]

Their enterprise led to some enlargement of the College Street school and
the establishment of a similar group of lecturers as the Portland Street
school. They flourished and died within the second quarter of the century as
the primacy of Scotland in the provision of medical education was eroded
by developments in London:[36] by mid-century medical teaching had become
concentrated in two institutions—Glasgow University and Anderson's
University (as it was then named).

This contraction of teaching opportunities was balanced somewhat by the official requirement made of all the GRI staff from 1830, that they give clinical lectures during their periods of office.

The seventies saw the next medical change in educational provision, as the long overdue move of the University from the city centre to the western outskirts was carried out: not only considerations of convenience for staff and students but also more pressing claims of the expanded Glasgow population for concomitant hospital facilities prompted the establishment of a second large voluntary hospital immediately adjacent to the new academic site. The subsequent transfer of the most senior and distinguished physicians and surgeons from the GRI to the purpose-built teaching accommodation of the Western Infirmary (1874) prompted swift reaction on the part of the Royal's Board of Directors. The prestige of the GRI, acquired over almost a century, could not be allowed to wane: and it could best be ensured by the setting up of a Royal Infirmary School of Medicine. Clinical facilities for medical students would continue as before to the benefit of Infirmary finances and hence to that of patient care; and attachment to a medical school provided career opportunities for an extra number of Glasgow doctors (along with modest emoluments). Ideas of expanding the concept of the educational facet of the GRI into an institution of a more general nature were abortive in all but a change of name; St Mungo's College (1889) led a rather precarious existence for thirty years and was then (1910) honourably absorbed into the University Medical School with the establishment in the GRI of two St. Mungo professorial Chairs (of Medicine and Surgery) and two other endowed Chairs (of Pathology and Obstetrics and Gynaecology).

The emergence of St Mungo's College was paralleled by moves to provide medical education for women in Glasgow. The two could not be combined for what were at the time irreconcilable social attitudes, and separate facilities were organised (1890) in the recently-established Queen Margaret College (1883): responsibilities for these were handed over to the University in 1892 (see Chapter Nine, note 7 below).

Towards the end of the century, private enterprise raised its head in that field for the last and all too brief time. The Western Medical School (1880) provided tuition in a limited range of subjects; it appears to have been the brainchild of a group of young and ambitious medical men, who wished to create their own opportunities to gain experience—the teaching market was still a fairly free one for those able to test it.

The rapid widening of opportunities in medical education was less a question of pressure of students as the twentieth century approached than of demands of the medical curriculum; University professors no longer had time to be literati or general practitioners—the accumulated body of medical knowledge was vastly enlarged as a result of specialisation, research work and the development of new techniques and diagnostic tools in the wake of technological advance. Medical education required an expanding work-force and the Glasgow doctors were willing recruits.

As in the hospitals, a career structure developed in education: a free-lance

lecturer in the early 1800s could aspire to join first a group of teachers
(College Street School), then to appointment on the staff of Anderson's
Institution. This in itself denoted success, but a Professor there was not
slow to transfer to the University if opportunity offered.[37] Later, the
appointment of Demonstrator in any of the 'schools' of the eighties and
nineties could mark the beginning of an academic medical career. At the
other end of the scale, experienced members of the profession without
teaching appointments found a prestige-conferring role as examiners—
the arbiters of the whole elaborate process of producing medical manpower.

The financial rewards of educational activity are not easy to assess. The
eighteenth-century University foundations were handsomely endowed
(Physic—£270, Anatomy—£250) compared with the early nineteenth-century Regius Chairs (Surgery—£50, Midwifery—£50), which carried the
same rewards as the privately-endowed Waltonian lectureships. Later,
peculiar circumstance and internal politics at Glasgow University resulted
in some of the new medical chairs providing no salary:[38] but by 1876 a
rather more equitable position was in evidence and all the medical
professors received at least £100 per annum (although those of Physic and
Anatomy continued at their traditional figure).

There was in addition, direct income from students' fees which depended
upon the size of the class. Fees at GU were 3 guineas for lecture courses and
for practical classes and numbers in the Anatomy class varied between 100
and 200 for most of the first fifty years of the century. Fee income in the last
three decades of the century helped to finance the equipment and assistance
necessary to the teaching of an increasingly science based curriculum: on
balance and with the exception of the GU Anatomy chair (total emoluments
£1095 in 1876–77), University medical appointments alone were not
lucrative, being mainly £250–£300 in 1876–77.[39] But the dignity and prestige
they conferred undoubtedly provided wider opportunities for financial
gain.

Extra-mural fees often undercut those of the University, at 1–2 guineas
per course, and again numbers fluctuated. In 1882, the GMJ reported that,
at 800, the medical student population was the highest ever and other
sources[40] suggest that the number increased to around 1000 by 1900.
Clinical lectures given by appointed physicians and surgeons augmented
Infirmary funds and the doctors' salaries—in 1857, when students usually
paid 5 guineas for a year's instruction, the GRI collected about £1020, of
which £452 was paid out to the four lecturers concerned in proportion to the
number of students choosing to attend each one.

At all times, and not surprisingly, a large proportion of the Glasgow
medical corps was a product of the city's medical school, in that first
medical qualifications were either of the Faculty (Membership, Licence or
later, Double or Triple Qualification) or the University of Glasgow degree.[41]
The rest, overwhelmingly, had Scottish diplomas: though Glasgow was an
importer of students and an exporter of qualified medical people, it was
rare indeed to find a medical 'incomer' from south of the Border.[42]

(d) Outdoor services

TABLE 15

Medical posts: 'outdoor' appointments

	1800	1825	1851	1861	1871	1881	1891	1901
Municipal								
(a) Town's Hospital		6						
'Districts'								
Appointments		6						
(b) Police Districts			2	5	7	7	7	9
Appointments			2	5	7	10	7	9
Poor Law								
Number of parishes			4	4	4	4	3	2
Number of parochial district surgeons			17	21	26	19	17	16
Total of appointments		6	19	26	33	29	24	25

Source: Various, including directories, Annual Reports.

Glasgow carried a tradition of looking after its poor—apart from the conscience of its medical men, the town sought to provide medical service for the needy,[43] which was first institutionalised in the Town's Hospital. By 1816 the demands made upon the Surgeon to the Hospital prompted a recommendation to the Town Council that a domiciliary service be organised on a 'district' basis and that the poor, on attestation by the local minister or elder, should be treated as a charge upon the Town's Hospital. As Glasgow's size increased, so did the number of 'districts', until, in 1845, when this municipal service was transferred to the statutory Poor Law, there were 16(+ 1 'extra') District Surgeons employed by the Directors of the Hospital.[44]

These early District Surgeons were mainly Faculty members, occasionally young men, fairly recently qualified, but most of them practitioners of quite long-standing, or of a later considerable repute.[45] Nor was it beneath the dignity of a professor to undertake district work—George Watt of Anderson's University was Professor of Medical Jurisprudence in 1840 and a District Surgeon. Remuneration was very modest at 10 guineas per year, with occasional bonus payments at times of fever epidemics:[46] nevertheless, it would seem that civic duty and some philanthropic impulse kept this service manned by reputable practitioners of the day.

Similar comment can be made of the Police District Surgeons, another

Service which had functioned well enough on almost minimal staffing until the acceleration in population growth after 1850. Civic employment conferred recognition and status, and demanded as pre-conditions adequate academic standing.

The Poor Law of 1845 saw the regularisation of medical care for the sick poor and removed the prime responsibility from the individual doctor and the local community; the State assumed control over the structure whilst failing to contribute to its finance, so that working conditions and remuneration varied widely over the country. There was no staffing difficulty in Glasgow, and the withdrawal of the former Parochial Surgeons (most of them, in 1840, Members of the Faculty) from the new-style service created opportunities for others—though there was no security of tenure, there were more than enough practitioners wishing to take advantage of the remuneration offered for these part-time posts. In 1850, City Parish appointed twelve surgeons at salaries of £45 per annum;[47] by the end of the century this had risen to £65 per annum whilst Barony Parish offered £75 per annum in the eighties.

The parochial force was an increasingly graduate one

	Graduate	Non-graduate	Ratio
1851	4	13	1:3.2
1871	16	9	1:8.1
1891	15	3	5:1

which, (though not exactly parallel) reflected the general change in the qualifications of the medical profession. In spite of a long campaign to establish security of tenure (gained under the Local Government Act of 1894) it would appear that this was unlikely to be a burning issue in Glasgow, since many parochial officers served for at least ten years and a few as long as twenty years.

It is difficult to generalise about the social role and status of the parochial medical officer. Was it the refuge of the incompetent, a bolt-hole? On balance, this is doubtful. The appointments were made by the Parochial Boards and the salaries were paid by rates levied upon the community—it is highly probable that the non-professionals involved in the relief of the poor would demand value for money and that the competence of the medical appointees would be of some weight in the decisions made. Since tenure was not secure until 1894, performance of the Parochial Medical Officers must have demanded effort—negligence was unlikely to be tolerated and, although the work was probably depressing, it must have afforded recompense, be it purely economic or largely altruistic, depending more upon the attitudes of the individual than upon a societal view of the work. The posts meant different things to different people—as already mentioned, a source of dependable income (for a stated short period only, during most of the century), as a base from which to progress to a thriving practice, or to other kinds of medical appointment.[48]

It is conceivable that by the end of the century, when tenure was assured and the Parochial Officers (in England at least) had become a body sufficiently conscious of a distinct group identity to form an official Association,[49] the Poor Law doctors had acquired respect and some degree of status. Legislation (Public Health (Scotland) Act, 1867) brought responsibility for administration of Public Health under control of the Board

TABLE 16

Public medical appointments

	1800	1825	1851	1861	1871	1881	1891	1901
Prison	1	1	1	1	1 + 1a	2	4	4
Police force								
Under Public Health Act 1867								
MOH (City)					1 + 1a	1	1	1
Vaccinators					5	5	5	5
MOH (District)					3	4	5	2
Forensic			1	3	3	2	2	1
Factories Act		1	3	3	3	3	8	7
Miscellaneous	1	2	4	2	1	2	1	12
Total	2	4	9	9	19	19	26	32

Note: 'Miscellaneous' includes at various times: Quarantine Surgeon, Inspector of Madhouses.
The MOH (District) were appointed to areas around the city proper (e.g., Partick, Pollok): their number decreased with extension of the city boundaries.
'a' denotes 'Assistant'.
Source: Various, including directories, Burgh Records.

of Supervision and indicated that Poor Law medical work could be conveniently combined with that of Public Health. There was, indeed, one worthy Glasgow gentleman who was simultaneously for a period Parochial Medical Officer, Police District Surgeon and Medical Officer of Health for the same district, and who probably regarded general practice as incidental: occasionally also, a parochial appointment was held along with one in a charitable medical institution.[50]

(e) Public appointments

Included in this group are medical officers attached to local government institutions and those required by a variety of legislative measures enacted during the nineteenth century (but excluding the Poor Law (Scotland) Act). All were part-time appointments, with the exception of the Medical Officer of Health for Glasgow which, having been instituted as such in 1863 in the person of William T. Gairdner, became a full-time post when he was succeeded in 1872 by J. B. Russell.

All (including the Police District attachments above) confirmed some degree of prestige and some demanded extra qualifications—for instance, under the Burgh Police (Scotland) Act 1892, a Medical Officer of Health appointed after 1894, must, in addition to meeting the usual registration demands, also hold a Diploma in Sanitary Science, Public Health or State Medicine. It was, in any case, rare, for a non-graduate doctor to be appointed to these services and there was always a number of Faculty Fellows engaged in this kind of public medical work—it did not conflict with concepts of professional status. Throughout the second half of the century, the medical élite of Glasgow were more evident as Police and Public Health officers than as parochial ones; and whilst some doctors in the former group were simultaneously teachers in recognised educational institutions, the latter never were.

Public appointments were salaried[51] and their proliferation could provide, by judicious combination, a highly successful career in medicine, as is illustrated by William McGill.

He was licensed by the Faculty in 1848, and probably left Glasgow for a while,[52] but was back by 1861, having acquired the licence of the RCPEd. (1859). In that year he was serving as a Parochial Medical Officer, as Surgeon to the Police Force and as a Police District Surgeon (Central). Two years later, he became a FFPSG and in 1867 took the degree of MD: by 1871, he had moved from Duke Street to George Street—western migration was an indication of prosperity. Ten years later he was established in the newly developed western area of Hillhead and at this date (1881) was no longer a parochial surgeon but retained his police work. In 1891, he had relinquished all salaried work and had moved yet again, to Blythswood Square—this, though eastward, brought him into an area associated for half a century with medical practice at its social 'best'.

Experience in this type of appointment could also provide a springboard for quite a different career. William Macewen graduated from Glasgow University in 1869 and, after serving as House Surgeon at the Glasgow Royal Infirmary, was Assistant Surgeon at the Town's Hospital (City Poorhouse) in 1871. From there, he moved to become Casualty Surgeon to the City's Police Force and, by 1881, was established in Bath Street, with appointment as Surgeon to the Royal Infirmary and lecturer in Surgery, Clinical Surgery and Medical Jurisprudence in the Glasgow Royal Infirmary. He became Regius Professor of Surgery at Glasgow University in 1892, Surgeon at the Western Infirmary and was knighted for his service to medicine (see Chapter Five).

(f) 'Other attachments'

TABLE 17

'Other' medical attachments

	1800	1825	1851	1861	1871	1881	1891	1901
Total medical force			240	222	236	280	403	558
Number of doctors having 'other' medical attach- ments			15	35	56	67	97	128

Source: Post Office Directories; Medical Directories.

There is a tremendous number of institutions and organisations, both charitable and business, mentioned in the medical directories by those doctors who had some kind of professional association with them. It was a recognition of competence, bestowing a degree of status, which bore a direct relationship to the prestige of the body employing the medical services: where these were voluntary, extra credit accrued.

The whole spectrum of the Glasgow profession, from University Professor to ordinary GP, was involved in 'extra' associations—from charitable non-medical institutions (Houses of Refuge, Reformatories, Blind Institution)[53] and voluntary military groups (Lanarkshire Rifle Volunteers) to those connected with the economic life of Glasgow.

A healthy and active work-force was an increasingly important factor in industrial and commercial enterprise both locally and nationally and medical practitioners were called upon for appropriate advice and help (with suitable return to themselves) in the efficient management of labour. State intervention in industrial and commercial organisation resulted in some regulatory legislation (Factory Acts, Infectious Diseases Acts, Quarantine Acts, Vaccination Acts), involving to varying degrees medical assessment or therapy with respect to the workforce. Local enterprises began during the nineteenth century to retain the services of a medical man: Tennant's of St Rollox pioneered this. Insurance was a developing support system for both business activity and the individual: in its schemes for the latter, medical facts were essential to the deployment of actuarial skills, and the growth of insurance companies provided increasing requirements for 'Medical References' or 'Medical Officers'. The large, nationwide, prosperous companies tended to retain the senior and most reputable members of the Glasgow medical establishment—an exercise in mutual enhancement of prestige.[54]

The Provident Societies or Associations point to the early self-organisation of labour and to trade groupings. Both, by their corporate use of doctors, reflect from a different angle the conception of the importance of good health and the value of medical services to the working man, particularly after mid-century.[55] They were regarded somewhat ambivalently (as were the Dispensaries) by the profession. In 1872 fees ranging from 2s. 6d. to 5s. per annum, paid to the doctor for each member of a Society and covering attendance and necessary medicines, were regarded as derisory and demeaning in some quarters; whilst an average fee of 'nearly 1/6 per visit' was looked upon as equivalent in acceptability to the rewards of trade or parochial medical work.[56] The modest practitioner, without other professional appointment, was happy to retain this small degree of security—as many of them did for decades.

Since success, like money, generates itself, it is to be expected that, in a widening field of opportunities, there would be pluralism: this is indeed the case with Glasgow's medical profession.

TABLE 18

Total of medical appointments, whether full or part-time, available in Glasgow

	1800	1825	1851	1861	1871	1881	1891	1901
Hospital	7	12	29	39	60	88	164	227
Dispensary	1	4	2	8	10	24	34	41
'Outdoor'	1	6	19	26	33	29	24	25
Educational	10	16	15	15	20	47	73	96
Public	2	4	9	9	19	19	26	32
Totals:	21	42	74	97	142	207	321	421

Source: Various, as for previous tables.

The most frequent combination throughout the century was hospital (excepting parochial) appointment and teaching post—indeed, it was automatic in the last three decades or so, as the vital association of academic theory and clinical observation developed as the basic philosophy of medical education. There was some plurality in hospital and dispensary attachments; a surgeon at the Royal might serve in a similar capacity at one of the small specialist hospitals or at a general or special dispensary.[57] 'Specialities' were pursued at 'Consultant' level along with general hospital work.[58] Simultaneous appointments were also held at a less exalted level.[59]

The established profession deflected criticism and acquired grace by acting as Consultants to other charitable organisations (Deaf and Dumb Institute, Charity Asylum, etc.) or as Medical Officers for other worthy causes (Seaside Homes, Training Home for Nurses).

In the middle ranks, particularly in the second half of the century, employment by industrial concerns and by some insurance companies was a valuable addition to a minor professional appointment to a small hospital or dispensary: and for those doctors who had no other medical connections, the work for insurance companies bulked large. It was not completely spurned by the élite, but it would appear that, having served its economic purpose in the early days of a career, subsequent success led to the abandonment of commercial links.

5. The achievement: a profession with status?

It is fairly obvious that following the profession of medicine did not provide a simple means of earning a living unless there were family resources in reserve. Looking at the nineteenth century and the progress of the profession, it would seem that by enhancing its image and consolidating its status in general, medicine by its very desirability was perpetuating the dilemma between freedom of action and financial security. Discussion in 1894, commenting on the growth of medical aid associations, charitable medical services and the ratio of doctors to population, concluded that

> the struggle for existence generally within the ranks of the medical profession had become annually more keen.[60]

Economic side-lines were necessary—at the beginning of the century the modest practitioner kept a shop and traded: at its end, a connection with an insurance society provided a minimal guaranteed income. The climate was ripe for the exchange of a degree of freedom for a degree of security—in the shape of State intervention to match the needs of the doctors with those of the community.

The National Insurance Act of 1911 was generally welcomed by the bulk of medical manpower, although Glasgow's Royal Faculty of Physicians and Surgeons[61] considered that the scheme was derogatory to the profession. Its Fellows could afford literally to take this attitude, which in any case reflected the feeling of only a fifth or so of the city's doctors (see Table 4). Their views, along with those of the other Royal Colleges, were largely ignored by those directly concerned with the legislation.

The Act heralded a fundamental change of principle and set the course for the eventual organisation of a comprehensive Health Service in 1948. Wage-earners were to be made less dependent upon charitable enterprise for medical care and in an adaptation of the Victorian Samuel Smiles' philosophy of 'self help', were to make present compulsory contribution to potential future needs. At the same time, the doctor was to become the focus of medical service as insured patients were directed to him: he no longer had to compete with hospital out-patient departments.

Medical demands have continued to grow and so the corps of dedicated and efficient practitioners has increased, to cope with both the continually expanding area of what is medically possible and the more sophisticated ideas of what constitutes 'health care'.

Chapter Three

RONA GAFFNEY

Poor Law hospitals 1845-1914

1. The Scottish Poor Law and medical care

The establishment of systematic medical care for paupers in Scotland arose out of the provisions of the Poor Law Amendment Act of 1845, the single most important piece of Scottish Poor Law legislation until the Local Government Act of 1929. The 1845 Act regulated Poor Law administration by establishing a two-tier system—a pattern which was to be followed in Scotland in Government regulation of Public Health in 1867 and Education in 1872. At local level the Act set up more than 800 Parochial Boards, managed by board members who were annually elected by the rate payers; nationally, a Board of Supervision was established to oversee the working of the Act.[1] This Board consisted of nine members, made up as follows: the Lords Provost of Edinburgh and Glasgow, the Sheriffs Depute of the counties of Perth, Renfrew, and Ross and Cromarty, the Solicitor General for Scotland, and three persons appointed by the Government. As its name implied, the Board's duties were primarily supervisory. It could initiate inquiries, give or withhold approval for parish building plans, and it decided on matters of dispute put to it by parishes. It could also outline its policy on important issues, such as the employment of paid nurses, by means of advisory circulars. But while these activities had some effect in influencing events at parish level, the Board had few powers of compulsion and where a parish chose to remain deaf to the Board's advice it could, on the whole, pursue its own course unhindered. The individual parochial boards retained a great deal more power and independence of action than their English counterparts, so that rates, Poor Law services, and the conditions in Poor Law hospitals in Scotland could and did vary considerably from parish to parish.

The issue of medical care was always an important one for Parochial Boards because the Scottish Poor Law had insisted from the first that state aid to the poor could only be given to those persons (and their dependents) who were *both* poor *and* disabled in some way. Though the Amending Act of 1845 made many changes in the organisation and administration of poor relief, it did not alter this basic principle. Therefore in Scottish poorhouses and in parish outdoor relief rolls, the proportion of paupers in need of medical care was always very high. The 1845 Act was specific about the clear responsibility which each parish bore for the medical treatment of its paupers and it provided the basis for an extensive Poor Law hospital service which could be expanded as required:

> In all cases in which poorhouses shall be erected or enlarged or altered . . . there shall be proper and sufficient arrangements made for dispensing and supplying

medicines to the sick poor, under such regulations as the Parochial Board shall make and the Board of Supervision shall approve; and there shall be provided by the Parochial Board proper medical attendance for the inmates of every such poorhouse and for that purpose it shall be lawful for the Parochial Board to nominate and appoint a properly qualified medical man who shall give regular medical attendance at such poorhouse and to fix a reasonable remuneration.[2]

2. The Glasgow Parishes

In 1845 the Glasgow area was divided among four parishes: the City of Glasgow, Barony, Govan and Gorbals. These parishes were far from uniform in size population or wealth. Only the City Parish and Gorbals were entirely town parishes; both Barony and Govan contained quite extensive rural areas within their bounds as well as important urban areas.

The City Parish encompassed most of central Glasgow north of the Clyde, and its population in the mid-nineteenth century was around the 170,000 mark. Though smaller than Barony in terms of population, it always had the largest pauper roll. This was due to the prevalence of slum areas and common lodging houses within its boundaries, and to the likelihood of vagrants being sent to the City poorhouse by the Police, Harbour or Customs officials. Gradually the City Parish's unenviable lead in pauper numbers was whittled down as its slums were cleared by railway developments or the activities of the City Improvement Trust from the 1860s onwards. The rapid extension of Glasgow's urban area into the rural parts of Govan and Barony parishes in the later nineteenth century also helped to equalise conditions.

Barony Parish also lay north of the Clyde and had an area of 13.91 square miles and a population in the middle nineteenth century of just below 290,000, making it the most populous parish in Scotland. It included not only large areas of northern and eastern Glasgow, but fairly large stretches of farm land and several independent urban communities like the burghs of Maryhill, Springburn and Hillhead. This overlap of parochial with burgh authority caused some problems in the administration of the Nuisance Acts and Public Health legislation, but was immaterial to the provision of Poor Law services.[3]

Govan Parish straddled the River Clyde and at 28,489 acres it was the largest in area of the four. Its mid-nineteenth-century population was around 150,000. As well as encompassing a fair-sized landward area, the parish included the village of Govan, the burgh of Partick, and a large portion of the area of municipal Gorbals. The parish of Gorbals was adjacent, the smallest in area of the four (6940 acres) and wholly urban in composition. It had a small population of little more than 10,000 and a very low average valuation for rating purposes. Since this was coupled with a very high level of pauperism, Gorbals could only meet its requirements by resorting to monstrously high assessment rates, reaching 16 per cent or 17 per cent in many years, while the rate in nearby Govan Parish remained at between 4 per cent and 5 per cent. Rates at this level burdened the already poor population of the parish and often barely managed to bring in the minimum needed for poor relief. Recognising its serious difficulties, the Gorbals Parochial Board tried, unsuccessfully, to unite with other Glasgow parishes in 1869. Finally, in January 1873, Govan was persuaded to take Gorbals into combination. A further important alteration in the Glasgow parish system took place twenty-five years later when the parishes of City and Barony merged in an attempt to bring greater uniformity to the provision for paupers in the city.

The three larger Glasgow parishes possessed poorhouses incorporating hospital sections; until its combination with Govan in 1873, Gorbals dealt with its indoor poor by sending the ordinary poor to Govan poorhouse, hospital cases to Glasgow Royal Infirmary, and lunatics to asylums elsewhere. The poorhouse maintained by City Parish had been in existence long before the Poor Law Amendment Act of 1845 and had developed from the eighteenth-century Town's Hospital (1733), a refuge for the sick and destitute. By the 1840s, the original building in Clyde Street had become inadequate, so when the premises of the Royal Lunatic Asylum in Parliamentary Road became vacant in 1843, they were acquired by the parish authorities and became the nucleus of a new poorhouse. There was no special separate hospital building, but the hospital section of the poorhouse regularly treated in excess of 5000 patients a year, while at any one time it was generally dealing with over 400 cases.

Barony's parish poorhouse was opened in 1853. It was built at Barnhill, near Springburn and its hospital section dealt with around 150 cases at any one time, rising to an average of about 300 cases by the 1890s. In September 1880 a separate hospital block was erected at Barnhill and in March 1887 two cottage hospital units were built in the grounds to accommodate sixty extra patients. After the merger of City and Barony parishes in 1898 some changes were made in hospital provision for the new larger parish. The old City Parish poorhouse in Parliamentary Road was closed and the valuable city centre site sold to a railway company. Barony poorhouse at Barnhill now dealt with all the ordinary poor while hospital cases were catered for in three new, purpose-built hospitals opened between 1902 and 1904. The largest of these, at Stobhill, was designed to provide more than 1700 beds, mainly for chronic and long-stay patients, with special wings for all the sick children of the parish and for the treatment of tubercular patients. Two new district hospitals, one in Duke Street and one at Oakbank, provided between them more than 500 beds for the treatment of acute medical and surgical emergencies.

Govan Parish established its original poorhouse in Eglinton Street, in former cavalry barracks, but the building was inadequate in size, layout and security. The parish acquired land at Merryflats, near Ibrox, in 1867, and its new poorhouse was opened there in 1872. This building contained separate, though linked, sections for ordinary inmates, hospital patients and for lunatic cases and is still in use as the city's Southern General Hospital. In comparison with the other two major Glasgow parishes, Govan poorhouse was relatively small, its hospital section generally dealing with between 150 and 200 patients at any one time.

3. Conditions in Poor Law hospitals

The kind of treatment which was available for Poor Law patients varied from parish to parish, but was in general always less attractive than that which was currently offered in voluntary hospitals. Throughout the entire period under consideration, Glasgow's voluntary charity hospitals maintained a very high turnover of cases and had long waiting lists of patients anxious for treatment there. Most of these people considered parish medical care to be a second-best choice, a prospect which would be avoided while there was still any hope of admission into one of the city's general or specialist charity infirmaries. The reasons for this preference were quite clear: voluntary hospitals provided a higher standard of care, employed good medical staff and better nursing staff than parochial institutions, and offered more comfortable, or at least less harshly discouraging physical surroundings. The unappealing aspects of parochial medical care were not imaginary nor were they accidental. They derived from the deliberate policy of Poor Law managers. Their concern for strict economy in parish medical spending seems to have had little connection with the absence of funds. Since most parish income came from a local assessment which could be fixed by the Parochial Boards themselves according to their needs, it was rare to find them in a position of real financial difficulty.[4] Between 1845 and 1914, deficits between income and expenditure in Glasgow parish accounts occurred infrequently and seemed to be only the result of a temporary miscalculation of the year's needs when setting the annual poor rate. However, despite this apparent financial security, parochial managers had strong incentives for being economical: they were rate payers themselves and had to face annual elections. In these circumstances it was their constant preoccupation to keep the poor rate within reasonable bounds; in any case parochial managers shared with their electors strong opinions on poverty which ensured that they provided no more than a basic minimum medical service. It was often held that pauperism was encouraged by lenient treatment and could only be controlled effectively by firm and repressive action by those in authority. Self-help was the recommended course of action by which all right-minded citizens ensured their survival and comfort in hard times, unemployment or sickness. The basic premise was that no-one had the moral right to expect society to look after him if he failed to do so himself. Poor Law provision existed for humanitarian reasons and not because society wished to support those they considered lazy or improvident. This reasoning remained basic to the approach of the parochial board managers even though they gradually eliminated the most unpleasant features of life in Poor Law institutions.

Parochial managers, then, eagerly embraced the concept of 'less eligibility' which had quickly become a part of the outlook of those working with the English Poor Law and it gained ground in nineteenth-century Scotland despite the legal differences between the two countries. The theory that at least part of the poorhouse should be run as a 'test' house to weed out the undeserving from the deserving became accepted Board of Supervision policy by the 1850s. The Board issued a circular of advice on this matter to all parochial boards in 1850:

> So long as relief to the poor was looked upon by the givers and the recipients as the fulfilment of a charitable rather than a legal obligation, poorhouses were naturally regarded merely in the light of almshouses for the reception of the more deserving amongst the aged, infirm or friendless poor. . . . But now there is a strong pressure on Parochial Boards from a class whose claims it would be unsafe to admit without testing the truth of the allegations on which those claims are founded. For this purpose a well regulated poorhouse is the best of all tests. While it furnishes sufficient and even ample relief to the really necessitous, it affords the only available security that the funds raised for the relief of the poor are not perverted to the maintenance of idleness or vice. But a poorhouse will be totally useless as a test, or rather it will not be a test at all, unless it is conducted under rules and regulations, as to discipline and restraint, so strict as to render it more irksome than labour . . . to those who are not truly fit objects for Parochial relief.

The circular went on to differentiate between the treatment of 'test' and of genuine cases, noting that poorhouses ought only to house two classes of pauper, other groups being awarded outdoor relief.

> *Class 1.* comprises all destitute persons who are incapacitated by youth or old age, or by disease, whether mental or physical, from contributing in any way to their own support and who . . . cannot be adequately maintained and cared for by means of out-door relief, except at a cost exceeding that for which they can be provided for in the poorhouse.
> *Class 2.* and to whom it is particularly applicable either as a test or as affording the means of needful restraint, consists of applicants for or recipients of relief of every kind whose claims are doubtful. . . . If Parochial Boards desire to discourage indolence, to detect imposture, and to reform or control vice, they must make *work, confinement* and *discipline* the conditions upon which paupers of this class are relieved.[5]

From this period, and in response to frequent reminders from the Board of

Supervision, most of the larger Scottish poorhouses employed task- or labour-masters and organised programmes of disciplined work in laundry, needlework, oakum picking, etc., for their 'test' cases who generally comprised malingerers, dubious medical cases, habitual drunkards, deserted wives, and women with illegitimate children. The success of these labour programmes required a strict classification of inmates according to character and needs, but it was always difficult to ensure that a real difference existed in the treatment of 'test' and genuine pauper cases. In practice, and especially when parish hospitals shared the same buildings as the general poorhouse, the concern of parish authorities to curtail severely the physical comfort and moral sympathy for their 'test' cases necessarily rebounded on the paupers and particularly on their sick patients. As a result of this general attitude of strict, cheese-paring economy, Poor Law hospitals lagged far behind voluntary hospitals in the introduction of new medical techniques or practices which were developing at an increasing rate in the late nineteenth and early twentieth centuries. For example, the technique of antiseptic surgery, pioneered by Lister and his associates at Glasgow Royal Infirmary had been accepted by the younger generation of surgeons and diffused into many large hospitals, but it was considered to be an unjustifiable refinement in parochial institutions a decade later.[6] So, in 1879 Dr Robertson, City Parish poorhouse medical officer, explained his current evaluation of antiseptics to his Medical Committee, basing his conclusions on financial rather than medical considerations:

> He has a high opinion of their efficacy and has constantly prescribed them in the treatment of surgical cases in the poorhouse. He at the same time states that it is right to add that considering that this is a Parochial establishment, he has not thought himself justified in ordering the more expensive apparatus and appliances employed in many general hospitals.[7]

Though the Medical Committee authorised Dr Robertson to undertake a 'somewhat more expensive mode of treatment of the cases' if this would result in greater benefit to the poor, their approval of the extra expense was guarded and it is clear that the doctor was expressing orthodox opinion on the relative positions of parochial and voluntary hospitals in the league of medical spending. Similarly, other parochial doctors found it difficult to persuade their boards to provide even minimal facilities for the hospital. Boards were reluctant to accept, for example, that separate rooms for operations were essential in mid-nineteenth-century hospital practice. Though parochial hospitals dealt with far fewer acute surgical or accident cases than voluntary hospitals, they did, nevertheless, undertake some major surgery during the average year. Records show that operations included amputations of fingers, breasts and limbs, the excision of cancerous bones, the removal of tumours, and even, optimistically, skin grafts for burns. The custom during the 1850s, 1860s and 1870s had been to perform these operations in the common wards, either in the patient's own bed or on a table brought in for the purpose. In a report dated as late as

1884, Barony's poorhouse Medical Officer wryly noted the drawbacks of this system:

> The want of an operating room had been much felt. At present all operations must be performed in a ward or ward kitchen, within sight and hearing of other patients. . . . Operating in a ward where other patients are lying is highly inconvenient to the operator and trying to the feelings of the other patients.[8]

A makeshift operating theatre was set up in Barnhill that very year, but City poorhouse did not even achieve that level of sophistication until 1892. By comparison with the standards of the city's voluntary hospitals, the facilities and equipment available for parochial hospital use were always very limited, spartan and out of date.

In addition to such disadvantages, poorhouse doctors had to face an even more basic problem in the shape of serious and prolonged shortages of beds and ward space. This problem grew as did the population and the numbers of paupers in Glasgow, and it probably reached its peak in the 1870s and 1880s. Overcrowding and shortage of beds were at their worst where hospitals had to share accommodation with the general poorhouse. As long as the hospitals were integral parts of the larger poorhouse, they were used as part of the general accommodation pool when space was at a premium. This meant that on the rare occasions when the hospital section was uncrowded, it could expect to receive an overflow of non-sick inmates. This policy seemed only sensible to harassed poorhouse governors, who were all too often faced with the puzzle of too many inmates and too few beds. The report made by the Board of Supervision inspector on a visit to City Parish in 1880 gives an idea of the straits to which governors were forced when overcrowding became really serious:

(a) During a part of last winter the population was as much as 300 above the authorised limit.

(b) The overcrowding was thus serious and the classification entirely destroyed.

(c) This excess in numbers was met by laying beds on the floor and also by placing bedsteads together in pairs and accommodating three paupers in each pair. . . .

(d) The tests suffered to such an extent that it was necessary to discharge in batches onto the out-door roll, inmates who, under an effective test, would have discharged themselves.[9]

In this kind of situation, the use of spare hospital beds, where they existed, appeared to be one of the most attractive alternatives open to governors. Naturally, the practice was viewed differently by medical officers because it ensured that hospitals remained crowded to capacity even when the incidence of illness was relatively low. This in turn meant an unremitting strain on the very sparse sanitary facilities and on the overworked staff. It also meant that the admission of genuine sick cases could be delayed since the free beds were given over to another use. However, though the intrusion of poorhouse difficulties into hospital affairs was always in the background, it never occupied the centre of the stage simply because the hospital section itself was usually too fully occupied by the sick to offer vacant space to anyone else.

Because large numbers of patients were normally treated in parochial hospitals, and since parishes were unwilling to spend money on extra building, it was usual to find that these hospitals were very cramped. During the busiest times it was not uncommon for medical officers to have recourse to making patients share beds, especially in children's wards. The following examples are from Barony Parish reports:

1. 1884. Hospital—In this department the accommodation does not afford a safe margin for ordinary occasions, thus during the past winter 25 children were at one time bestowed in 18 beds.[10]
2. 1886. I beg to inform you that the ward for the treatment of skin diseases (children) is overcrowded, there being 5 children in excess of the number of beds.[11]

In addition, more beds were set up than wards could accommodate comfortably, and medical officers had to press into service rooms which were unsuitable for hospital purposes. The net result was the creation of conditions which did not make for the comfort or quick recovery of sick patients and which, in some cases, came close to the lowest limits of accommodation sanctioned by the Glasgow local authority in its sanitary regulations for the city. For example, this is an extract of a report prepared for the City Parochial Board after an internal inquiry into the state of its hospital section in the early 1880s:

Mr. Robb submitted his statement, which he had prepared after careful inspection of the premises. After describing the range of buildings used as the male hospital, the ceilings of the first and second stories he considers are a fair height, but the height of the ceilings of the attic flat being only nine feet, the air is close and stifling, and he considers that flat especially unsuitable for hospital purposes. There is no bathroom accommodation, and the two small apartments used for W.C. and scullery have neither light nor ventilation, except when the doors are open. . . . In the female hospital the ceilings are unsatisfactory. . . . He considers the centre building very unsuitable for its purpose and by no means healthy as the cubic content of the sleeping apartments containing three beds allows only 333⅓ cubic feet of breathing space for each individual, while the apartments containing two beds allow only 320 cubic feet for each. He understands that this state of matters constitutes a contravention of the Police Act of 1862, which allows not less than 350 cubic feet for each individual. The apartments were originally constructed for a single inmate each.[12]

Since no major building was undertaken by City Parish at this time, it is presumed that conditions remained fairly similar until the end of the century.

The whole question of 'cubic air space per bed' was a difficult one. The Board of Supervision made no formal recommendation on the matter, but its visiting officers took care to point out that the standards in City and Barony were lower than even the minimum generally accepted by other medical authorities of the time. The City Parish's own medical officer had undertaken, in 1876, a careful comparison of the space allowed to patients in his hospital and that allowed in London workhouse hospitals, in the Glasgow charity infirmaries, and in the newest Scottish poorhouses to be approved by the Board of Supervision, Govan and St Cuthbert's (Edinburgh). On examining this report, the City Board came to the startling conclusion that at least 100 extra beds would be needed for their sick and infirm inmates if they hoped to achieve the same standards. Nothing, however, was done in the immediate future to put this recommendation into practice, and the City Parish hospital continued, like Barony, to provide grossly substandard services even though its managers were fully aware of the deficiency.

WCs, sinks and baths were always in short supply and successive reports indicate gross breaches of the most elementary sanitary rules. For example:

1. Barony, 1883. Visiting Officer's Report. The occupants of wards 141 (skin diseases) and 142 (venereal) use the same W.C., in which there are two seats, and the same bath. One lavatory with two basins and one W.C. is used by 41 patients, of whom six are lying-in patients, and there is no bathroom for these persons.[13]

2. City, 1882. Report by Dr. Littlejohn of the Board of Supervision. This report could be expanded into a small volume were each sanitary defect in these buildings pointed out and described. . . . The dishes are washed and stored in the water closets. In one case the dishes were piled around and up to within 2 or 3 inches of the earthenware basin which was exposed to view. There is no bath for the use of the female venereal ward and the children are bathed in a wooden tub which contained a bowl and, therefore, appeared to be used for washing dishes in. The nurse admitted that she sometimes emptied water, which had been used for washing children with this disease, into the sink which is provided for washing dishes in. . . . The walls of the staircase were in some instances streaming with wet, and clothes were spread out to dry on the railings. Clothes were sorted on the floor of a sick ward.

   I am unable to suggest either structural or sanitary alterations which would render this institution a suitable one for the accommodation of paupers.[14]

Faced with such intractable problems, it was difficult for medical officers to carry out their duties effectively. They were already restricted by their parishes' low level of expenditure on medical equipment; this reluctance to accept the need for larger and better hospital premises made things worse. Medical officers found themselves forced to be selective in their admissions. Since there was often not enough room for all, only the most serious cases could be accepted. Therefore the ordinary poorhouse wards generally housed convalescents who had been dismissed from hospital early (poor-houses did not share the voluntary infirmaries' advantage of convalescent homes), and sick people who were marginally less ill than those who rated a hospital bed. The following extracts indicate how harassed medical officers tried to keep their hospitals functioning in spite of almost overwhelming difficulties:

1. Barony, 1884. The average number under treatment in the hospital has been exceptionally high, the wards being constantly full. As showing the strain on accommodation, I may mention that the largest number of beds ever vacant was 30, while frequently there were no vacant beds at all, patients having to be discharged to make room for fresh admissions.[15]

2. Barony, 1886.

   Inspector of the Poor   14th March, 1886.
   Dear Sir,

   I beg to inform you that last night, at eleven o'clock, I was called to visit a woman named Mary Heron in the female Probationary Ward. She had been in the Probationary Ward since Thursday. When I saw her last night she was sitting on the floor gasping for breath and was so ill that she was unable to speak. As there were nineteen persons in seven beds, I deemed it advisable to remove her to hospital.

   A bed was made up on a chair, and one of the patients roused out of her bed to sleep upon it, and Mary Heron placed in the bed vacated by the patient. There were nine women and one child waiting in the female Probationary Ward for admission to hospital. A woman was sitting by the fire with a child on her knee, and she complained that she would have to sit by the fire all night. I offer no comment on these facts as I think it must be evident to you that increased hospital accommodation is very much needed.

   William Core, Medical Officer.[16]

Pressure upon accommodation was a feature of voluntary hospital life, too, at this period. However, this never became such a preponderant issue there for three reasons: first, voluntary hospitals had no obligation to provide for a certain class of the population as parochial hospitals did, so they could limit admissions before they caused serious harm to the internal conditions of the institutions; secondly, voluntary hospital managers were willing and, indeed, enthusiastic to expand their premises during this time—they never managed to keep pace with demand, but they did avoid complete stagnation;[17] thirdly, as teaching centres, most voluntary hospitals had staff who were closely interested in medical advances and this, along with their own high standing in the medical profession, ensured that standards remained moderate even in times of great demand.

The severe overcrowding and substandard hospital buildings in Poor Law establishments were greatly alleviated by the new parish hospitals built in the early twentieth century after the merger between City and Barony Parishes in 1898. The complete separation of hospital from poorhouse and of acute cases from chronic and infectious ones which subsequently occurred, was a great improvement and seemed to foreshadow the creation of an acceptable, comfortable, rate-supported hospital system for the city.

However, the difficulties of the old Poor Law were not resolved at a stroke. Since potential patients were still filtered through the Poor Law system, which required application for poor relief at the office of the Inspector of the Poor or at the poorhouse, many hiccups developed in the smooth running of the various hospital machines. Comments in parish Minutes between 1904 and 1906 indicate that the classification plan frequently failed and that patients often did not reach the appropriate hospital. Similarly, though new hospital buildings ended the worst of nineteenth-century hygiene and sanitation scandals, there was no major change in admission policy by parochial boards. Poor Law managers continued to exercise strict checks on the eligibility of persons who applied for hospital care and they showed no desire to amend legal restrictions and to extend their services more generally amongst the community. Such changes in hospital buildings and services as did take place seemed to be entirely the result of a need to deal with repeated Board of Supervision complaints on hospital standards coupled with a hope that a merger between City and Barony Parishes would rationalise hospital provision and make it less expensive.[18]

4. Doctors and patients

Poor Law Hospitals were unattractive to doctors and patients. The medical jobs were frustrating, physical conditions poor, and boards of management parsimonious. Patients were often long-term residents who suffered from chronic, incurable or 'uninteresting' ailments.[19] This ensured that medical men who could choose would seek employment elsewhere. Wage scales for poorhouse Medical Officers were similar to those offered to the Superintendents in voluntary general hospitals, but the parochial jobs never attained the same degree of respect or status. The undeniable drawbacks of Poor Law work did not, however, discourage all medical applicants. The work presented few challenges and so perhaps less worry over treatment.

A parochial doctor did not have to undertake much specialist medical work because, in the Glasgow parishes at any rate, parochial boards subscribed to various voluntary hospitals where they sent any special or unusual cases which arose amongst the patients. Consequently, special knowledge of the treatment of, say, eye or ear diseases was relatively unimportant.

With a few honourable exceptions,[20] it seems likely that parochial medical officers did not represent the cream of the medical profession. Perhaps parochial board members preferred an unimpressionable medical officer who would conform to their policy of strict economy. This concern created a kind of self-fulfilling prophecy when it came to the selection of their medical officers. Parochial hospital conditions sometimes deterred energetic doctors from seeking permanent jobs there; and Boards themselves distrusted ambitious doctors who might cause trouble. In 1876

Barony Parochial Board dismissed its Resident Medical Officer, Dr Strethill Wright, when he published an exposé of conditions in Barnhill poorhouse hospital.

Therefore, in the main Poor Law doctors seem to have been made up of two broad types:

(1) Young men who usually became assistants or short-stay medical officers. They took on the parochial job for the experience it offered, but moved on as soon as a better opportunity presented.

(2) Long-stay medical officers who appreciated the security of a regular income.

Patients in the Poor Law hospitals were usually the very poor, a disadvantaged group unable to exert any social pressure.

Parochial hospitals often found themselves supporting a sizeable proportion of chronic patients for very long periods. A report from Barony Parish in 1893 gives some idea of the numbers involved here:

The number of patients in hospital at this date is 376, 51 of whom have been over two years in hospital. These may be classified as follows

Over 2 years but under 3 years—17		
3	4	14
4	5	8
5	6	4
6	7	2
7	8	2
8	9	1
Over 9 years		3
	Total	51[21]

Comparing this situation with that in voluntary hospitals, where special permission had to be sought from boards of management if consultants wished to treat a patient for more than forty days, it is clear that the patient population in Poor Law hospitals was composed of a much greater proportion of intractable and indeed incurable cases. Most patients suffered from illnesses such as tuberculosis, bronchitis, cancer, or 'degenerative diseases': many were in fact terminal cases who would never return to their homes.

However, the type of illness suffered by patients was not the only, or even a reliable, criterion for differentiating between Poor Law establishments and others. It was not always an easy or straightforward matter to be treated in a parochial hospital. Admission was governed by fairly rigid rules—derived from the 1845 Act and from subsequent Board of Supervision regulations—by the initiative of individual Parochial Boards, and by the exigencies of accommodation. Patients might be admitted to hospital directly from the poorhouse, on the order of the medical officer. This was the easiest means of obtaining Poor Law hospital attention since all the

formalities surrounding entitlement to poor relief had already been overcome when the inmate first entered the poorhouse as an ordinary pauper.
Similarly, individuals already on the parish outdoor relief roll could easily
be transferred to hospital when such care was deemed necessary by the
medical officer, bed space permitting. However, many people who accepted
outdoor poor relief refused residence, dreading the social stigma of the
poorhouse. Even where hospital care was urgently needed it was not
uncommon to find resistance, as was reported at a City Parish meeting in
1880:

> Dr. Walker (the District Surgeon) explains that the case of Mrs. Patterson is
> clearly one for an hospital, but as she declined to go into the poorhouse, he is
> willing to do everything in his power to relieve her and will order a water bed at
> once, and supply any other articles. Mr. J. M. Cunningham appeared before the
> committee and stated that he made no complaint but that the family were unable
> to provide lint and other necessary bandages for the woman's bed sores.[22]

In such cases parochial boards had no powers of compulsion although they
could decide to continue home visits by their district surgeon or abandon
aid altogether.

Because the basic structure of the Scots Poor Law required evidence of
disability as well as destitution, a fair proportion of first-time applicants for
relief *were* more or less hospital cases. When an application for poor relief
was received, an examination by the district surgeon followed, the Inspector
of the Poor recommended the type and extent of relief to be given, and the
board's Relief Committee took the final decision. When the applicant
obviously needed hospital treatment, the process was speeded up as much as
possible, though it was never supposed to exceed 24 hours in any case. The
district surgeon's report was designed to elicit a basic picture of the
applicant's social and medical condition, but even with such information it
was quite possible for the mechanism to break down, leaving a hapless
pauper without the urgent attention he needed. If a pauper were judged too
ill to be moved to the poorhouse, there was very little in the way of alternative medical care. He remained dependent upon the goodwill of the
district surgeon to provide limited medical care at home. A further problem
frequently arose over the board's determination to stick to the formal requirements of the law when extending relief. They generally refused to
admit anyone who was above the level of a pauper, especially if their treatment were likely to be long or expensive. A precise line, in terms of income
or status, was never drawn between paupers and non-paupers, and this
whole question of defining when a person was entitled to poor relief in
Scotland was one which continued to cause trouble. Broad guidelines were
laid down in several circulars from the Board of Supervision, but even these
changed in emphasis according to prevailing trade conditions and the
decisions handed down in various important court cases. For instance,
during the serious trade depression of 1878–9, the Board of Supervision
offered advice which seemed to herald a departure from the stringency of

the 1845 Act, suggesting that 'in considering the question of disability in the case of a person really destitute, the Inspector should not carry the letter of the law to an extreme'.[23] This liberal and humane interpretation of what constituted a basis for poor relief would seem to have warranted local boards extending aid to some categories of the able-bodied and their sick or healthy dependants. Less than a decade later, however, the Board of Supervision changed its policy entirely and issued stern warnings against such liberality.

In practice, and despite Board of Supervision pronouncements, the answer to the basic question 'when is a person a pauper?' lay with the local boards. This question, and the related ones of how to deal with non-paupers, was one which was usually 'decided on its merits', and it varied over the years and in different parishes. In the Glasgow parishes, the official attitude seems to have been fairly strict. Until the mid 1870s, there appears to have been some laxity in allowing medical aid to non-paupers,[24] but this did not continue. Though the *precise* criteria for giving or with-holding medical aid are difficult to find, two general rules seem to have been followed in City, Govan and Barony Parishes:

(*a*) Medical relief in hospital or on the outdoor roll was most frequently given when the person involved was the family bread-winner—naturally enough, since this sort of case satisfied the twin conditions of disability and destitution. The decision on indoor or outdoor treatment was based on the seriousness of the case and on the amount of money coming into the family from other sources. In this light, hospital treatment was sometimes offered as a test of the validity of a man's claim for relief.

(*b*) Where a wife or child was ill and the man of the family able-bodied, medical aid was generally refused, even when the family could not afford private treatment. In the following example, the City Parochial Board showed itself very unwilling to grant proper hospital treatment to a wife in this position:

> 1896. John Canning, 19, Canning Place, applied for admission of wife to the poorhouse. Married, 55, badge-porter, earns 15s. to 18s. per week. Wife, 37, certified 'abdominal cancer'. No family. Rent 13/6, two apartments, sunk, fairly clean and furnished. Refused relief on 10th August and on same day Sheriff granted order to relieve. 1/- interim grant on 12th August. Settlement Ireland. Since refusal given, a nurse was attending from St. Elizabeth's Home [charity nursing organisation] and applicant lodged a complaint of inadequate relief. Decision—out-door medical relief granted.[25]

The Local Government Board (the successor to the Board of Supervision) entirely supported this parish decision, and while recognising that 'the whole wish of the applicant would appear to be to have his wife admitted to a hospital where she may get the attention which her case requires',[26] they did not recommend that the parochial hospital should undertake the treat-ment. Instead, a list of charitable agencies was supplied, which they felt was more appropriate in cases like this.

Therefore, parochial hospitals were only obliged to deal with sick paupers and their dependants. Other classes of poor—the sick dependants of able-bodied men, the unemployed, the poorly paid—had to find their own medical assistance, generally in charity hospitals. This dividing line between Poor Law and charity patients was felt by many to be a useful distinction. It isolated the lowest class and prevented the spread of the contagion of pauperism to the respectable poor. However, such a sanguine outlook neglected the significant fact that charity hospitals were never capable of treating all their applicants for admission and that they therefore operated a policy of selection by which the more acute, interesting, unusual, and curable cases were accepted while the residue was abandoned.

5. A satisfactory system?

By 1914 the Glasgow parish councils (successors to the parochial boards) had provided three large custom-built hospitals and two poorhouse hospital sections, staffed by qualified people and equipped to deal with most medical problems. These hospitals were without doubt an important part of the city's health care provision and indeed in the Poor Law Report of 1909 were recognised as such. The commissioners in condemning others praised one—'Glasgow with its three new Poor Law Hospitals being to some extent, an honourable exception.'[27]

But it was clear that Poor Law hospitals were underfinanced, doctors rarely chose to work there, patients were often debilitated from years of poor feeding and poor housing. Only those to whom choice was denied agreed to enter such hospitals. Given these inbuilt disadvantages it is hard to see in the years up to 1914 how Poor Law hospitals could have been considered a nucleus of a community hospital service. A major injection of capital as well as a fundamental change of attitudes was necessary and although Poor Law hospitals became Municipal hospitals in 1929, many continued to be prejudiced against them. With the advent of the National Health Service in 1948 they did enter into a new phase, becoming part of a modern hospital service.

Chapter Four

FRANK RICE

Care and treatment of the mentally ill

1. Origins and early growth

An examination of the treatment of mental illness in the Glasgow Asylum for Lunatics[1] in the nineteenth century gives a clear indication of the achievement of the community in Glasgow in trying to come to terms with this type of disease, which remained both difficult to define and to cure. It is also possible to use the Glasgow experience as a case study to illustrate events elsewhere in Scotland where similar initiatives and the response of seven other Royal Lunatic Asylums made a major impact in the attempt to cure mental illness.

Any temptation to regard mental illness as a phenomenon peculiar to the industrial epoch has to be rejected after even a cursory glance at the literature available. Scholars such as Alexander and Selesrick,[2] and Rosen[3] and Szasz[4] have shown that references to the mad can be traced as far back as Biblical times. Moreover, whereas antique ideas on madness were characterised by religious, daemonic and magical themes, a positive medical attitude had its origins in Graeco-Roman and early Arab times. Research indicates that the concept of an 'asylum', while rarely put into practice before the modern age, does certainly predate it, with the Spanish claiming the first such institution in Valencia in 1409.

There are valid reasons for regarding the later decades of the eighteenth, and early years of the nineteenth centuries as being a critical time in the evolution of care and treatment. Central to this theme is the clear evidence that lunacy, to use a contemporary term, aroused more interest than hitherto. Statistics from most European countries indicate a sustained increase in those known to be lunatic during the early nineteenth century. The alarm felt by people of the time is adequately expressed by John Reid, a London physician, who wrote in 1808, that 'Madness strides like a Colossus in the country',[5] and a year later that 'more people are mad than are supposed to be so'.[6]

At the beginning of the nineteenth century specialist institutions for the lunatic became general. This 'great incarceration of the insane', as Foucault sees it,[7] had in fact been going on in Europe since the middle of the seventeenth century. Both Prussia and France had already built vast, castellated institutions, the origins of which Scull has recently attempted to explain. He believes that, it was a vulnerability to outside attack which forced the 'continental absolutisms' to incarcerate their internal 'problem populations'.[8] Whether this was the case or not is open to conjecture, but it is true that the United Kingdom government embraced institutionalism later, and in a less severe form, than on the continent. In this country, poorhouses, houses of correction, prisons and hospitals took in their quota of mad people prior to the nineteenth century, but many such persons at this time had to rely either on their kin or on community resources. It was in 1808 that the state (in England and Wales) made its first hesitant moves with a permissive Act to establish county asylums, but it was not until 1845 that a national 'organisation of insanity' was established. In Scotland, similar but by no means parallel moves were made in 1857. Certainly, by the middle of the nineteenth century, the asylum had emerged as the organisational solution to the problem of insanity both in Europe and in the United States.

Furthermore the era of the French Revolution provided the first glimpses of what was later known as psychiatry. Throughout most of the eighteenth century the practice of medicine, which was developing rapidly in the field of physical illness came to extend its influence to the sphere of mental disorder. In the Age of Reason, medical men were well placed to argue that madness, or 'non-reason' was not the result of divine intervention or demoniac possession, but a malfunction of the body, an 'illness'. Hence the eighteenth century medical men prescribed a whole series of remedies, blood-lettings, vomits, purges, blisters and the like in an attempt to 'cure', or alleviate this. The 'success' of this lowering treatment was often to produce patients who were listless. Ironically, at a time when medicine was beginning to establish its position, it was to receive the first of many serious challenges to its competence. Undoubtedly influenced by the Romantics' stress on 'feelings' the 'individual' and 'liberty', a new approach to the mad, known as 'moral management of the insane', was initiated towards the end of the eighteenth century. In practice the older medical orthodoxy prevailed in many quarters and, indeed, as the nineteenth century wore on, the eventual outcome was to be a synthesis of the two schools' ideas. But in its original form, moral management, as illustrated by Tuke, Pinel and Esquirol was largely anti-medical in its approach. It emphasised the humanity of those unfortunate enough to lose their reason, and called for greater freedom for the lunatic within a pleasant, healthy, therapeutic milieu. The total abolition of restraint at Lincoln and Hanwell between the years 1829–35 was perhaps the apex of this movement in Great Britain.

Moreover, innovations in the classification of insanity can be seen in the early nineteenth century. There were however serious methodological difficulties as aetiological explanations vied with symptomatic descriptions to create some very dubious nosological distinctions. Local doctors were often keen to add their own (often florid) 'causes' of insanity. But, in terms of this general survey of developments, one could suggest that there were three main initiatives during the nineteenth century. Firstly, Philippe Pinel, in his *Traite medico-philosophique sur L'Alienation Mentale* emphasised environmental factors in the origins of insanity and proposed 'only four forms of mental illness, mania, melancholia, dementia and idiocy'.[9] These terms came to be widely used during the nineteenth century. Secondly, Wilhelm Griesinger was the doyen of those German doctors who sought to move the study of madness away from the ideas of 'romantic poetry'. He preferred instead a clearly somatic explanation for the disorder, and pioneered neurological research into the brain, regarding this as the seat of mental illness. This view became popular in the latter half of the century. And finaly, Emil Kraepelin, towards the end of the nineteenth century, is largely credited with transforming earlier nosologies into the beginnings of the classificatory systems with which we are familiar today. In Kraepelin's work the two major functional psychoses were described for the first time; the manic depressive syndrome, and dementia praecox, which was named schizophrenia by Eugen Bleuler in 1911.

While it is clear then that significant developments in the history of the mentally ill took place both prior to and following the decades mentioned earlier, nevertheless those changes which took place at the turn of the nine-teenth century must be regarded as crucial. How effective these changes were, in the long run, is a matter of some debate, but to contemporary eyes, there was much that was valid in these reforms. The objective of this chapter is to consider how far this 'age of improvement' in lunacy care affected Glasgow.

2. Glasgow Asylum for Lunatics: life in Dobbie's Loan

Despite the opening of the Glasgow Royal Infirmary in 1794, there was no special provision for the mentally ill of the city and its environs until well into the nineteenth century. There may have been some small private mad-houses in the city towards the end of the eighteenth century, offering a rudimentary service. But apart from the 'trade in lunacy' the only other place of refuge for the insane was the lunatic ward of the poorhouse, known as the Town's Hospital; this building had been opened in 1733 and over-looked the River Clyde. Its location was indeed a drawback as, not infre-quently, the 'mad cells' were flooded with water;[10] moreover, the regime practised a 'depository' policy as far as lunatics were concerned. No attempt was made to treat or 'cure' cases; instead they were merely 'put away'.[11]

It was principally out of a desire to improve this state of affairs that reform came to Glasgow. Mercantile initiative rather than civic or medical zeal was the motivating force, and one individual Robert McNair, a sugar merchant, is clearly described in most of the relevant documents, as the 'founding father'. He[12] had been elected Baillie in 1805, in which capacity he served as a director of the Town's Hospital. He was shocked by the state in which the insane were kept. McNair decided that something must be done.

It was proposed at the outset merely to renovate the existing Town's Hospital. But when it was discovered that the original appeal launched by McNair had realised approximately £7000 the first proposals were dropped, and plans drawn up for the construction of a separate lunatic asylum.[13]

Three acres of lands of Mrs Rae Crawford, immediately west of the intersection of Parliamentary Road and Dobbie's Loan were settled upon (1808–9) at a cost of £764 9s.0d. Within that setting, Mr William Stark constructed a form of Panopticon consisting of a central complex from which projected diagonally four divisions of wards each three storeys in height. Walls continued outward from the termination of each wing to the surrounding boundary within which space were to be found the grounds. Each storey of each wing constituted a ward, consisting of a row of chambers along one side and an oblong gallery on the other. The total construction cost of this project to 27 December 1814 was £16,434 4s.5d. The building was opened on 1 December 1814 and ten years later acquisition of a Royal Charter gave to the city the Glasgow Royal Asylum for Lunatics.

In the beginning, the Royal Asylum certainly appeared to correspond to the model of the humane therapeutic community envisaged by the 'moral managers'. Only forty-four patients were admitted in 1814 and the 'rural and verdant nature'[14] of the environment to the north of the city fulfilled the criterion that a house for the insane be at a distance from urban congestion. Separation of the patients according to sex and class, yet another objective of Pinel and his contemporaries was achieved, and rudiments of 'milieu therapy' and positive treatment were practised. Moreover, acquisition of a Royal charter was not merely a legal formality; in a more significant way it designated the Glasgow house as one of that group of institutions, the Scottish Chartered Asylums. These eventually totalled seven in number, and among their distinguishing features was a near total absence of any public funds or legislation associated with both their establishment and function and an identification, on the part of management, of the houses' role as charitable institutions.[15] In this regard, the Glasgow regime was initially envisaged as catering for both 'respectable' middle class and working-class patients, and a scale of fees was drawn up to reflect this stratification.[16] Pauper patients were supposed to be maintained in the poor house.

The problem of the pauper lunatics was to become one of the most intractable which faced the Lunatic Asylums. Whenever new accommodation for lunatics was opened patients appeared and quickly filled the vacant places. The availability of the asylum was sufficient to attract from the surrounding communities patients formerly invisible to the authorities. The administrators of the Glasgow Lunatic Asylum always drew a distinction between 'private', fee paying patients and those 'public' pauper inmates whose admission was paid for by the respective parishes.

A general increase in admissions, from forty-four in 1814 to 202 in 1842 was to place an intolerable strain on the fabric. In addition the Asylum was increasingly surrounded by encroaching urban sprawl. Alterations to the structure were carried out but by the late 1830s it became clear to the directors that these modifications were only short term remedies. As a result, a decision was taken in 1839 to abandon the Dobbie's Loan site and move the entire institution.[17] Sixty-six acres in the northern portion of the lands of Gartnavel, three miles from the city centre were purchased at a cost of £10,185. In January 1841, Charles Wilson was appointed the architect and the result was two distinct buildings, a Gothic 'West House' for the private patients and a much plainer 'East House' for the paupers. The total expenditure on the new buildings, in 1843, was £55,497 15s. 5d. and operations commenced there in June of that year.

In Scotland no major government action was taken with regard to lunatic patients until 1855 when a Royal Commission[18] was appointed. This action reflected the increasing strain under which the seven Royal Lunatic Asylums were working with a constantly increasing patient load. After the Royal Commission had reported the *Lunacy (Scotland) Act of 1857* followed. Among the many provisions of this first, major body of legislation on the mentally ill in Scotland was a clarification of what constituted insanity, a tightening-up of the law on the subject, the establishment of a national co-ordinating Board of Commissioners in Lunacy, and the division of Scotland into separate lunacy districts in which publicly-financed district asylums were to be built. All previously existing institutions for the insane in Scotland were to be brought under the purview of the new nationwide organisation, the contribution of the poor houses and private madhouses was to be phased out, and an administrative distinction drawn between district institutions practising a depository 'psychiatry for the poor' and the 'Royal' houses developing their curative initiatives for fee-paying patients.

Over the next forty years parochial boards slowly and reluctantly shouldered responsibility for their lunatic patients. Glasgow built district Asylums at Woodilee, Lenzie (1875), Kirklands Asylum (1881) and Gartloch Asylum (1896). Govan opened a parochial Asylum at Merryflats (1873) and a district Asylum at Hawkhead (1895).

The table shows the large increase in admission of patients between 1830 and 1840 which required the managers to undertake the removal to Gartnavel. Once established in new spacious premises admissions rose

TABLE 19

Patients at Glasgow Asylum for Lunatics

	1814	1820	1830	1840	1850	1860	1870	1880	1890	1898
Patients at 1 January		106	114	155	487	500	545	529	480	414
Admissions	44	87	89	149	393	204	326	113	135	171
Dismissals										
Relieved	3	20	24	19	243	58	89	51	54	58
Cured		44	45	81	171	96	147	42	51	74
Patients at 31 December	40	112	123	183	425	502	561	514	476	424

Source: AR of GAL.

rapidly, reflecting the inevitable pressure of pauper patients upon the available resources. The population of Glasgow was rising rapidly but it would be unwise to assume more mental illness although more putative mental patients did become visible to the authorities. With the opening of the district Asylums after 1870s the Royal Asylum ceased to be under such pressure. The drop in the number of admissions after 1880 is quite striking.

By the end of the nineteenth century the original vision of Robert McNair of merely improving conditions in the old Town's Hospital had been greatly enlarged. The city could boast four asylums within its environs, one of which, the Royal, had developed a medical reputation worthy of respect. But despite the growth of institutional support, the pressure of admissions continued to handicap the efficiency of the house, and it was partly as a further attempt to alleviate that pressure that psychiatric wards were later established in three general hospitals, the Eastern General, the Southern General and Stobhill. It should be noted that the district asylums continued to be administered by their respective boards until 1929, when they were taken over by the Corporation of Glasgow, and these, with Gartnavel Royal, passed into National Health Service control in 1948.

3. Gartnavel: moral management

Having outlined the administrative structure of mental care and treatment in Glasgow, a study of the Royal Asylum is now proposed, covering the early and middle decades of the century. It should be understood that the terms 'care' and 'treatment' were often virtually synonymous: proper care of a patient could in some cases be regarded as a means of therapy. In others medicinal remedies were applied and could be more clearly categorised as 'treatment'.

In common with the other chartered asylums, it was some time before the managers of Glasgow Asylum for Lunatics appointed a full-time, resident physician superintendent. Until 1840 well-known members of Glasgow's medical establishment 'visited' the Asylum to supervise care and treatment: the resident superintendent, often married was able to deal with day-to-day medical and domestic matters. Pressure of numbers which involved the move to Gartnavel possibly brought about a radical re-organisation in the staffing of the institution in the course of which Mr Hutcheson underwent a metamorphosis. With the establishment of the 'Physician Superintendent' came the additional appointment of 'Non-resident Surgeon' (see Chapter 2 above).

Certain innovations, not all of them beneficial in both the treatment and classification of the insane can be detected from that time. Drs William Hutcheson and Alexander MacIntosh were active during the middle of the century while in 1873, Dr David Yellowlees was appointed and later became the first lecturer in Mental Diseases at the University. Hutcheson clearly saw his task as being a moral manager; writing in the *Annual Reports* he averred that

All the patients are addressed and treated as rational and accountable beings—Harsh words and gestures are avoided.[19]

The patients 'under proper restrictions' were encouraged to 'congregate together' for work, exercise, entertainment and religion.[20] There is much to suggest that this was no mere delusion on the management's part. A rigid division was maintained between both the classes and the sexes in recreation

TABLE 20

Officers of the Asylum

Period	Resident Superintendent	Superintendent/ Apothecary	Visiting Physician	Physician Superintendent
1814 to 1840	Wm Drury 1814–24	J. M. Probyn 1824–7 H. A. Galbraith 1827–38 W. Hutcheson 1838	Dr R. Cleghorn 1814–20 Dr J. Balmanno 1820–40	
1840 to 1849		Dr W. Hutcheson 1840–49		
Post 1849				Dr A. Mackintosh 1849–74 Dr D. Yellowlees 1874–1901 Dr R. R. Oswald 1901–21 Sir D. Henderson 1921–32 Dr A. McNiven 1932–65 Dr G. C. Timbury 1965–80 Dr W. E. S. Kiernan 1980–

Source: AR of GAL, see also F. J. Rice,
Strathclyde undergraduate dissertation 1974.

and dormitories. At Gartnavel after 1843 Glasgow adopted the Edinburgh model, of building two separate units. Hence when the Royal Commissioners visited the asylum in 1855, they found that the West House, for private patients held about 100, while the pauper East House could hold about 350. In the former, wards or 'galleries' as they were called of which there were eighteen contained, according to the Commissioners' estimation, 2360 cubic feet per patient while the separate 'bedrooms' and 'sitting rooms' had an average space of 1792 feet. In the East House, there were, in 1855, about twenty wards ranging in size from twelve to thirty-five beds except for three smaller wards for violent patients. 'The average space in this division was 865 cubic feet per patient',[21] wrote the Commissioners.

Many of the pauper wards were described by the Commissioners as 'dark, damp and smell offensively'.[22] They noted that in some places the bedding was made up on the floor, without actual bedsteads, while in others beds made of iron and mattresses of straw was the norm. Each bed had only one sheet changed once a week. It was standard practice for incontinent patients to have their beds placed over leaden troughs sunk in the floor into which passed the urine.

This state of affairs can be best contrasted with the 'service' offered the highest fee paying patients at Glasgow. One hears from the Commissioners that the sleeping rooms were all 'fully and comfortably furnished' the walls 'variously papered' and the corridors 'carpeted throughout'. Most of the latter contained pianos and time-pieces, most windows had curtains and the general effect was 'one of elegance and comfort'.[23] In one such corridor were to be found 'three gasaliers, two rosewood tables, a piano, ottomans, small tables for occasional use, Elizabethan and other chairs'.

Thus it can be seen that in terms of the environment and accommodation of the Glasgow Royal Asylum, a sharp distinction was drawn between the provisions for the paying patients, which any moral manager would have found satisfactory, and that for the pauper inmates which left much to be desired. In prosecuting this enquiry, an attempt will now be made to enquire into the extent to which 'milieu therapy' as exemplified by work, exercise and recreation was practised at Glasgow.

Dr Hutcheson expressed the view, which was very much in keeping with the moral management othodoxy, that 'one of the most beneficial means in the treatment of the insane'[24] was occupation. It prevented the mind from dwelling on its delusions and also put an end to the restlessness which Dr Hutcheson felt attended certain forms of the disease. And it would appear that, as far back as 1817, the Glasgow Asylum was busy putting these ideals into practice. At that time

2 looms and 5 spinning wheels are generally kept at work, clothes are made or mended, stockings or worsted gloves are knit and occasionally a little muslin is flowered.[25]

By 1821, male patients were working at tailoring, shoemaking, joinery and bookbinding, while spinning, sewing and washing were the main female occupations. At first the work done was for the use of the Asylum alone, but, after 1839 some of the produce was marketed. It is difficult to assess the quality of the work done although the amount produced was impressive. In 1840 the weaving department produced 200 yards of handkerchiefs, the tailors made 15 frock coats and 17 dress coats while the wrights made 21 beds and articles such as rosewood work boxes, book stands, a mahogany work box, writing desks and 10 chests of drawers. Moreover, produce marketed by the asylum contributed to the institution's finances. Indeed, so central to the regimen did this aspect of its affairs become that one hears that the Weekly Committee, in September 1837, drew up plans for full workshops 'in order to extend this most important means of moral treatment'.[26]

It was in another aspect of milieu therapy, exercise, that the Glasgow Royal Asylum seemed wanting. While the extensive lands at Gartnavel were put to use in this direction it must be recalled that such a boon was granted only to the non-violent patient. The inmates who could not be trusted were confined to the 'airing courts'. The Commissioners were especially critical of Glasgow, pointing out that, at the time of their visit, there were two airing courts for 67 private patients and 3 courts, one of them very small, for 329 paupers.[27]

The third aim of management, having occupied and exercised some of the patients, was to provide recreation and amusement. This was an objective looked upon with favour. As the directors wrote in 1839,

> In the evening, after the labour and exercises of the day, the Patients may be seen in the well-lighted parlours, billiard rooms and galleries, cheerfully employed in reading, playing backgammon, cards or billiards, or relaxing themselves with the flute, the violin, or the pianoforte.[28]

Judging by the evidence, there can be little doubt that the pioneering practice of moral management was practised in Glasgow in connection with milieu therapy. Although Glasgow's management could have done more as far as the paupers were concerned, this failure must be seen within the context of a highly class divided society. Apart from this the Royal Asylum fulfilled the criteria. More specifically, however, moral management insisted not only on an adequate environment for the patient, but that more should be done for them in the way of occupation, exercise and recreation. These objectives were also realised at Glasgow, although it would appear that the Directors were less partial to providing exercise than the other diversions. But moral management was not merely about humane caring for the insane, it signified also a particular attitude to the treatment of such persons: this aspect of the Glasgow Royal Asylum's work must now be looked at.

4. Care and treatment

With the appointment of full-time resident medical superintendents in the 1830s the Royal Lunatic Asylums of Scotland moved into a different era.

For the men who took up these important posts had identified themselves with the care of the mentally ill and were keen to associate themselves with successful treatment. The most important figure was Dr David Skae medical superintendent of the Edinburgh Royal Lunatic Asylum at Morningside from 1846 to 1873. As early as 1844, a year before Griesinger's major contribution was published, Dr Skae wrote in the Annual Report for that year that 'insanity is a bodily disease affecting the brain, the organ of the mind'.[29] And in a later lecture on the legal aspects of insanity, read to the Royal College of Surgeons of Edinburgh in 1861, Skae postulated insanity as being 'a disease of the brain affecting the mind'. Dr Mackintosh of Glasgow, while a less distinguished figure than Dr Skae, nevertheless, had something similar in mind when he wrote in 1860 that 'hereditary tendency and the condition of the brain induced by previous attacks are probably the two most frequent sources of this predisposition (insanity)'.[30]

Three cardinal conclusions can be drawn from this position occupied by Skae. In developing this clearly somatic approach to insanity he was flying in the face of the theories of Pinel, Tuke and other moral managers who had given the environment a much more important role than the brain in their aetiology of insanity. Moreover, it is clear that Skae was at the forefront of research in his field, developing ideas very similar to those evolved by the German somaticists. And finally, as Fish expressed it, it was Skae's 'clear, medical approach to insanity which led him to classify mental illnesses according to aetiology.[31]

Victorian nosologies of insanity were biased towards an aetiological rather than a symptomatic base. Dr Skae played an important role in the development of that position. In his presidential address to the annual meeting of the Association of Medical Officers of Asylums (the forerunner of the Royal Medico-Psychological Association) in 1863, he pointed out that as the same physical disorder could cause quite different mental symptoms, a systematic classification was in practice not very useful. Hence it was necessary for the physician to trace the natural history of the disease. What is fundamental however is that Skae, in common with many of his contemporaries, was led, by this position, to postulate some very tenuous 'causes' of insanity.[32]

The appendices of the *Annual Reports* contain abstracts of the 'supposed causes of insanity', taken from the Case Records and referring to the predisposing as opposed to long term factors involved. Among the more significant 'causes', for the years 1830–70, were 'anonymous approach', intemperance, hereditary predisposition, pregnancy and associated disorders, religion, syphilis, disappointed love and masturbation.[33]

Now while it is difficult to understand how certain of the above conditions actually 'caused' insanity, nevertheless references to the medical reports contained within the *Annual Reports* and to the Case Histories indicate that the abstracts reflected the type of cases coming before the doctors.

It has already been noted that Dr Mackintosh in Glasgow referred to the importance of 'hereditary tendency and the condition of the brain' as a frequent source of insanity.[34] And in sampling the Case Records one learns that, for example the predisposing cause of Miss G's insanity, for which she was admitted in July 1838, was 'second cousin insane'.[35] The mother and sister of Miss D, incarcerated in August 1839, 'were insane'[36] while the predisposition of Miss R, an admission in 1841 was 'brother and sister insane'.[37]

Drinking was frequently cited as a cause of insanity. Dr Balmanno wrote for example in 1833 that 'among the exciting causes of mania we regret that we have still to mention the abuse of spiritous liquors—it would appear that lunacy, may be occasioned from that source'.[38] Moreover, references to drinking as a 'cause' abound in the Case Records. In January 1831, Miss N, 'having been jilted in love now drinks heavily'[39] was placed in the Glasgow Royal. Hence the exciting cause was 'disappointed affection and abuse of ardent spirits'.[40] In May of that year, Miss R, who 'liked drink' was described as having 'an exciting cause which appeared to be intemperance'.[41]

Pregnancy and associated conditions were believed to cause insanity in women. Thus in May 1831, a woman was admitted where the 'exciting cause' was 'child bearing'.[42] Menstruation or rather lack of it was also frequently blamed. In 1832, for example, the physician wrote that the exciting cause of Miss K's case, brought on in March 1832 was 'deficiency of menstruation'.[43] In 1864 one finds a whole series of such instances. The record of Miss B, admitted in February of that year reads,

> About 12 months ago, menstruation was irregular and finally suppressed. About that time she was depressed and gloomy and talked a good deal about religion. In this way it may have been ascribed as the cause.[44]

Miss P admitted likewise in February 1864 had not menstruated for eight weeks and 'this had probably some connection with the cause of insanity',[45] while Miss S admitted in April of that year had written on her record that 'some months ago menstruation ceased and the mental symptoms became greatly aggravated'.[46]

Many patients were committed apparently suffering from religious fanaticism. Thus for example, Miss T admitted to Glasgow in April 1839 owed her condition to 'religious troubles'.[47] A more thorough citation was that of Mr B incarcerated in January 1840. This patient appeared to be suffering from religious persecution as it was stated in the record that he was 'fearful of the Jesuits and thinks they observe his actions', and that he spoke of 'the growing ascendancy of the Catholics who would not allow him to remain in Glasgow'.[48] In addition to religious fanaticism, another source of worry for the physicians was masturbation. Dr Mackintosh writing in 1861, stated that he had been 'thoroughly impressed with the conviction that masturbation is a more fruitful source of insanity than is generally supposed'.[49] He cited the incidence of nineteen cases, in that year as insanity 'the physical cause of which is masturbation'.[50]

Although the Glasgow physicians in common with their contemporaries, regarded 'cause' as essential, they did pay attention to what they thought were symptoms. In this regard, Skae's four main categories, illustrated early in this chapter, were used at Glasgow. Of the cases admitted, mania was regarded as the most numerically significant, followed by dementia, melancholia and idiocy.

In this respect, it should be recalled that Pinel's view of mania was that it was the agitative state, and under this head would be included most violent and/or bizarre behaviour. And, as a result, we learn that Miss G, admitted to Glasgow in July 1838 'raved indifferently on various subjects'.[51] Miss H, incarcerated in January 1842, suffered from mania indicated by 'irritable temper, violent language, dislike of friends'.[52] Mr S taken to Glasgow Royal in March 1847, was in 'a state of violent mania',[53] at this point. According to the Records, he raved incoherently and engaged in such actions as throwing off his clothes, rubbing the wall with his hands, tearing bed-clothes, swearing and striking anyone who came near him and talking incoherently. Mr P was in a 'high state of maniacal excitement', when he was admitted in April 1847 and proceeded to scream, dance and rave. Another instance of mania, that of Mr S admitted originally in October 1838, was described in the Records as follows 'a few days after the pre-liminary symptoms of restlessness, the patient has again become maniacal, highly destructive, mischievous and filthy'.[54]

The less numerous citations of dementia did nevertheless conform to the Pinelian criteria of complete loss of intellectual abilities. Mr D incarcerated in December 1846, appeared 'sullen and dull' on admission and would not utter a word. 'To the physician, this patient looked like one far advanced in dementia.'[55]

There were numerous references to melancholia in the Records although these were less easy to categorise. Pinel had argued that melancholia did not necessarily mean sadness but included that state, and/or elation, although both feelings appeared to be excited by a single idea. Miss A admitted in April 1838, exhibited great mental depression and despondency in religious matters. She believed that she was possessed by an evil spirit, under whose impulse she thought and acted:[56] she was a suicidal case. Mrs D admitted in August 1839 with depression was regarded as melancholic and said 'the devil had power over her'.[57] Miss R incarcerated in October of that year, similarly for depression, had a 'constant suspicion of her neighbours in-juring her by supernatural means'.[58] Miss K placed in April 1840, again for depression, regarded herself as 'not fit for the world'[59] while Miss R who had been admitted in March 1841 for want of sleep and lowness of spirits felt that everything had gone 'wrong in the family'.[60] Pinel's con-cept of fixation on one idea in melancholia is well brought out in these citations.

The asylums also accommodated cases of idiocy or what would today be called mental retardation. Moreover, the physicians, in common with their contemporaries elsewhere, developed their own nosological distinctions. Hence, in addition to the Pinelian standard types, a variety of other classi-fications, and sub-divisions was noted. Shortly before his death, Dr Balmanno drew up his own nomenclature, which included both monomania and pantomania and such exotica as onomania, which this physician denominated as a type of intemperance.

These Victorians concerned with the classification of mental illness were also involved with the concept of general paralysis of the insane. As Fish points out, Skae was to regard 'general paralysis as the paradigm of mental illness'.[61] There is considerable doubt over its initial recognition as a disease entity. Skae himself recognised Haslan as the first medical man to describe the illness whereas a contemporary scholar, Vieda Skultans thinks Esquirol was the pioneer.[62] According to her, the earliest English physicians to mention it were Connolly, Buckwell and Maudsley.

A reading of the Glasgow Case Records for the 1850s and 60s brings to light increasing reference to general paralysis: and whatever the clinical source there is no doubt that, by the end of the nineteenth century, cases of dementia paralytica as it was alternatively known were being treated in most asylums. At about the same time, the definite association between syphilis and general paralysis was established. The growing incidence of this condition is mentioned by Skultans who cites the report of the English Commissioners in Lunacy—between 1901 and 1911, post-mortem examinations revealed that over 70 per cent of asylum patients were suffering from general paralysis at death.

At Glasgow Royal Asylum then from the 1840s, a medical policy of describing both the 'causes' and symptoms of insanity was practised. This is illustrated by the patient Case Records. It remains now to consider how such cases were treated.

It was customary for the physician superintendent to avoid giving these patients who were only mildly affected any formal treatment, for milieu therapy sufficed. For those who were more seriously 'ill', more stringent procedures were necessary, and there is strong evidence that the Glasgow Royal was practising the old methods well into the nineteenth century.

Dr Hutcheson indicated his preferences, writing in 1841, that 'in mere insanity', general bloodletting was never necessary: however, local bloodletting could be allowed. Also counter irritations applied to the scalp were 'useful' while a succession of blisters were the 'best means'. Purgatives were also important, while tartar emetics (tonics and narcotics) were also given. Finally, Dr Mackintosh averred that 'the warm bath', with cold applied to head, in many cases calms the patient.[63]

The Case Records reveal that Mrs M admitted to Glasgow in 1840 was bled as was Miss L in the same year. Mrs M admitted in March 1831, had her 'head shaved and cold poultices applied'.[64] A Miss M admitted at the same time, had the similar experience of having her 'head shaved and blistered without marked effect'.[65] Miss A (May 1831) had 'blisters and leeches applied to the head'[66] while Miss K (June 1832) had, among other things, 'blisters placed on her head'. Miss A (April 1838) had her head shaved and a cold cloth applied, while leeches were applied to her genitals.[67] In April 1863 Mr McL was 'to have a blister at the nape of the neck'.[68] Mr S admitted in September 1851 had 'leeches used'[69] upon him, while Mr K in October of that year had 'his head shaved, blister, cold applications' written on his Record.[70] The latest comment to be found concerning this practice was in March, 1854, when a blister was applied to Mr K's neck.[71]

Purgatives were also frequently noted. Miss E (December 1830) had purgatives given as was Miss N in January 1831. Miss R incarcerated in May 1831, had been 'purged freely'[72] while Miss K (June 1832) had 'drastic purgatives'.[73] Miss G (April 1840) was put on 'nauseating doses of tartar emetic', with gentle alternatives of Gregory's mixture.[74] These treatments, as with the others, continued well into the 1850s and 1860s.

In addition other remedies were used such as baths, narcotics and medicinal alcohol. Miss K was given warm baths. There were also occasional references to the medicinal use of narcotics. Thus Mr B admitted on October 1851 to Glasgow Royal received 'a grain of opium'[75] while Mr W incarcerated in June 1852, was given 'three grains of opium'.[76] Mr C (November 1856) was given enormous doses of opium and its preparations, while 'cannabis indica' was tried without effect.[77] Finally, there were frequent references to the use of medicinal alcohol. Miss McM placed in March 1838, was given a 'bottle of porter'.[78] Mr S who was admitted in March 1847, as a violent manic case was ordered to have a glass of whisky immediately, while later the treatment was changed to gin.[79] Mr G (June 1847) was to have a 'glass of brandy'.[80]

Clearly then a study of the Case Records indicates that the eighteenth century medicinal remedies were widely practised in Glasgow. These were the means by which many patients were treated. There remained a final initiative left open to the doctors when confronted with the violent patient and that was mechanical restraint and seclusion.

As we have seen elsewhere, the Royal Commissioners, in their *Report* noted that in the chartered asylums

> personal restraint, by the application of the straitwaistcoat or of straps or muffs, is almost entirely banished.[81]

But the Commissioners had reason to believe that seclusion for long periods was frequently used. Skae of Edinburgh believed that mechanical restraint was sometimes necessary but he was forced to practise seclusion because of lack of adequate accommodation. Dr Hutcheson of Glasgow was more forthcoming. In 1841, he placed the Glasgow Royal in the forefront of the 'non-restraint' movement by claiming that during the previous three years, personal restraint had been modified and almost abolished. During the last year, he was able to 'abolish it altogether and the result hitherto has been altogether satisfactory'.[82] As a result, this physician believed that, not only were the patients quieter and more orderly, but a 'great saving of glass, furniture, bedding, etc. had been achieved, the amount of seclusion diminished and the patients habits much improved'.[83]

Did these comments give the whole story? There seems to be no evidence in the Case Records of devices such as the whirling chair, nevertheless mechanical restraint was probably used. In a record written for Mr P in October 1860, there is unambiguous reference to a patient whose 'arms and hands are under mechanical restraint'.[84]

Seclusion or solitary confinement certainly was often used at Glasgow. Thus Mr M admitted in November 1846, became so violent that he had to be 'secluded'[85] and Mr D incarcerated a month later, was placed in seclusion; while the records of both Mr P and Mrs T admitted in the Spring of 1847 state on both 'let him be kept in seclusion'.[86] There was also frequent reference to violent patients being 'transferred to No. 3', which, on further enquiry, turned out to be a seclusion room.

From the patient Case Records of the Glasgow Royal Asylum during the early decades of the nineteenth century it would appear that the medical management preserved the older, eighteenth-century ideas of treatment until well into the nineteenth century. This state of affairs has to be contrasted with the therapeutic aspects of 'care' which, as practised in Glasgow during this time, was roughly in line with the reforms of Pinel, Tuke and the other moral managers.

5. A successful institution?

The Royal Asylum played an important role in the 'organisation of insanity' in nineteenth-century Glasgow. It was an authoritarian body, incorporated by Royal Charter, with its own legal identity, and powers and privileges recognised by law.

The Asylum was originally built on Dobbie's Loan in 1814 on a 'green fields' site to the North of the city. With the encroachment by the prosperous growing city the Asylum managers moved to a new splendid site at Gartnavel. Their removal in 1843 enabled them to institute new therapies of farming, gardening and outdoor pursuits for their patients.

The physician superintendents in Glasgow were interested in improving the methods of treatment for lunatic patients and made valiant efforts to effect a positive therapeutic policy designed to cure and to return patients to the outside world. But old traditions die hard, and it is clear from the Case Records that the old eighteenth-century 'remedies' of bloodletting, purges, vomits, leeches and blistering, opiates and alcohol were regularly used. The attractions of such remedies were very real, for asylum staff found that patients weakened by any of these treatments were debilitated and therefore amenable.

Nor was the Royal Asylum in Glasgow exceptional in combining milieu treatment with various less pleasant methods of control. Other Royal Asylums faced similar problems of overcrowding and understaffing. Even today, despite Pinel's original vision that the mad be 'unchained' either physically or metaphorically and with new interpretations by R. D. Laing and Michael Foucault, it is clear that the practice in the mental hospitals cannot always attain the perception and understanding of the theorist.

Chapter Five

DAVID HAMILTON and MARGARET LAMB

Surgeons and surgery

1. 'A hazardous practice'

Before the advent of antiseptics in the operating room, surgical practices were limited and their use hazardous. Joseph Lister, newly appointed Professor of Surgery at the University of Glasgow (1860), was almost certainly the first surgeon anywhere who, after performing operations in the 1860s at the Glasgow Royal Infirmary, used an antiseptic treatment to stop the spread of fatal infection. Lister left Glasgow in 1869 to return to Edinburgh. Later, William Macewen, also at the GRI and later at the Western Infirmary, made further progress by introducing techniques of aseptic surgery.

As a result of these major changes the status of the surgeon changed. In the first half of the century the 'surgeon' in Glasgow had been a general practitioner who commanded a limited repertoire of surgical procedures. By the end of the century the surgeon armed with new and remarkable surgical skills, had emerged as a prestigious hospital-based specialist far removed from the more humble general practitioner.

Joseph Lister became Baron Lister, the first medical peer, while William Macewen was knighted. The honours granted to these men reflect the growing authority of the surgeon resting on their success and the ever-widening scope of their operations.

2. Before Joseph Lister, 1800–1861

Glasgow Royal Infirmary opened in 1794, but was not fully functional until 1799: hence it is convenient to start an analysis of its figures at 1800.[1] The medical records of the Glasgow Royal Infirmary give a good insight into the number and scope of operations undertaken there. It is, however, important to realise that the surgical operations of the Royal Infirmary were by no means the sum total of all such work carried out in Glasgow. Since the surgeons of the hospital were the general practitioners of the town, taking it in rotation to work in the hospital, they also undertook the surgical procedures of the day in the patient's own home, be it a poor patient sustained by the parish Poor Law, or a paying private patient.[2] In addition there were operations carried out on the inmates of the Town's Hospital (see Chapter Three above). Thus the operations recorded in the Royal Infirmary represent only a part of Glasgow surgery and, since the surgeons were young when on the hospital staff, in their later and more experienced years, they were often working entirely outside the hospital.[3] It may be also that patients were chosen for admission to the Royal Infirmary for social rather than clinical reasons—for instance when the person could not be looked after in his/her own home.

There were other facets of the Infirmary's admission policy. Patients unlikely to recover were discouraged and were supposed to be removed within forty days. The managers complained in their Annual Report of 1809 that on one day during the year they had 'no less than twelve incurable patients'. Such cases could have a distinctly adverse effect upon mortality figures.

The cases treated in the surgical wards and the number of operations carried out in the Infirmary are shown in the first part of Table 21. The figures suggest that the pattern of the practice of surgery was stable and the increase in the number of cases treated and operations performed merely kept pace with the growth in population. The most frequent cause of admission to the surgical wards was for 'common ulcers'—perhaps leg ulcers resulting from nutritional deficiency—which at times made up 25 per cent of the in-patients. Next in incidence were simple fractures, 'indigestion' and bruises and sprains (each about 10 per cent of all admissions). Of the operations, about one third were amputations, usually for compound fractures. There were also frequent attempts to remove superficial cancers and surgery for anal fistulae. No figures for the death rate from surgical operations are given in the Annual Reports of this period, but an estimate of mortality from one major surgical cause of death—compound fracture of a limb—is available from these brief Reports. Survival after this fracture was good in the years 1829–33 and 1835–37 by the standards of the day, since mortality was only about 25 per cent. But in 1834 and later from 1838–40 the death rate rose to about 50 per cent.

During this period the method of organisation of the staff and their appointments did not change. Four surgeons (i.e. general practitioners) were appointed to the hospital for two years. Thereafter, they were eligible for re-election after a two year interval, serving again for two years. They were called the junior and senior surgeons in their first and second periods of service. Their duties probably involved about two hours hospital work per day with recall for emergencies, being summoned for a consultation by messengers.[4] No operation could be carried out without such consultation between at least two surgeons, a stipulation probably necessary on account of the high mortality from surgery.

The Royal Infirmary was unusual in paying its staff although two years of 'service gratis' was a preliminary requisite and until 1810 the surgeons, in their second term of office, received £10.00 per annum: this was increased to £20 from 1810 onwards. From 1833 the surgeons received £30 per annum. During this period the surgeons' pay was lower than that of a physician whose professional status was traditionally higher and who from 1833 onwards received £50 per annum. Like many other hospitals, the Royal Infirmary in Glasgow benefited from using unpaid student labour as 'dressers', appointed from among the senior students. It was the practice in

TABLE 21

Hospital Cases in Glasgow 1800—1900

Year	Population in 000's	Medical Cases	Surgical Cases	Dispensary Cases	Accident Cases	Accident as % Surgical Cases	Surgical Operations	Operative Mortality	Operations per 1,000 Population	Surgical Cases	Surgical Operations	Operations per 1,000 Population
				Glasgow Royal Infirmary (1794)						GRI, Western Infirmary (1874) Victoria Infirmary (1890)		
1800	77	489	314				41		0.53			
1810	100	656	401				30		0.30			
1820	147	1211	487				66		0.44			
1830	202	1312	698				129		0.63			
1840	255	1254	1176	7501			120		0.47			
1850	329	937	1229	4578	459	37.1	186	15.7	0.55			
1860	395	1527	1612	10,811	617	38.2	228	7.8	0.67			
1865	435	1959	2472	11,730	833	33.7	310	12.5	0.61			
1870	478	1971	2334	13,973	1064	45.6	470	6.8	0.98			
1875	495	2719	2393	18,876	1144	47.8	422	12.0	0.85		657	1.32
1880	511	2397	2733	21,232	1151	42.1	952	3.7	1.86			
1885	538	2161	2782	23,732	1139	40.9	848	6.1	1.57	4483	1642	3.05
1890	566	2183	3150	26,644	1338	42.5	1152	5.3	2.03			
1895	655	2215	3604	27,053	1290	35.7	1668	6.8	2.54	6563	3370	5.08
1900	740	2198	4058	33,108	1692	41.7	2247	6.7	3.03	8007	4531	6.12

Blank spaces in the table indicate non-availability of statistics.
The great increase in surgical operations during the last quarter of the 19th century is reflected in the figures for 1900—in spite of steadily growing numbers carried out at the GRI during that period, by the end of the century only 50% of infirmary operative cases were found in the GRI, following the provision of facilities at the GWI and VIG.

Source: Population figures estimated from Census figures: AR GRI; C. I. Pennington, 'Mortality, public health and medical improvements in Glasgow 1855-1911', Stirling Ph.D., 1977.

London hospitals to charge a fee to the dressers, but in Glasgow, the Scottish tradition of inexpensive education obtained and no fee was required. Slightly senior to the dressers were the clerks, or house surgeons, who were appointed each year: one or two were attached to the surgical wards. They were resident in the hospital and also spent one year in both the fever ward and the medical wards.

Before 1831, physicians to the hospital were 'specialists' who did not do any surgery, but after that date the 'pure' physician had disappeared and the general practitioners could also take up appointment as physician to the Royal Infirmary.[5] Thus, it was possible for an individual doctor to be appointed to the Royal Infirmary, first as a surgeon, then as physician.[6] The hospital doctor therefore was not a specialist in Glasgow at this time. The situation was probably similar elsewhere. Only in Edinburgh and in London would there be enough business for the successful physician to maintain a specialist practice.

Throughout the nineteenth century the population of Glasgow was expanding greatly,[7] and by the 1840s the number of surgical cases rose to equal and exceed those classified as medical. With increasing industrial activity there were many accidents on the railways, in iron foundries, collieries, building works and shipping in the harbour (both on board ship and on the quays). Alcohol abuse was often mentioned as a contributory cause of all

FIGURE 1.—*Surgical operations Glasgow Royal Infirmary 1810–1900.*

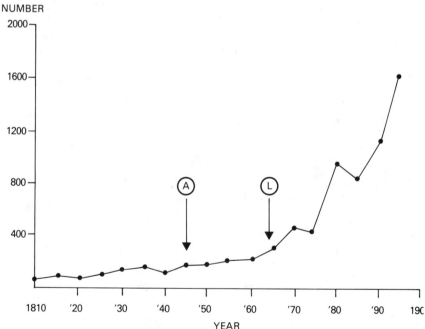

Also shown are the dates of the introduction of ether anaesthesia (A) and Lister's early use of carbolic acid antisepsis (L). (*Source:* AR GRI.)

types of accident. The managers prided themselves on accepting such cases promptly, as emergencies, although their enthusiasm was tempered by the extra financial burden this entailed. Later, to the managers' satisfaction, working men in the big factories began to collect subscriptions for the Infirmary themselves. The grateful managers received increasingly large sums annually from these 'operatives' who were happy to subscribe to the hospital, although they had neither admission rights nor a place on the governing body of the hospital. The first of these many contributions was in 1817 from Barrowfield Mills, where five guineas had been collected. By 1840 such monies had become substantial, being about 10 per cent of the total income in that year, and rising to 33 per cent of the total income in 1870.[8] There was increasing pressure on the hospital's resources from the number of accident cases in the 1840s and 1850s. In 1859, a new surgical wing was built which increased the number of beds in the hospital to 200. The high ceilings and broad wards of the Infirmary (which can still be seen) testify to an increasing concern with ventilation as a method of combating infection.

Similar pressures were felt by the medical and surgical staff; larger numbers of out-patients were presenting themselves at the Infirmary's Dispensary and the wider range of surgical problems resulting from indus-

FIGURE 2.—*Mortality: compound fracture and amputation of lower limb, Glasgow Royal Infirmary, 1842–1900.*

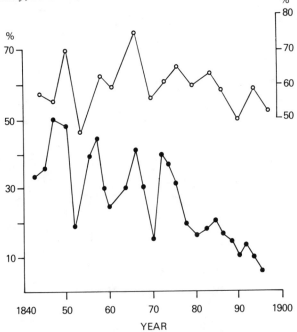

Open dots: mortality from amputations of leg or lower leg, solid dots: mortality from compound fractures of leg. (*Source:* AR GRI.)

trial accidents required more urgent and more considered attention than had been necessary in earlier years.

The ability of the surgeons to undertake successful operations did not change, until the 1860s. It is of special interest to note that although ether anaesthesia had been introduced in 1846,[9] and could thereafter be generally available, this in itself had little or no effect on either the number of operations undertaken (Figure 1) or on mortality after surgery (Table 21). Apparently therefore the only effect of the use of anaesthesia as far as the Glasgow Royal Infirmary is concerned, was to make surgery more humane. The pattern of surgical admissions remained the same: leg ulcers continued to dominate. However, as a result of accidents, simple and compound fractures were rapidly increasing in importance, putting burns, sprains and 'indigestion' into joint third place.

From 1850 the Annual Reports of the Royal Infirmary became more detailed allowing mortality after surgery to be calculated (Table 21). The overall rate is of little value, particularly later in the century, since its significance depends on the proportion of serious and minor surgery treated. But the death rate for individual surgical problems is of great interest. In Figure 2, the death rate for compound fractures of the leg is shown. It is argued here that the variation in mortality figures, following fracture treatment or amputations may have been affected by external causes. It is tempting to see some correlation between post-operational mortality and some typhus epidemics. The typhus epidemics were in 1841–2, 1846–8, 1853–4 and 1864–6.

Because of increasing patient numbers it was decided in 1835 to add to the number of surgeons, thus allowing one member of staff to be present at certain hours in the 'Waiting Room' of the hospital. The total period of service of the junior surgeons was extended from two to four years because a stint in the dispensary was done in the first year and possibly because more experience was required for the in-patient work.

In 1855, the continuing pressure of work led to an increase in tenure of the surgeons from four to five years. Those appointed had usually been qualified for about ten years at the time of their attachment to the Royal. The first year was now devoted to the busy dispensary and the next four to the surgical wards, although by 1868 the four dispensary surgeons and the Infirmary surgeons may have been two distinct groups. After one year 'out', the surgeon was eligible to be re-elected for a further spell in the hospital. Both the physicians and surgeons received £50 per annum. In 1841, Mr Hilliard had been appointed a cupper and bandage-maker to the Infirmary—an additional post reflecting the extra work-load.

In 1857, the demand on the surgical side was such that further 'junior' surgeons were appointed to look after the out-patient work of the dispensary, making three in all, each at a salary of £30 per annum. The Annual Report hints that the previous system had been unsatisfactory because the surgeons occasionally failed to report for duty. There were now forty patients per day attending the dispensary and the two new 'extra' surgeons were solely employed there. The original plan was to have two surgeons appointed for four years, renewable for four years after that, and ineligible for one thereafter: they needed only to be six years post-licensing. Whatever the original intentions, the effect was that this long period of hospital attachment meant that a career structure came to be established, since these 'extra' dispensary surgeons were eligible for later appointment to the Infirmary wards. The shorter period required after licensing and the lower salary made the dispensary surgeon the first grade on a ladder of promotion, in contrast to the earlier scheme of a general practitioner 'taking his turn' in the hospital. In 1868, two further 'extra' dispensary surgeons were appointed, making four in all, thus firmly creating a professional hierarchy, along with a hospital salary scale, and resulting in the emergence of the 'consultant' in a pre-eminent position.

3. Antiseptic and aseptic surgery, 1861–1900

Although there was continuing search for ways of making surgery safer, Joseph Lister (1827–1912) appears to have been the first to consider together the 'Germ Theory' of Pasteur and the effectiveness of certain chemicals in the treatment of sewage[10]—and then to apply his deductions to surgery. The resultant 'antiseptic' treatment of wounds, involving the use of a solution of carbolic acid[11] became standard Listerian practice. Later Lister used a patented 'carbolic spray'. This pioneering work was carried out in the Glasgow Royal Infirmary to which Lister was appointed surgeon in 1861. He came from Edinburgh after a valuable period of work with James Syme and developed some of the main features of the antiseptic system during his years at the Glasgow Royal Infirmary; patients under his care had a better survival rate and his work pointed the way to great change in the potential development of surgical techniques.

It is generally said that Lister met with considerable opposition in trying to establish his methods so it is interesting to note the reaction of his contemporaries in Glasgow.

At the time of his arrival, surgeons were much concerned with mortality in the wards; they viewed patients' prospects with a good deal of apprehension, but were comforted by the reflection that the hospital was in a very good sanitary condition and that wards in the new surgical hospital were

> . . . so well ventilated, so clean and airy that operations of the gravest nature may be undertaken with a prospect of success as great as, if not greater than, in private houses.[12]

As a safety-net, even if the dreaded hospital diseases did occur, the available accommodation made it possible to close the ward for a time and prevent the spread of infection.

Lister published the first accounts of his own work in 1867,[13] and it would appear that his ideas though regarded sceptically elsewhere had taken firm root at the Royal. Reports of cases by the attendant Surgeons[14] in the *Glasgow Medical Journal* (1868–9) clearly reflect this and seem to indicate that even if the theoretical basis of his work was not fully understood, the impressive results of antiseptic treatment demanded that its practice be followed. Not that they accepted Lister's rule completely—they used their discretion on when and how to use carbolic acid and critically compared its use with other methods:

> . . . I have tried the plan of exposure without dressing, so much recommended by Professor Humphrey of Cambridge: but I have not succeeded nearly so well with it as with light antiseptic dressings, which in my opinion ought to be frequently changed and well-protected from the escape of the carbolic acid.[15]

By 1870, George Buchanan was no longer apprehensive, as he had been in 1862 about using his surgical skills:

> . . . opening large abscesses . . . under the antiseptic method have come to be interesting surgical manipulations.[16]

Ebenezer Watson agreed with him.[17] Buchanan was also convinced of the value of Lister's work in limiting the degree of handicap which often resulted from surgery. Reporting on cases of compound fracture:

> In no instance did union fail to occur and in some cases the bones were so comminuted and the laceration so great that I have no hesitation in saying that a few years ago the limb would at once have been removed as irreparable. For such accidents carbolic acid has worked wonders.[18]

And following conservative treatment for a compound fracture of the thumb (which would previously have been amputated):

> Upon the whole the use of the antiseptic treatment will much reduce the number of operations about the hand in our next year's report.[19]

Lister continued his work on return to Edinburgh in 1869 and the modifications in technique which he introduced over the years appear to have been quickly adopted by the Glasgow hospital surgeons. In January 1871, Dr Dewar was using 'green protective and lac plaster' as dressing—but two months later, he adopted 'new carbolised gauze'.[20]

Lister's successor, G. H. B. MacLeod, in a Clinical Surgical Report (GRI) commented:

> The compound fractures of long bones which are admitted into our hospital are, as a rule, very severe and most anxious cases. . . . Still in no department of surgery has greater improvement been made of late years than in the management of these cases. For them the antiseptic treatment has accomplished wonders, and, when it can be fairly carried out, success is the rule, and failure the exception.

At the same time, acutely observing that,

> The most difficult questions frequently arise regarding the management of these
> fractures, as the success which so generally crowns the use of carbolic acid is apt
> to induce us to undertake what is beyond our art . . .[21]

In fact, the only dissenting voice at the Glasgow Royal Infirmary seems to
have been that of Dr Morton who in 1872 had not been persuaded by
Lister's methods, but perversely chose to report using another 'antiseptic'
dressing; the lack of its success possibly reinforced his thinly-veiled
criticisms of the new procedures.[22]

So it would appear that in Glasgow at least, antiseptic techniques became
firmly established as routine in most hospital wards, including those of the
Western Infirmary. By 1880, they were no longer worthy of special note in
the *GMJ*. And, importantly, a new generation of students was being introduced to these practices as accepted fact, so that young general practitioners
could share in the greater confidence with which surgery was undertaken.[23]
One of these students was William Macewen (1848–1924).[24] He entered
private practice but also became police casualty surgeon which would give
him a steady income (see Chapter Two above). There seems little doubt that
police duties proved an invaluable apprenticeship to a surgeon's career,
providing as they did a regular steady supply of injured patients. Macewen
was appointed in 1877 as Surgeon to the Glasgow Royal Infirmary, an
astonishing promotion for a man of twenty-nine. No doubt Macewen's
excellence had been noted but it is almost certain that his appointment to so
prestigious a post reflected not only the expansion of 'consultant' jobs but
also the removal in 1874, to the newly opened Western Infirmary, of the
most senior medical academics. Macewen remained at the GRI until 1892
when he was appointed to the Regius Chair of Surgery by the University of
Glasgow. From that date until 1924 he was based at the Western Infirmary.

Macewen's energies were concentrated upon three aspects of surgery:

(1) his share in the development of aseptic surgery,
(2) his work on bone,
(3) pioneer work on the brain.

Macewen had been a student of Lister's at the GRI in the 1860s and he
remained a firm supporter of Listerian methods. Once in a position of
authority at the GRI he attempted to make advances, introducing a new
discipline and new techniques leading to what has been called 'The Ritual of
the Surgical Operation'. Macewen pushed ahead attempting to remove all
the possibilities of chance infection from the operating room. He was
probably the first to sterilise 'operation materials and dressings'. He
experimented extensively, in the effort to obtain a reliable way of preparing
and disinfecting absorbable ligatures, sutures and drainage tubes. Macewen
is well-known as the pioneer of sterilisable white coats in the operating
theatre. As a result of all these efforts aseptic surgery was the rule in
Macewen's operating theatre followed by aseptic healing.

Macewen appears to have been drawn into the field of bone surgery by the need to find some way of aiding children suffering from rickets in Glasgow. Much of his detailed observation is discussed in the book *The Growth of Bone* which he published in 1912. Almost at once on being appointed to the Royal he began to tackle the problems of limb deformation resulting from rickets. During these years Macewen performed hundreds of operations (osteotomies), becoming expert at relieving ricket conditions.

But there can be no doubt that Macewen's greatest contribution came in his surgical work on the brain and spinal cord. Progress in these areas required the development of exact anatomy, correlated with advances in the field of physiology, pathology and the (then) new science of histology. Macewen worked intensively making careful observation before operating and his work on the brain reflected his precise scientific methods.

As a result of Lister and Macewen's work and that of other able Glasgow surgeons hospital mortality rates fell (see Figure 2) and the poor fled less often from hospital.[25] The need for a subscriber's line for hospital admission fell further into disuse as patients presented themselves at the hospital dispensary for treatment and were admitted, either out of compassion or as providing useful teaching cases. By the end of the century, surgery in the homes of the poor had almost disappeared, and even the rich considered entering the new small nursing homes, instead of being operated on in their own establishments.

The striking feature of this period was the rapid increase in the number of surgical operations carried out in Glasgow Royal Infirmary (Table 21), and the gratifying drop in mortality. Glasgow Royal Infirmary was no longer the only hospital carrying out surgery. The opening of the Western Infirmary (1874), the Victoria Infirmary (1890), the Royal Hospital for Sick Children (1882) and the Samaritan Hospital (1886) meant more work in other hospitals' surgical wards and theatres. Some of the surgical operations there are also recorded in Table 21.

When deaths from compound fractures in the Glasgow Royal Infirmary are looked at in more detail (Figure 2) it can be seen that the cycles of mortality characteristic of the period prior to 1870 disappeared and a more even decline appeared. The mortality from leg amputation, whether 'high or low', continued to be considerable until the end of the century. Actual numbers of amputations decreased suggesting that patients so treated were already critically ill and therefore that amputation may have been a last desperate procedure.

The major expansion of surgical practice was based on the appearance not only of novel types of surgery but also of safe but relatively minor surgery. Tonsillectomy, dating from 1885 soon became fashionable. But attempts at more heroic surgery were less successful. Abdominal surgery was attempted in 1877, mainly for obstruction of the bowel, but between 1877–88 only three patients survived from twenty-nine such operations. Brain surgery (trephining) had almost a 50 per cent mortality until 1900 and nephrectomy was doubtless regarded as equally experimental—there were five attempts in 1895 to remove a kidney but none of the patients survived.

The number of surgeons appointed to the Glasgow Royal Infirmary was increased from five to six in 1882, and the dispensary surgeons had increased from four to six in 1854, changing in name to 'Assistant Surgeons'. To prevent confusion, the resident, unpaid, 'Assistants' were renamed 'House Surgeons'. The beginnings of specialism within the hospital were seen with the appointment of an ear surgeon. The increasing number of operations strained the capacity of the single operating theatre, and in 1882 two smaller ones were opened. In the same year the hospital obtained its first telephone which permitted urgent surgical consultations.

4. A favourable progression?

With the techniques at their command in 1900 surgeons were far removed from their brethren of one hundred years before. This was reflected not only by their numbers and status but also by the sum total and variety of surgical techniques successfully undertaken. There are, however, some surprising findings and new uncertainties. How many surgical cases were undertaken in hospital which would have earlier been done at home? The rise in hospital surgical operations seen in Figure 1 may not reflect the changes in the whole city. Nor do we know the numbers of operations carried out in the poorhouses, though there is evidence that surgery was carried out there less frequently towards the end of the century, suggesting that the voluntary hospitals took in paupers with interesting surgical conditions.

The main surprise is that the availability of anaesthesia from 1847 onwards did not have any immediate effect on surgical practice. Since the benefits to the patients were undoubted and the methods were quickly and widely used, the conclusion is that mid-century surgical practice was limited not by the pain caused, but by the complications, notably post-operative infection or blood loss. Only when these were controlled could surgery advance.

And so the emphasis in Glasgow must remain on Lister's and Macewen's work. In surgical circles it was a time of great excitement and great controversy. As has been shown, most surgeons working in Glasgow were anxious about their patients' survival and were willing to use (and perhaps modify?) Lister's new methods. But as is so often the case, notwithstanding the dramatic response of James Greenlees, the first patient Lister treated,[26] there was no magical formula which was successful every time.

The figures for the results of surgery in mid-nineteenth century Glasgow show that evaluation of any innovation in groups of patients was difficult since spontaneous fluctuations in mortality occurred.[27] Indeed, the period in which Lister started to introduce the antiseptic method in his wards (1864–5) was the start of declining mortality for compound fractures in the whole hospital. This fact was pointed out at the time by some of Lister's critics.[28] Later, there was a slow but steady decline in mortality from compound fractures no doubt due to improved surgical methods as well as to more skilled nursing.

But there were almost certainly other factors relating to the general good health of the patient. If patients were better nourished (as they might have been in a prosperous late Victorian Scotland), then they would be more resistant to infection. Some surgeons, opponents of Lister, who were working outside of Glasgow, were puzzled by their good results (without benefit of Lister's methods) and may have had better fed patients in their care.[29] Nevertheless there were many case reports in the *GMJ* in the 1860s and 1870s where surgeons recommended 'fortifying diets', thus suggesting that many patients were ill-nourished.[30] In these cases surgeons feared that the patients could not sustain the shock of surgery. It also explains the relative immunity of the rich patients to infection, a fact noticed by mid-nineteenth-century surgeons, since this could be the result of their better nutrition, and not their isolation, when operated on in their own homes.

It is clear that many factors contributed to the availability of more sophisticated surgical techniques in the late nineteenth-century Glasgow. The opportunities for advancement in this sphere of medicine depended in large measure on new discoveries in anaesthesia, antiseptics and aseptic techniques. But notwithstanding these impressive new skills, which brought honour and prestige to the surgeons developing them, the basic good health of the patient and his nutritional habits was also a basic pre-requisite for successful surgery.

Chapter Six

CAROLYN PENNINGTON

Tuberculosis

1. The decline in mortality

The decline in mortality that took place throughout the United Kingdom from approximately the middle of the nineteenth century has until recently been commonly assumed to be due to improvements in medical care. It has seemed to be an inescapable conclusion that the erection of a large number of new hospitals in towns and cities throughout the country during this period must have had profound effects on health.

The role that hospitals have played in the decline in mortality, however, has been seriously questioned. McKeown and others have argued that in the eighteenth century the contemporary rise in population owed little to hospitals, which indeed probably did more harm than good.[1] Medical measures, with the possible exception of inoculation and vaccination against smallpox, were of little value, surgery was unsafe and very limited in scope, and few of the drugs then available had any therapeutic value.

With the introduction of compulsory vital registration it became possible to examine trends in the death-rate with greater certainty. Analysis of mortality data shows that the increasing life expectancy in England and Wales in the nineteenth century was due to a decline in the incidence of infectious diseases (tuberculosis, typhus, typhoid, scarlet fever, diarrhoeal diseases, smallpox, whooping cough, measles and diphtheria). It is generally accepted that this was primarily due to improvements in living conditions; to a lesser extent changes in the virulence of certain diseases also played a role. The fall in mortality from these diseases owed little to hospital care as relatively few cases were admitted to hospital until at least the end of the century. Medical treatment was also not important since no effective treatments were available at this time for these conditions.[2] Lower mortality owed little, therefore, to advances in medical knowledge or to greater provision of hospitals. The rising standard of living, and in particular improved diet which increased resistance to some infectious diseases, probably accounts for some of the greater life expectancy. Hygienic measures introduced by sanitary reformers account for the reduction in typhus, typhoid, and diarrhoeal diseases and changes in the causative organism for the decline in scarlet fever.

In Scotland and in Glasgow the fall in mortality that occurred between the 1860s and the first decade of the twentieth century was, as in England and Wales, largely attributable to the decline in infectious diseases, although Glasgow was notable in that a much larger proportion of its mortality decline was due to respiratory diseases of all kinds than was the case nationally.[3] In particular, the fall in deaths in Glasgow from non-tubercular respiratory diseases accounts for a much higher proportion of the overall mortality decline than it did throughout Scotland. This was the most obvious difference between the Glasgow and the Scottish experience. Mortality rates from pulmonary tuberculosis (as for other forms of respiratory disease) were much higher in Glasgow in the 1860s than in Scotland as a whole but the decrease in pulmonary tuberculosis accounts for much the same proportion of the drop in overall mortality in the city as it did nationally. Other infectious diseases declined from comparably high levels in Glasgow but the pattern of mortality trends from these conditions was similar to that in the rest of Scotland. Mortality rates from all infectious diseases in Glasgow remained higher than the national rates.

2. Respiratory diseases

Informed contemporary observers were well aware of the extremely high death rates from respiratory diseases that prevailed in mid-nineteenth-century Glasgow. William Gairdner, professor of medicine at Glasgow University and the city's first (albeit part-time) medical officer was conscious of the problem. He noted in 1870 that fatal as the common infectious diseases were 'They were not comparable, in their effect on the death rate, to the diseases of the respiratory organs, which, taken in aggregate caused considerably more than a third of the whole mortality'. Pulmonary tuberculosis accounted for a seventh of total mortality and such acute respiratory diseases as bronchitis, pneumonia, and pleurisy for a further fifth. Gairdner went on,

> . . . if means of prevention could be applied to the acute diseases of the lungs and air passages and to consumption in Glasgow so as to diminish their fatality by (say) one-third or one-fourth, a far greater saving in life and suffering would be effected than by any other sanitary interference whatsoever.[4]

Gairdner was being prophetic in writing this in 1870 but it is doubtful whether the fall in mortality from respiratory diseases and pulmonary tuberculosis that took place thereafter owed much to sanitary or medical measures.

Although Gairdner and Dr J. B. Russell, his successor as Glasgow's medical officer of health, were well aware of the extent of the problem posed by respiratory diseases and consumption, they concentrated on more immediate public health concerns. The efforts of the sanitary department were directed to the obvious problems of the time, the control of smallpox and the fevers. When these were mastered the infectious diseases of childhood had to be controlled. To this end infectious disease contacts had to be traced and where necessary vaccinated or isolated, houses disinfected and hospitals provided. The voluntary hospitals of Glasgow, the three infirmaries and the children's hospital, directed much of their attention to

treating acute conditions particularly those amenable to surgical intervention. It was left to the poor law hospitals to provide the available
hospital care for respiratory diseases and pulmonary tuberculosis which
were then considered to be chronic problems (see Chapter Three above).

3. Tuberculosis

For most of the nineteenth century, consumption (the commonest and most
prevalent form of tuberculosis) was not regarded as a condition susceptible
to public health surveillance and intervention. This was largely because it
lacked the immediate, rapid, visible signs of other infectious epidemic
diseases, because it was not known to be infectious, and because no
effective treatment existed. Dr Russell, speaking on the control and prevention of infectious diseases in 1878 noted that, 'sufferings from bronchitis or
consumption may not affect us much, except through our poor-rates'; while
typhus, smallpox and scarlet fever, 'invade our homes and compel interest
if not sympathy, even from the most selfish'.[5] Thus pulmonary tuberculosis
and other respiratory diseases presented themselves as conditions that
pauperised families (often over a long period) and were therefore problems
for the Poor Law rather than as diseases striking down the healthy indis-
criminately and rapidly. It was to the latter that public health measures were
directed.

The aetiology of tuberculosis was unknown until Koch demonstrated the
causative organism in 1882 and thereby established beyond doubt the contagious nature of the disease. A large range of treatments was available for
consumptives up to this time[6] which can be taken as an indication that none
was really effective. It also suggested that medical men were unsure of the
nature of the disease they were attempting to treat.[7]

Once it had become known that the tubercle bacillus was the sole cause of
all forms of tuberculosis an attempt could be made 'to adapt to tuberculosis
the great principles of prevention and treatment that were proving service-
able in the case of other infective diseases'.[8] Many years later Professor
Robert Philip, the pioneer of the treatment of tuberculosis in Scotland,
described the 'flutter' caused in laboratory medicine by the announcement
of the tubercle bacillus in 1882 as 'one of the romantic memories of
medicine'.[9]

4. 'On the prevention of tuberculosis'

Although Russell, as medical officer of health was inundated with work he
did not shrink from new tasks and new responsibilities. From 1889 when he
published 'Sanitary requirements of a Dairy Farm' he was active in taking

measures to control TB and ensure that Glasgow would pursue an active policy against so damaging a disease. Russell was concerned both with bovine and pulmonary TB.

In Glasgow the first official steps against tuberculosis were those taken to prevent the sale of contaminated milk and meat. In 1889 the sanitary department won a test case in the courts over the sale of a tuberculous bullock carcase which had been condemned as unfit for human consumption (under section 26 of the Public Health (Scotland) Act 1867). By this time the general public in Glasgow were being made aware that tuberculosis could be spread in the milk and meat of infected cattle. The *Glasgow Herald* carried a series of articles on the relationship between infected meat and milk and the spread of tuberculosis.[10] Further prosecutions followed this test case. This was a move in the general public interest, the local *Sanitary Journal* noted, in the interests of the working classes especially 'to whom unscrupulous butchers . . . are only too ready to dispose of unsound meat, disguised in the form of minced meat or sausages'.[11] The Glasgow Police (Amendment) Act of 1890 extended the local authority's power of prosecution and seizure and set up an inspection staff which watched railway stations, wharves, etc. to ensure that unsound meat was not brought into the city illicitly. This system soon meant that Glasgow was no longer, as Dr Russell put it, a market for 'the farmer's casualties' and 'the speculations of the carrion butcher'.[12]

These efforts to control the sale of tuberculous meat probably had little impact on the spread of non-pulmonary tuberculosis, as the chief source of infection is not meat but untreated milk. It is possible that disease may result from the consumption of raw or undercooked tuberculous meat, but this is uncommon.[13] It is, however, much easier to control the sale of meat than to monitor the condition of milk which was brought into Glasgow from farms in the surrounding area; to determine the presence and source of tubercle bacilli, bacteriological examination of separate samples from each farm would be required. The Glasgow Police (Amendment) Act gave powers to weed out obviously tuberculous cows from city byres and to examine cows in the rural areas which supplied the city. Unfortunately there were no effective means of enforcing this latter measure for some years.

In Glasgow a more concerted attack on tuberculosis followed the report that Dr Russell made on the subject at the request of the committee of health. In December 1891 the Medico-Chirurgical Society of Glasgow, an organisation to which many of the most eminent Glasgow doctors belonged, resolved that a memorial should be presented to Glasgow Town Council calling its attention to the fact that tuberculosis was now considered to be an infectious disease and asking that this matter be considered with a view to protecting the community from infection. A committee of the society, which included Joseph Coats (president of the society and the first professor of pathology at Glasgow University) and Professor Gairdner framed the memorial. This authoritative statement pointed out that tuberculosis was an infectious disease (though heredity and acquired susceptibility might be important factors). The commonest form of the disease was consumption of the lungs and infectious consumptives 'almost constantly spit up matter which is loaded with the infective microbe'. While tuberculosis might not be as infectious as typhus or smallpox it could be compared in infectivity with typhoid. Yet tuberculosis had more disastrous results than all the other infectious diseases put together and was probably under-reported, if anything, in the Registrar General's mortality returns. The memorialists congratulated The Town Council on its action in prohibiting the sale of tuberculous meat and milk and suggested that a start be made to reduce infection from consumptives. They concluded that Glasgow's 'splended sanitary organisation' should do much 'to cleanse our city from some of the principal causes of the widespread prevalence of this, its greatest plague'.[14]

In this way the medical establishment of Glasgow put pressure on the Town Council to take action against what was now perceived to be an infectious disease. The degree of infectivity of consumption continued to be a matter for debate. The memorial was submitted to the committee of health in January 1892 and the medical officer, Dr Russell, was delegated to report on the matter. In December 1895 Russell submitted his conclusions,[15] discussing the mode of spread of the tubercle bacillus in some detail. Contaminated milk and meat were sources of non-pulmonary tuberculosis (particularly, in the case of milk, in children) and therefore, ought to be regulated. Pulmonary tuberculosis (phthisis, or consumption) accounted for three-quarters of deaths from tuberculosis in Glasgow and so it was clearly the greatest problem. Russell relied heavily on Cornet's work on the mode of spread of pulmonary tuberculosis, which he quotes extensively.[16] Cornet, as Russell noted, had shown

> that sputum is practically the only source of infection in phthisis; that where there is no sputum there is no infection; that the sputum is not infectious unless it dries; that it cannot dry excepting under certain conditions, perfectly easy to be avoided;[17]

Russell's conclusions and recommendations were based on these premises.

Local authorities were faced with a new problem when they considered how they should tackle pulmonary tuberculosis. It was not, Russell considered, an infectious disease 'in the popular sense'. The popular view of an infectious disease was one 'from which there is no safety save in keeping away from it.' Those with infectious diseases faced social ostracism even in the middle classes. 'The West-end fear of infection', Russell noted, 'is indiscriminating even to absurdity.'[18] If pulmonary tuberculosis were to be treated in the same manner as other infectious diseases restrictions would have to be placed on a large number of people. Russell considered that the isolation of consumptives and other draconian measures that were being suggested in Prussia and elsewhere were unnecessary. He was aware that even in the absence of public health measures to control consumption mortality from the disease had fallen by 47 per cent in Glasgow in the twenty-five years from 1860–4. Russell believed that general hygienic and environmental improvement held the greatest hope for the continued improvement in consumptive mortality. Clearly he had little expectation of medical treatment for consumption.

Russell believed that sputum from consumptives or dust from dried sputum were the vehicles for spreading pulmonary tuberculosis. He therefore held that it was unnecessary to isolate consumptives as the infection could be limited by proper control and disinfection of sputum and by consumptives sleeping alone. Russell was mistaken in this, as it was later shown[19] that tubercle bacilli are carried in the minute moist droplets expelled from the nose and throat of someone with open pulmonary tuberculosis when coughing, sneezing or talking loudly. Dust from sputum is probably less important than droplet infection in the spread of tubercle bacilli. Nevertheless Russell's recommendations were based on the sputum and sputum and dust hypothesis. As he believed that the risk of infection was so limited he thought that it was not necessary to make pulmonary tuberculosis a compulsorily notifiable infectious disease. The dangerous cases were those in advanced stages of the disease for whom some sort of home or hospital was required. This might present difficulties as local authorities had no experience of providing hospitals for incurables. It was also essential to disinfect homes after a death had occurred from pulmonary tuberculosis. The remainder of Russell's recommendations are confined to advocating education about tuberculosis. He suggested that his report should be published for the benefit of the medical profession and that a short popular leaflet on the subject of consumption, similar to that which was produced about scarlet fever, should be published and distributed. Further steps were obviously required to control the milk supply; the services of a veterinary surgeon were urgently required to test dairy cows. Individual municipal departments all had a role to play in controlling unfit and overcrowded houses, in encouraging the use of parks and open spaces and in discouraging spitting in public places and so on.

A special sub-committee on the prevention of tuberculosis was appointed to consider Russell's report which was duly endorsed. The most obvious immediate results were the further measures taken to control Glasgow's milk supply. In 1897 a veterinary surgeon was appointed who was able to test suspect cattle in city byres. His task was made easier two years later by the appointment of a bacteriologist who could test milk samples (as well as other specimens). Legislation to control milk supplies continued to be extended. Following the recommendations of the Royal Commission on Tuberculosis in 1898 a Dairies, Cowsheds and Milk Shops Order (1899) was issued which extended the prohibition on the sale of milk from diseased cattle to include that from tuberculous animals. In 1900 powers to control cow byres in Glasgow were made more rigorous when it was agreed that byres should be licensed under the terms of the Cattle Sheds in Burghs Act (1894) only after a joint report by the medical officer of health, the sanitary inspector, and the veterinary surgeon (or any two of these). These efforts may well have reduced the amount of tuberculous milk actually produced in Glasgow but milk from rural areas was outside effective control of Glasgow officials and enforcement of national legislation in country areas was variable.

Attempts to improve the safety of milk supplies received a set-back in 1901 when Koch announced at a London Congress on Tuberculosis that bovine tuberculosis bacilli were non-pathogenic to human beings. A Royal Commission on Tuberculosis (Human and Bovine) was set up to investigate this claim and it established that Koch was mistaken. Glasgow's medical officer used the occasion of the publication of the Third (Interim) Report of the Royal Commission, which showed that bovine TB could be spread from cows with forms of tuberculosis other than tuberculosis of the udder, to add weight to his demand for more control of conditions on dairy farms supplying Glasgow by rural local authorities.[20]

Thus efforts to improve the safety of milk supplies continued but many years elapsed before safe, pasteurised milk replaced untreated milk in Glasgow. Milk-borne tuberculosis continued to be a major cause of disabling disease in Glasgow children.

Pulmonary tuberculosis confronted Glasgow's public health doctors with a much more complex problem than was the case with other forms of the disease. Dr Russell was convinced that its decline, which was clearly evident from mortality data, had occurred without any special prophylactic measures and was therefore due to what he described as 'general hygienic measures'.[21] He did not advocate a rigorous policy of isolation and segregation but rather general environmental improvement which would make the city less crowded and polluted. As he remarked, 'Sunlight is the only disinfectant which sustains the man while it kills the microbe.'[22] Clearly sunlight should be encouraged within the city by controlling air pollution from industrial and domestic chimneys, restricting very high buildings, checking overcrowding within buildings, and by providing parks.

The other main recommendation of Russell's report was to inform the public of the facts concerning tuberculosis. To this end Russell's report 'On The Prevention of Tuberculosis' was published primarily for the benefit of the medical profession and a synopsis of the report entitled 'A Popular Exposition of the Modern Doctrine of Tuberculosis with Applications' was printed for the use of nurses, district visitors, and teachers. A popular leaflet 'Hints on the Prevention of Consumption' was prepared. By the end of 1896 140,000 copies of this leaflet had been distributed throughout the city by commissionaires and sanitary inspectors and a further 6000 copies were issued to be distributed by doctors, dispensaries, hospitals and nursing institutions.

5. The National Association for the Prevention of Consumption

The Glasgow medical establishment again figured prominently in pressing for improved facilities for consumptives when efforts were made to have sanatoria established in the west of Scotland. The late 1890s saw growing national concern with the problems of tuberculosis. In 1898 members of the medical profession founded The National Association for the Prevention of Consumption and other forms of Tuberculosis with the Prince of Wales as its first president. The aims of the Association were to influence public opinion through scientific meetings and public lectures, to found sanatoria, and to encourage research.[23]

Early in the following year in Glasgow the sub-committee on the prevention of tuberculosis asked the medical officer and other public health officials to consider whether a branch of the National Association should be set up in the city. Later in the year the Lord Provost was approached by the secretary of the Medico-Chirurgical Society asking for his help in arousing public opinion on the problem of consumption. The matter was considered and members of the Medico-Chirurgical Society again met the sub-committee in February 1901, when it was decided that a public meeting should be held to raise support for setting up a local branch of the National Association for the Prevention of Consumption. A public meeting was duly held in the banqueting hall of the City Chambers on 22 March 1901 and was chaired by the Lord Provost and supported by Principal Story and other Glasgow medical and civic notables. Resolutions were passed supporting the establishment of a Glasgow branch of the National Association for the Prevention of Consumption and endorsing the need for sanatoria.[24] A major part of the Association's work in the west of Scotland was the establishment of Bellefield Sanatorium at Lanark which was opened in 1904 with thirty (later fifty-two) beds for male patients of the 'artisan and commercial classes'. It was supported by contributions raised by the Association's Ladies Auxiliary and a large capital grant from Glasgow Corporation.[25]

Sanatoria, often modelled on the principles used at the famous one at Nordrach in the Black Forest, were being set up throughout the country at this time. Treatments for pulmonary tuberculosis which stressed the importance of a good diet and fresh air long antedated Koch's discovery of the tuberculosis bacillus. Some proponents stressed the importance of high altitude in the situation of the sanatorium, others a cool dry climate, a sunny situation, the absence of dust, or the value of ozone. In general, the management of cases in sanatoria involved living out in the open air for as much time of day and night as possible, rest or carefully graduated exercise, a good diet, and health education.[26] The value of such a regimen is now open to doubt, since its use had not been very critically examined. However, at this time, it was the approach which held out most hope of a cure to consumptives although we can see that its main advantage probably lay in isolating cases from the community. Effective and reliable treatment of pulmonary tuberculosis was not possible until streptomycin was introduced in 1947.

Some contemporary doctors were convinced nevertheless of the value of sanatoria. Dr Beatson at a public meeting in Glasgow, for example, referred to 'Scientific and reliable evidence' of their value.[27] But Dr Johnston, the medical officer at the City Poorhouse, who later held a similar position at

the two district hospitals of the Parish of Glasgow at Oakbank and Duke
Street, was among those who doubted that the therapeutic value of
sanatoria could be attributed to their special situation on some high hillside
or bracing rural position. 'Given two Sanatoria, one on a breezy common,
the other in the heart of a city,' he noted 'and let each receive all cases of
phthisis who apply for succeeding periods of six or twelve months, it has yet
to be proved that the latter would show the higher mortality.'[28]

6. Pulmonary tuberculosis and Poor Law hospitals

General hospital care for consumptives, as for those suffering from other
forms of respiratory diseases, was largely provided in Glasgow in Poor Law
hospital wards in the poorhouses of Barony Parish (at Barnhill), City Parish
and the parish of Govan (at Merryflats). As Dr Robertson, the medical
officer at the City poorhouse noted in December 1868, the most important
diseases treated in the poorhouse 'both in point of numbers and severity'
were diseases of the chest including pneumonia, bronchitis, and phthisis.[29]
Admissions and mortality from these diseases always rose in severe, cold
weather and there were constant references in winter months to the
increased number of patients coming in 'suffering from the ordinary
troubles which are most abundant at this season, chiefly those of the lungs
and heart'.[30] Deaths from phthisis make up a considerable part of total
mortality in the hospital wards, half of those in the month to mid-March
1896, for example.[31]

During the latter part of the nineteenth century the treatment of the sick
in Scottish poorhouses had improved greatly (see Chapter Three above).
The introduction of trained, paid nurses was a major step forward and no
longer were the sick left to the mercies of resident, unpaid, pauper, 'nurses'.
Pressure from officials of the Board of Supervision for the Relief of the
Poor had led to this important change and the Board continued to press for
further improvements of hospital facilities in poorhouses.[32] Lack of suitable
accommodation for treating the sick at both the old City poorhouse and at
Barnhill was an important factor which led to the amalgamation of the two
parishes in 1898 to form the new parish of Glasgow. One of the first actions
taken by the new parish was to make plans for purpose-built hospitals for
the parochial sick. Thus the special needs of the sick poor were getting more
recognition in Glasgow.

With the publication of Dr Russell's report on tuberculosis in 1896 the
particular requirements of the consumptive sick within poorhouse hospitals
became obvious and important changes ensued. The report must have come
to the attention of some member of the parochial council of City parish for
soon after its publication a member of the council (a Dr McLaughlin)
moved a resolution that all cases of phthisis in the poorhouse should be put
in separate wards.[33] The medical officer of the poorhouse was asked to

report on the matter and he suggested that a copy of Dr Russell's report should be sent meantime to each member of the poorhouse committee. Dr Johnston (the medical officer) submitted his report in September 1896 noting that on a specified day in June of that year there was a total of 122 phthisis cases in the poorhouse. Seventy had been in the hospital and a further fifty-two (who were considered to be capable of work) in the rest of the poorhouse. Because of a lack of special accommodation only forty-five of the hospital cases were segregated in special wards. Johnston did not appear concerned that twenty-five consumptives should be in ordinary hospital wards since he was convinced that phthisis would not pass from patient to patient 'where the sputum is kept in closed spittoons, regularly cleansed, containing water or carbolic acid, and where the floors are constantly kept clean, and soiled bedclothes removed'.[34] Clearly, like Dr Russell, Dr Johnston believed that sputum was the sole source of danger to those who came in contact with consumptives, and concluded that he did not think it possible to segregate all consumptives within existing poorhouse buildings. Once the new parish of Glasgow was set up in 1898 it was possible to provide special purpose-built wards for consumptives in the new parish hospital at Stobhill: beds for 120 phthisis cases were included in the plans. In Govan poorhouse at Merryflats on the south side of Glasgow all cases of pulmonary tuberculosis were isolated from 1900 onwards and in 1909 special new wards were opened.[35]

At Stobhill hospital the open air method of treatment was tried from the middle of 1904. Twelve selected consumptive patients were housed in two tents in the hospital grounds. The medical officer reported that two of the patients had been cured, since they had no physical signs of consumption and no bacilli were found in their sputa. It was noted that the patients greatly appreciated this form of treatment.

There was still insufficient accommodation at Stobhill for treatment of consumptives on modern lines and so it was proposed that a sanatorium block should be built. A delegation, which included the medical officer, visited the Victoria Hospital for Consumption in Edinburgh to seek Dr Philip's advice and was impressed by the wooden shelters that were in use there. It was agreed that twenty similar shelters should be built at Stobhill in which consumptives could benefit from living in the open air in all weathers. This form of treatment proved popular, for the medical officer requested in 1909 that a further five shelters should be provided as there were always more male patients who could benefit from such treatment than could be accommodated. How effective such a regime was is another matter. Patients lived outside in these shelters day and night. According to the medical officer in October 1905, they were quite satisfied and some of them even said they did not want to go back to the ward despite the fact that the weather had been cold and foggy. This form of open air treatment together with a 'liberal' diet was the contemporary method of management. Nevertheless, Dr Core the medical officer at Stobhill, when asked by the parish council in December 1906 how many curable cases of pulmonary tuberculosis there were in the hospital, replied that judging from the past comparatively few cases had been cured. 'Such cases do not usually come under my notice until the disease has advanced beyond expectation of a cure.'[36] Clearly open air treatment was no panacea.

The fact that so many patients with pulmonary tuberculosis only entered Stobhill when their condition was advanced probably contributed to the lack of success. In the four years to 1911, 70 per cent of deaths from phthisis in the hospital occurred within three months of the patients' admission. Patients sought admission, an investigator noted, 'for their own advantage or the *financial* relief of their households; the sanitary welfare of their family or of the public has little or no share in determining application for admission or length of residence.'[37]

Once it had been established in the 1880s that pulmonary tuberculosis was contagious the attitudes of hospital authorities on all sides changed. On the one hand medical officers in Poor Law hospitals were concerned to segregate as many of their consumptive patients as they could, while on the other hand the voluntary hospitals in Glasgow, which were able to select their medical cases, became less ready to admit consumptives to their wards. Glasgow's medical officer Dr A. K. Chalmers gave figures to a meeting of the National Association for the Prevention of Consumption in 1910 showing that the admission of patients with phthisis had fallen from 15 per cent of all medical admissions to the general, voluntary, hospitals in the years 1880–4 to only 2.9 per cent of medical admissions in 1907.[38] The Royal and Western Infirmaries continued to treat some consumptives as in-patients but 'do not lay themselves out to do so'. Such cases were either patients with surgical or other complications of their condition or were admitted through an initial error in diagnosis. These 'are willingly retained on account of their value as clinical material in a hospital which is an adjunct to a medical school', it was noted. The new Victoria Infirmary on the south side of the Clyde did have seven beds in two small wards especially for consumptives but only some fifty cases a year were treated.[39] Thus it fell increasingly to the Poor Law hospitals to provide medical care for those with pulmonary tuberculosis.

In the 1870s Dr Russell had noted that phthisis made itself manifest to the general public as a rise in the poor rates. The association between phthisis and poverty had been evident for many years. A medical inspector of the LGB, Dr Thomas Dewar, was struck, when he studied the disease in Glasgow in 1911, by the close relationship between the two and stressed this matter in his report. 'Phthisis is a cause of poverty' he wrote 'and poverty is a predisposing cause of phthisis, facilitating, if not inducing, its acquisition, reducing resistance, hastening its extension, and diminishing the chance and hope of recovery.'[40] Pulmonary tuberculosis confronted both the Poor Law authorities and the public health authorities with a dilemma because of the close association between the disease and poverty and poor housing. As Dr Chalmers noted in 1905 pulmonary tuberculosis would only be prevented 'by removal of the conditions which foster it'. The disease flourished 'because of the low standard of housing we are still perforce compelled to accept'.[41] Chalmers found that the incidence of pulmonary tuberculosis (as measured by death rates from the disease) was directly related to house size; those in the smallest and most crowded houses had the highest mortality rate from the disease. Mortality was also highest among labourers and lowest in the professional classes. Consumption was therefore 'relatively more prevalent where house-room was most restricted, where wages were always low and possibly irregular, and where, probably, food also was on a correspondingly restricted scale'.[42] Those ill with consumption were compelled to resort to the Poor Law for both medical treatment and support of their dependants. Often they were only prepared to do this when the disease had advanced beyond treatment. Yet it was the public health authority which should have been preventing the disease while it was the aim of the Poor Law to preserve an individual's economic independence. The surest way of accomplishing the latter was to maintain individual health and this was easiest 'when the economic status is maintained.'[43]

7. The dilemma of the Local Government Board

At the end of the century the Local Government Board found themselves in something of a quandary. As Dr Leslie MacKenzie, the medical member of the LGB noted, it was no direct part of a parish council's duty to prevent infectious disease. Its duty was the control and prevention of pauperism. But pauperism was a major cause of pulmonary tuberculosis and as the Poor Law had to provide for the sick poor it had been providing medical treatment for the consumptive poor.[44] In 1899 the Board had begun to assess the extent of the problem when it asked poorhouse officials for details of the number of phthisis and other cases of tuberculosis in the poorhouses and the provisions that were available for their treatment.[45] Later Poor Law officials were urged to segregate consumptives within poorhouses.[46] An important development occurred in 1903 (Dr J. B. Russell was then medical member of the LGB), when the Board stated that phthisis was to be regarded as an infectious disease in terms of the Public Health (Scotland) Act 1897, and provisions made for it accordingly. An LGB circular of 1906 obliged local authorities to deal with phthisis as they did with other infectious diseases and permitted them to add it to the list of diseases notifiable under the Notification Act.[47] The circular gave details of the various sorts of hospitals that were being provided. The LGB favoured a system of dispensaries similar to that pioneered by Dr Robert Philip in Edinburgh. In these, patients could be assessed and arrangements made for the necessary medical and hospital treatment, disinfection and so on. Such dispensaries would be managed by a medical officer of health and would provide a 'Central Bureau of Information' on all aspects of tuberculosis.[48]

Thus the LGB turned to the public health authorities to provide for the prevention and eventually for the treatment of pulmonary tuberculosis. The Board were taking steps to break the seemingly inevitable syndrome of

poverty, pulmonary tuberculosis leading to further poverty, poor housing
and nutrition which predisposed yet another generation to fall victim to an
attack of the disease. The local authorities were also expected to continue
with environmental improvement and health education.

8. Public health provision for pulmonary tuberculosis in Glasgow

In Glasgow not only was the LGB pressing for action against consumption
but pressure was growing in other quarters. Early in 1903 the managers of
the Royal Infirmary proposed that the limited system of notification of new
pulmonary tuberculosis cases by voluntary and Poor Law hospitals and
dispensaries should be extended, that domiciliary nurses should be
employed to educate people in their own homes and that disinfectants
should be provided by the Sanitary Department.[49] The Medical Officer was
asked to report and he requested that an assistant medical officer be
appointed to investigate the matter.

The report of the two doctors was submitted in November 1903 and
began, as had that of their predecessor Dr Russell in 1896, with a review of
the pattern of pulmonary tuberculosis mortality in the preceding thirty
years. It pointed out that there had been a continuous fall in mortality
which had begun well before the tubercle bacillus had been isolated or any
specific measures taken against the disease. This mortality decline was
attributed to 'the displacement of masses of population from areas which
were overbuilt, and from houses which were overcrowded'.[50] The disease
was most prevalent in very crowded areas of the city. The report concluded,
as had Dr Russell's, that the best hope for a further reduction in consumptive mortality lay in continued efforts to improve housing and the environment. The introduction of compulsory notification was not recommended
but it was suggested that the matter of providing isolation facilities for
advanced cases should be further considered.

Despite the medical officers' view that making pulmonary tuberculosis a
compulsorily notifiable disease was not warranted, public opinion in favour
of such a step was growing. Groups such as the Glasgow United Trades
Council, the Langside Ward Committee and the Mile End Ward Committee
urged the town council to take further steps to control the disease.[51] In
March 1903 the Glasgow Eastern Medical Society had recommended that
the Corporation should make pulmonary phthisis a notifiable disease in
terms of the Infectious Disease (Notification) Act of 1890. By 1906 Glasgow
Parish Council had added its voice to the demand for compulsory notification.[52] The medical officer was again asked to report on the matter in 1906
after the Corporation had received the LGB circular on the administrative
control of pulmonary phthisis. The medical officer concluded that the
system of voluntary notification was inadequate.[53]

There were legal difficulties to be resolved before pulmonary tuberculosis could be made a compulsorily notifiable disease. Authorities in Glasgow feared that if cases of the disease had to be notified then the city would be forced to pay for treatment for such patients. The Town Clerk of Glasgow noted that the whole point of the Public Health Act of 1897, 'is to give powers to the local authority not so much to interfere with individual cases of infectious disease as to prevent the spread of such among the public.'[54] The Committee of health recommended in October 1906 that compulsory notification be adopted but it was unclear how this should be done in the case of pulmonary tuberculosis. Using existing legislation involved problems, as the Corporation pointed out to the LGB. The Secretary of State for Scotland therefore introduced a short relieving Act which modified the 'over-stringency' of the Public Health Act of 1897, so that it could be applied to pulmonary tuberculosis without causing unnecessary hardship to individuals.[55] The disease became notifiable in Glasgow from January 1910. This measure facilitated the supervision, isolation, and treatment of pulmonary tuberculosis and it was made mandatory throughout Scotland under the Public Health (Pulmonary TB) Regulations issued by the LGB in 1912.

The Corporation was already taking active steps to provide dispensary treatment for consumptives. In March 1909 the sub-committee for the prevention of tuberculosis met representatives of the parish councils, the National Association for the Prevention of Consumption, Quarrier's Homes, Lanfine Home and Bellefield Sanatorium when it was agreed that the staff of the local authority should use parish council dispensaries on certain days for the treatment of consumptives.[56] The first dispensary specifically for the treatment of pulmonary tuberculosis had been opened in 1906 in the City's Sanitary Chambers and was run by the National Association for the Prevention of Consumption.

By the second decade of the twentieth century pulmonary tuberculosis was increasingly treated as an infectious disease and provided for accordingly. No longer was it regarded merely as one cause of pauperism and as such the responsibility of the Poor Law. Only a beginning had been made in providing the dispensaries and sanatoria that were required for a city the size of Glasgow and the continued downward trend in pulmonary tuberculosis mortality probably owed little to these innovations. The particular problem that pulmonary tuberculosis posed lay in the prolonged nature of the illness which frequently meant the lengthy incapacity of a wage earner. In 1910 at the Edinburgh meeting of the National Association for the Prevention of Consumption Dr A. K. Chalmers proposed that the Association recommend to the government of the day 'the desirability of considering a scheme of national insurance against the disease'.[57] The resolution was not carried. Clearly, however, the special needs of pulmonary tuberculosis demanded some special national provision. In fact despite the allocation of resources and the dedication of many doctors and nurses, TB remained intractable until the 1950s when effective drug treatment and better standards of nutrition ensured its virtual disappearance (see Chapter Ten below).

Chapter Seven

CHRISTOPHER SMITH

Medical radiology: its practical application 1895–1914*

1. Röntgen Rays

Probably no event of scientific importance has yielded such immense benefit to mankind as that resulting from the historic discovery of X-rays by Professor Wilhelm Conrad Röntgen, of Würzburg, on the evening of 8 November 1895.[1] In the present age it is not easy to appreciate the impact created by the advent of radiology in a world still largely unfamiliar with the use of electricity even for domestic lighting. For the first time physicians had at their disposal a means of examining internal anatomy without resorting to surgery.

Nonetheless, not all reaction was favourable. Confusing reports appeared in the popular press, leading to widespread misapprehension regarding this latest scientific development. Many people were concerned about invasion of privacy and the likely threat to public morals posed by a method of photography which rendered clothing invisible. There were demands for legislation to restrict X-rays, and in New Jersey a bill was introduced to prohibit the use of X-rays in opera glasses in theatres. Advertisements appeared proclaiming the merits of X-ray proof underclothing, while readers of a French newspaper were advised that wrapping important letters in tin foil would prevent their being read in sealed envelopes by means of X-rays. Reaction was sometimes expressed poetically as in the following, with the joyful final verse celebrating the fact that early X-ray photographs revealed little detail of soft tissue:

> Hech, sirs! ere Röntgen sent his rays
> Thro' this puir 'house of clay',
> Our fond trust was we surely were
> Sole tenants for our day.
>
> But now all's changed, that vandal light
> Spears through our vera claes,
> Our shoon are but as windock glass—
> We're seen frae head to taes.

* Appreciation is expressed to Professor J. M. A. Lenihan, Director, West of Scotland Health Boards, Department of Clinical Physics and Bio-Engineering and to Dr J. G. Duncan, Consultant in Administrative Charge, Department of Radiology, Glasgow Royal Infirmary, for their advice and encouragement in the course of these historical researches.

Later—
> Hoeray! he's foiled, he bored the skull,
> But canna grup the brain!
> Ma wee bit thochties—gude or ill—
> My ain! my vera ain!!

Glasgow Evening Times

Although, as the *Photographic Review* was able to assert, there was no 'humbug or fakery' attached to accounts of Professor Röntgen's own work, the same could not be said of subsequent reports emanating from all parts of the globe. A New York newspaper declared that, 'At the College of Physicians and Surgeons, the Röntgen rays were used to reflect anatomic diagrams directly into the brains of the students, making a much more enduring impression that the ordinary methods of learning anatomical details.' At a meeting of the Paris Academy of Science, Professor H. M. Murat of Le Havre stated that he had obtained results similar to those of Röntgen by the use of ordinary sunlight.[2] Elsewhere in France, the latest alleged application was in proving that of some ninety samples of wine submitted to X-rays not one was the genuine product of the grape—details of the method were not revealed!

Röntgen photography soon found its way into the law courts as evidence. In March 1896 at the Nottingham Assizes,[3] photographs taken by Professor Ramsay at University College were shown to prove the injury sustained to the feet of an actress who had stumbled on a faulty theatre staircase. Despite initial scepticism, the jury decided to award the plaintiff substantial damages. The legal implication for the medical profession was foreseen when the *British Journal of Photography* warned that this new method of diagnosis might 'become a tacit witness against them as well as a valuable helper'. An instance was quoted concerning an eminent photographic expert who in his youth had incurred a severe fracture of his forearm. The limb was set by a surgeon but remained deformed. When many years later an X-ray photograph exhibited the very faulty way in which the bone had been set, 'Its a good thing for him', said the victim, 'that the surgeon who set my arm is dead, otherwise I would certainly take action against him.'

The earliest practitioners of the 'new photography'—to use the popular description—were mainly scientists or electrical engineers. However, within a few months of the original announcement the first X-ray installations began to appear in hospitals under the direction of energetic medical staff, who would undertake such work in addition to their normal duties. They immediately found themselves having to tackle the problem of dealing not only with new patients, but also a vast backlog of subjects with unhealed fractures or other unresolved lesions, whom an X-ray examination might also benefit. From Germany came a strange story of a cook's assistant[4] who several years earlier attempted to commit suicide by shooting himself in the head with a revolver. After he had apparently recovered, he continued to complain of pains in the head and insisted that the bullet was still in his skull. His disbelieving doctors treated him as insane and arranged for him to be committed to the Nietleben Lunatic Asylum, where he remained until 1896 when a skull X-ray demonstrated the validity of his claim.

It was soon evident that exploration of the clinical application of X-rays had only just begun. An immense challenge faced scientists, engineers and physicians alike before medical radiology could be developed to anything like its full potential. Much pioneering work was carried out during the first years, notably in improving the design of X-ray tubes, developing more efficient fluorescent screens and photographic plates, and determining better methods of electrically energising the X-ray tube. One outcome was the reduction of exposure times from several hours in certain cases, to a few seconds or less, thus rendering it a practical possibility to obtain radiographs of even the thickest parts of the body. Moreover, greater comprehension of the mode of operation of X-ray apparatus enabled contrast to be so improved that soft tissue organs could be discerned.

Many pioneers in the field were to suffer severe radiation necrosis during those days before the damaging nature of X-rays was appreciated, leading eventually to great suffering and death from malignant disease. In May 1896 the *Lancet* suggested,[5] in view of the revelation that X-rays acted as a depilatory, that shaving might be dispensed with and the 'new barber' may possibly be one outcome of the 'new photography'. Even after the therapeutic value of X-rays in treatment of cancer became known, few associated that property with possible long-term effect on normal tissue. Indeed, for some time the scientific and medical journals published accounts of experiments in treating tumours, often adjacent to reports of 'peculiar' effects following exposure of the skin to X-rays. As the initial blistering and discolouration of the skin was similar to that produced by the sun's rays, and disappeared after a few weeks, it was widely disregarded, some even concluding that X-rays must be present in sunlight. In truth, there were those who had an intuitive awareness of the risk. Such was their dedication that nothing was allowed to impede progress toward making radiology widely applicable. At St George's Hospital, Hamburg, stands a memorial to the X-ray martyrs of the world. Unveiled in 1936, the stone bears the following inscription:

TO THE RONTGENOLOGISTS AND RADIOLOGISTS OF
ALL NATIONS
DOCTORS, PHYSICISTS, CHEMISTS, TECHNICAL WORKERS,
LABORATORY WORKERS WHO GAVE THEIR LIVES
IN THE STRUGGLE AGAINST THE DISEASES OF MANKIND.

2. Historical background

The serious study of the passage of electricity through a rarefied atmosphere, which must frequently have resulted in production of X-rays and ultimately led to their discovery, commenced around 1855. In that year, Heinrich Geissler (1814–79) glassblower at the University of Bonn[6] constructed the first practical mercury pump, and thenceforth perfected a technique for sealing platinum electrodes into an evacuated glass bulb, thus effectively creating the 'vacuum tube'.

In his presidential address to the Royal Society anniversary meeting on 30 November 1893,[7] Lord Kelvin anticipated great advance arising from research with vacuum tubes, 'If a first step towards understanding the relations between ether and ponderable matter is to be made, it seems to me that the most hopeful foundation for it is knowledge derived from electricity in high vacuum.' At that time, argument still raged amongst scientists as to the mechanism by which electromagnetic radiation such as light was able to travel through an apparent vacuum. The prevalent theory, formulated by the Dutch physicist Huygens in 1690, favoured the concept of an all-pervading medium termed the 'ether' which, although not of a material or 'ponderable' nature, nonetheless facilitated transmission of radiation.

Recognition by Röntgen of a 'new kind of radiation' which he called X-rays, with the ability to penetrate opaque solids, was to yield an important insight into the very nature of matter, and is widely regarded as the most important single step in the development of modern physics. The editor of the *Electrician* probably expressed the view of many scientists when he asserted, 'Intensely interesting as the structure and deformities and diseases of the hand must be to all of us, the thought that we may be on the brink of an experimental verification of the existence of longitudinal ethereal vibrations, within sight of a solution to the gravitation mystery, or about to extract from Nature the well-kept secret of the true nature of Electricity, renders the physicist temporarily oblivious to the exact condition and configuration of his phalanges or metacarpal bones.' Röntgen's contribution to physical science was formally recognised in 1901 when he became recipient of the inaugural Nobel prize for physics.

Despite important research with vacuum tubes over several decades by a host of workers including, Plucker, Hittorf, Goldstein, Crooks and Lenard, until Röntgen's sensational discovery the facet of these devices that impressed most was the colourful fluorescence produced by electrical discharge, often displayed for public appreciation. This later led one observer to comment, 'The Geissler discharge tube—the former beautiful plaything of the scientist—has proved the pioneer of the most wonderful discoveries and speculations that physical science of this or any generation has ever known.'

The rapid spread of knowledge that ensued following the discovery of X-rays must be attributed first and foremost to the enlightened attitude adopted by Röntgen, 'According to the good tradition of the German University Professors, I am of the opinion that their discoveries and inventions belong to humanity, and that they should not in any way be hampered by patents, licences, or contracts, nor should they be controlled by any one group'. No time was wasted in dispatching complete details of his work to scientific colleagues around the world, including Professor A. Schuster in Manchester, and Lord Kelvin in Glasgow. Kelvin received the communication just a few days before the end of December 1895, at about the same time as Röntgen's first publication 'Ueber eine Neue Art von Strahlen' was printed in the proceedings of the *Würzburg Physikalische Medizinische Gesellschaft*.[8] Although confined to bed as a result of a blood clot in the leg combined with an attack of pleurisy, Kelvin was excited by the discovery and wrote in reply, 'I was very much astonished and delighted. I can say no more just now than to congratulate you warmly on the great discovery you have made and to renew my thanks to you for your kindness in so early sending me your paper and the photographs.'

In that initial paper, Röntgen observed, 'If the hand be held before the fluorescent screen, the shadow (thrown by the X-rays) shows the bones darkly with only faint outlines of the surrounding tissue'. He included an X-ray photograph, or radiograph, of his wife's hand, certainly the first of a human subject. This was apparently made in order to explain to Frau Röntgen the nature of the important work that was making her husband late for meals and keeping him in his laboratory late at night.

Having recognised the significance of Röntgen's discovery, but being unable to pursue the matter personally, Kelvin at once passed the paper to his nephew, Dr James Thomson Bottomley, of the University Physical Laboratory. Bottomley was himself a distinguished scientist, and an active member of the Philosophical Society of Glasgow founded in 1806 'for the discussion of subjects connected solely with the arts and sciences'. It was therefore natural that he should communicate freely with other members of the Philosophical Society. Among these were two men—Lord Blythswood of Renfrew, and Dr John Macintyre of Glasgow Royal Infirmary—who were each to play a major role in establishing medical radiology on a practical basis in this country. Both were to be founder members and future presidents of the Röntgen Society, forerunner of the present British Institute of Radiology.

They were soon investigating the new phenomena with such success that on 5 February 1896, a joint communication by Dr J. T. Bottomley, Lord Blythswood and Dr John Macintyre, 'On the Röntgen X-rays, or the New Photography'[9] was read at a special meeting of the Philosophical Society of Glasgow. Even at that early date, Macintyre had assembled equipment with which he was enabled to 'demonstrate all the ordinary phenomena of photography of objects through wood, aluminium, black cardboard, etc, etc'. This apparatus he reported,[10] 'consists of a small battery, giving eight volts and six amperes; an induction coil, lent by Professor Jamieson; a very small Tesla coil, made by Messrs Baird and Tatlock; and a Crooke's (vacuum) tube, which was selected from the stock of Mr Otto Muller, of Glasgow'. Macintyre was already looking to improve both his apparatus and photographic materials, although he was wildly optimistic in predicting that, 'before long a portable and comparatively inexpensive apparatus will be at the disposal of the surgeon'.

Elsewhere, word spread with equal rapidity. In Manchester C. H. Lees, on behalf of Professor Schuster, exhibited copies of Röntgen's first X-ray photographs to the Manchester Literary and Philosophical Society on 7

January 1896. Arthur Stanton, one of Schuster's laboratory assistants prepared an English translation of Röntgen's German manuscript which was published in *Nature* on 23 January.[11] Immediately following Stanton's translation was an article by Mr A. A. Campbell Swinton[12] describing his own experiments carried out with only the newspaper reports of Röntgen's work to guide him. His article was illustrated with an X-ray picture of a hand, which is possibly the first radiograph to have been taken in Great Britain.

Coincidentally, on the same day as Röntgen's paper appeared in *Nature*, he gave the first public lecture and demonstration of the X-rays, to the Physical Medical Society of Würzburg. During the course of his lecture, Röntgen made another X-ray of a hand, this time of the anatomist Professor A. von Kolliker. To rapturous applause, Professor Kolliker proposed that the new radiation should henceforth be known as Röntgen rays, a term which is often used but has never been widely accepted. A variety of names has also been applied to the X-ray photographic process, including skiagraphy, shadowgraphy and electrography before radiography was adopted.

3. The beginnings of medical radiology

The new technique had already been put to practical effect in Vienna by Professor Mosetig,[13] whose experiments on two patients on whom operations were to be performed were said to have been attended with complete success. In one case, the position of a bullet embedded in the hand was located after all other methods had failed, whilst the other case revealed the exact nature of a malformation of the foot. Meanwhile, the *Lancet* reproduced an X-ray photograph of a fractured left fore-arm with 'union in faulty position', said to have been obtained in the State Physica Laboratory, Hamburg, on 25 January 1896.

By mid-February there were competing claims to have first put X-rays to clinical use in this country. At a meeting of the Royal Photographic Society on 28 January, Mr J. W. Gifford, of Chard, exhibited samples of his radiographic work including one showing an 'osseous protuberance of the metatarsus, occasioning distortion of the great toe'. Soon afterwards Dr Hall Edwards, a Birmingham general practitioner, radiographed a woman with a needle embedded in her hand. The needle was clearly seen and removed by the Casualty Surgeon at Queens Hospital, Birmingham. At about this time, Dr A. F. Stanley Kent was able to diagnose a fractured finger bone during a demonstration at St Thomas's Hospital and Dr J. Mackenzie Davidson of Aberdeen located a needle in the foot by means of X-rays.

James Mackenzie Davidson—he was later knighted—was to become the most celebrated of the early radiological specialists and his memory is perpetuated by an annual memorial lecture organised by the British Institute of Radiology. Born in South America of Scottish parents, he studied medicine in Edinburgh, London and Aberdeen, before becoming ophthalmic surgeon to the Aberdeen Royal Infirmary. He heard of Röntgen's discovery while travelling on the continent, and went immediately to Würzburg to find out all he could. In an account of a conversation with Röntgen, he recalled questioning him about his reaction to the first startling observation:

> I asked him, 'What did you think?' He said very simply, 'I did not think, I investigated.'

Mackenzie Davidson is best known for his work on stereoscopic radiology, and for his famous 'localiser' for ascertaining the depth of foreign bodies.

In Glasgow, John Macintyre refrained from laying claim to being first to apply X-rays in a manner to which he may well have considered no particular merit could be attached. His attitude is perhaps best summarised by the words he later used in an article published in *Nature*,[14] 'The serious investigator is more impressed with what has to be done, than elated with what has already been accomplished. It is with great pleasure that I read in the columns of *Nature* of the continued advances of those well fitted to engage in the study of the properties of Röntgen rays in the physical laboratory; and while we have reason to be pleased that the rays have been clearly proved to be of great value in the diagnosis of certain affections, every part of the apparatus must be investigated and improved upon before we obtain thoroughly satisfactory results.' This task Macintyre pursued with remarkable success, assisted by continued co-operation from Dr Bottomley and Lord Blythswood, and with a wealth of inspiration and practical guidance provided by Lord Kelvin.

4. Two enthusiasts, Lord Blythswood and Dr John Macintyre

When he received that original paper from Professor Röntgen at the end of 1895, Lord Kelvin (William Thomson, 1824–1907) was in his seventy-first year and nearing the end of a career that had placed him in the very forefront of physical science. He had completed a fifth successive term as president of the Royal Society, and in recognition of his pre-eminence and devotion to Glasgow, the City was preparing to officially celebrate in 1896 his golden jubilee year as professor of Natural Philosophy at Glasgow University. Although born in Ulster, Kelvin had formed a deep attachment to the city that he first viewed at the age of eight when his family moved there. He declined many attractive offers of posts elsewhere, including invitations in 1871 and again 1884 to become director of the prestigious Cavendish Laboratory in Cambridge.

Kelvin's nephew, Dr J. T. Bottomley (1845–1926) was also born in Ulster, and educated in Belfast and Dublin. He came to Glasgow University in 1870 to act as Arnott and Thomson demonstrator in his uncle's department of Natural Philosophy. His researches covered a wide field, and when he learnt of the discovery of X-rays he threw himself into the business of investigating their physical properties.

After his death in 1908, Lord Blythswood (Archibald Campbell, 1835–1908) was recalled[15] as one of those rare examples of Scottish landed gentry whose life could *not* be described as 'productive of no particular good to the community or the world at large'. Born Archibald Campbell in 1835, he was a direct descendant of the Douglases who played a prominent role in Scottish history of the thirteenth and fourteenth centuries. Blythswood's early life was spent as a soldier and he saw action in the Crimea where he received injuries from which he never fully recovered. This did not prevent him from pursuing an active political career after leaving the army at the age of thirty-three. He was principal founding member of the Glasgow Conservative Association and served as Member of Parliament for West Renfrewshire from 1883 until 1892 when he was elevated to the peerage.

However, the most remarkable aspect of the man was his passion for physical science. He established on his estate at Blythswood, Renfrew, a laboratory and workshop in which he constructed scientific instruments and pursued research of sufficient merit for him to be elected a Fellow of the Royal Society in 1907, an honour he cherished above all others. Blythswood had a particular interest in research with vacuum tubes and, in common with many researchers, was regarded as unfortunate not to have been the first to have discovered X-rays for he had obtained photographic action through various opaque substances before Röntgen made his memorable discovery. In fairness, what set Röntgen apart was his perception in discerning the true cause of such phenomena.

Lord Blythswood contributed greatly to the development of medical radiology in Glasgow by the practical assistance he rendered John Macintyre in a multitude of ways. Many instruments constructed in his laboratory found their way into the capable hands of Macintyre. His own researches into X-rays were essentially scientific and in this area he and Walter Scoble[16] made the first detailed study of the intensity of X-rays. Their technique of measuring intensity as an electrical effect provides the basis of the ionisation method still prevalent.

Dr John Macintyre (1857–1928) came from a background markedly different to that of his illustrious collaborators in X-ray research. The son of Donald Macintyre a tailor from Argyll, and Margaret Livingstone, a relation of the explorer David Livingstone, he was born in 1857 at 343 High Street in the district vividly portrayed in Thomas Annan's famous photographic work 'Old Closes and Streets of Glasgow 1868/77'. Even amidst the insanitary conditions of the age, High Street was singled out as a particularly unhealthy place. It is not surprising therefore that in his youth John kept poor health, as a result of which he was removed from school in the

Townhead area at the age of eleven. Doubtless his experiences during this part of his life helped him to form the resolve to pursue a medical career. When well enough, Macintyre appears to have accepted whatever work was offered. He tried a variety of jobs and by the age of twenty-one had saved sufficient money to keep him during his medical studies at Glasgow University. Having left school so early, Macintyre was largely self-educated. He developed a special interest in electrical engineering and prior to qualifying in medicine was involved in some form of electrical work within Glasgow Royal Infirmary.

John Macintyre graduated MB, CM in 1882. He gained experience working in London and abroad for three years before returning to Glasgow to take up a position as 'Electrician' to the Royal Infirmary, the first such appointment in Scotland and one of the earliest anywhere. It was at this time that he was made responsible for organising 'the equipment of the Royal Infirmary with electrical current for medical and surgical purposes'. This led, in 1887, to the institution of an electrical department in the hospital, with Macintyre in charge.

The foresight shown by the Managers of Glasgow Royal Infirmary during that period is emphasised by the fact that it was not until 1890[17] that Glasgow Town Council applied for and obtained a Provisional Order empowering and requiring them 'to provide electrical energy within a limited area embracing the principal business streets and premises on the north side of the river'. Even then, the corporation supply did not extend to the Royal Infirmary and it was several more years before mains electricity was available.

In the interim, Macintyre was also appointed Demonstrator in Anatomy in the Royal Infirmary School of Medicine, and Assistant Surgeon in the throat department, thus commencing a distinguished career in one of the less fashionable specialities. He became surgeon in 1892, and served as President of the British Laryngological and Rhinological Association in 1893 and also in 1900.

Macintyre's innovative ability was evident as early as 1885 when the *Glasgow Medical Journal* published his paper entitled, 'Some Notes on the Use of Electrical Light in Medicine',[18] the first of many important publications. In this paper, he described a variety of ingenious instruments he had constructed for the illumination and examination of body cavities. They employed small electric lamps and were powered by batteries so that they could be used in the patient's home in even the darkest room—·a distinct improvement over the use of flickering oil, gas or candlelight.

5. Early work at Glasgow Royal Infirmary

It is clear that by 1896 John Macintyre would have been well qualified to implement the clinical application of X-rays. Following the first successful experiments reported to the Philosophical Society of Glasgow, he set about improving his apparatus and radiographic technique. He soon realised that the most important part of the equipment was a well-evacuated tube, for which his first source was Dr Bottomley, an expert in this work who it was said, 'had exhausted some tubes so that only one hundred and forty seventh of one millionth part of one atmosphere was left inside of the tube'. Later Macintyre stated that he got his best results with tubes purchased from Newton & Company, the optical and scientific instrument business founded about 1700 by the family of Sir Isaac Newton, which had now turned to making X-ray equipment. The Tesla coil used in his original equipment was of no particular benefit and was discarded.

At the same time, Macintyre considered ways of improving definition in his X-ray photographs. In that first communication on the X-rays he had enumerated what are still regarded as the essential points of radiographic technique with respect to relative positioning of the X-ray tube, photographic plate, and object to be radiographed.

The earliest clinical example of radiography that Macintyre deemed worth communicating to the medical press[19] was of a woman referred to him early in March 1896 by Dr James Adam of Hamilton. The patient had four years earlier accidentally passed a needle into her wrist, but felt no pain for several years until the middle finger began to swell, apparently without cause. Radiographs of hand and forearm showed evidence of irritation at the ultimate phalanx and also showed the needle to the inside of the styloid process of the ulna. Macintyre pointed out that the experiment had revealed two distinct and different pathological conditions, one causing discomfort, and the other, the needle, evidently causing none.

Macintyre predicted that ultimately the taking of permanent photographs or radiographs, would be largely supplanted by the use of fluorescent screens which allow direct viewing of the X-ray image. His attention was directed to the choice and properties of fluorescent materials, including calcium tungstate which Thomas Edison the American inventor had informed Lord Kelvin by telegram gave 'splendid fluorescence'. He constructed a binocular cryptoscope, a device introduced by Professor Salvioni of Perugia but often attributed to Macintyre. For his own part, Macintyre was quite specific as to who was the real inventor, 'I desire it to be clearly understood that the entire credit of observation by direct vision and photography is due to Professor Röntgen and to him alone. All that the original discoverer left for anyone else to do was improvement in apparatus and practical application.' Macintyre's cryptoscope, described in the *Lancet* on 28 March,[20] comprised a fluorescent screen with attached binocular viewer. If the user placed the binoculars to his eyes and positioned himself and the X-ray tube on opposite sides of the object to be X-rayed, then an image on the fluorescent screen could be directly viewed.

Such was the improvement in technique achieved by Macintyre that by 16 March he reported, 'I have been able to photograph the internal wall of the cranium (in a dead subject), and by means of a binocular cryptoscope carefully worked out to see shadows of bullets placed therein. With the same instrument I have been able to see all the shadows of all the bones of the upper extremities and the majority of those in the lower. With regard to photography, the upper part of the spine has been photographed straight through the chest wall, showing six ribs with their attachments and transverse and spinous processes; in the ribs the intimate structure of the bones is clearly seen, and for surgical purposes I have been able to photograph the elbow joint with a sufficiently good result in one minute and three quarters exposure, using one of Newton's tubes.' Within weeks he had succeeded in completing a series of radiographs of the skeleton including pictures of the shoulder, hip, knee and vertebral column. This last view required the longest exposure, taking eighteen minutes.

Until that time, the work was conducted in his rooms at 179 Bath Street, but before the end of March, Lord Kelvin announced in a letter to the *Electrician*, 'Dr Macintyre has constructed an arrangement for use in the Royal Infirmary of Glasgow by which already in his own house he has examined bones of patients suffering from disease.' Soon afterwards the managers of the Royal Infirmary were persuaded to form a new branch of the electrical department of the hospital.[21] Drs Archibald Faulds and George McIntyre were appointed assistants to devote themselves to surgical, and medical cases, respectively. By now, the hospital was supplied with mains electricity as well as being equipped with a motor-driven dynamo.

The expanded electrical department was fitted out with all the modern apparatus including a large Wimshurst static machine constructed by its inventor Mr James Wimshurst. The static machine was a laboratory apparatus used for generating static electricity. For some years such machines provided an alternative to the induction coil as a means of producing the high voltages required for X-ray work. There were also induction coils, the latest mercury interrupter supplied by Baird and Tatlock, a specially constructed mechanical interrupter, and the new focus X-ray tube perfected by Professor Herbert Jackson of King's College, London University. In June, the *British Medical Journal* publicly announced that an X-ray laboratory had been established in Glasgow Royal Infirmary,[22] the first in a British hospital.

With this equipment, Macintyre and his assistants launched themselves into the work of coping with the large numbers of patients soon being referred to them for X-ray examination. From the outset he gave prime attention to his own speciality—'Although I have been engaged in the general application of Röntgen rays my main work will consist in its application to laryngeal surgery. This includes the examination of the upper part of the chest and the bones of the neck and face.' He enthusiastically described an interesting early case of a boy who six months previously had swallowed a halfpenny, which to his delight he was able to see by means of the fluorescent screen was impacted in the gullet. Lord Lister, discussing this case in his presidential address to the British Association in 1896, referred to the 'wonderful penetrating power which the rays had acquired'.

Meanwhile, the development of apparatus and techniques continued so that by May, Macintyre was able to announce that he had carried out X-ray photography of the heart and other soft tissues for the first time, 'I have now distinctly seen the cardiac area in the living subject, showing its right and left borders, base, and apex.'[23] His success was attributed mainly to a systematic study of the conditions under which X-ray tubes operated. With Lord Kelvin's ampere gauge and cell tester, he determined that the mercury interrupter was about six times more effective at energising the tube than the conventional form of interrupter. Thus, he was able to obtain a radiograph of the hand with one 'flash' of the tube (about one-fiftieth of a second).

Attention was turned next to detecting the presence of renal calculi.[24] A surgical colleague, Dr Adams, requested a radiograph of a patient upon whom he had previously operated. The X-ray indicated an obliquely-placed elongated deposit which was then removed during a second operation. At about this time a series of photographs of the pelvis was completed, including hip joint disease. It was reported that John Macintyre 'had been able to photograph the bones and flesh in such a way as to show hip joint disease with the internal pathological changes and external deformities seen on the same plate'. At the British Medical Association meeting in 1896, large photographs measuring 24 inches by 18 inches displayed by Macintyre were said to have proved the value of showing both sides of the body—'to compare, for example, healthy and unhealthy hip joints together on the plate'—now a standard procedure.

Macintyre's greatest technical achievement occurred during the latter part of 1896 when his advances in reducing exposure time enabled him to produce the 'first X-ray cinematograph ever taken'.[25] This film of the movements of a frog's legs was years later followed up by cine-radiographs of the human heart and lungs, and of the stomach after a bismuth meal. G. M. Ardran in 1973 wrote in a review article[26] dealing with cine-radiography, 'It is clear that Macintyre appreciated the two methods of recording movements using X-rays and paved the way for the future development of rapid serial radiography and cine-radiography.' The background to his innovation lay with earlier experiments in the use of a camera to photograph X-ray images from a fluorescent screen. This established the principle later adopted to considerable effect in miniature radiography of the chest used for mass screening.

6. The new electrical pavilion at Glasgow Royal Infirmary

Within a few years of the expansion of the electrical department to include X-rays, the number of patients had so increased that Macintyre was forced to ask for completely new facilities to carry on the work. During 1901 over 1400 X-ray photographs were taken of around 1000 patients, in addition to the 'very frequent use of the fluorescent screen'. The managers were again approached, and agreed to the erection of a new electrical pavilion.[27,28] The entire cost of the building and equipment was borne by nine wealthy subscribers of whom Lord Blythswood was one. Blythswood also contributed a massive static machine of the Wimshurst type, built in his laboratory at Renfrew.

In 1900 Macintyre had been appointed Consulting Medical Electrician and Dr John Gilchrist became Medical Electrician. Following completion of the new pavilion in 1902, Dr James R. Riddell succeeded to the post of Medical Electrician. He was joined in 1903 by Samuel Capie and in 1906 Archibald Jubb and Katharine M. Chapman were also appointed Assistant Medical Electricians. By 1916 the staff complement included four Assistant Medical Electricians as well as a Working Electrician.

On 5 July 1916 the *British Medical Journal* announced that the Merchant's House of Glasgow had offered to provide funds from the Buchanan and Ewing bequests for the payment of university lecturers in 'Electrical Diagnosis and Therapeutics' at the Royal and Western Infirmaries. James Riddell was first to serve in that capacity in the Royal and then from 1920 in the Western, at which time Katharine Chapman succeeded him both as lecturer and as Medical Electrician at the Royal Infirmary.

The increase in staff allocation to the Electrical Department reflected growing attendances. Between 1906 and 1914 the total numbers of patients dealt with per annum increased from 3140 to 6266, of whom 2730 (87 per cent) and 5725 (94 per cent), respectively, were referred for X-ray examination. The remainder, a steadily declining proportion, received electrical treatment, muscle testing, or electrodiagnosis.

It is worth noting that John Macintyre always demonstrated an astute awareness of possible danger when dealing with X-rays. He only once observed an effect on himself, a slight dermatitis 'after working for nights in succession with the left hand in front of the X-ray tube', which he reported in the *Lancet* in October 1896.[29] Great care was exercised in safeguarding his staff from any similar injury and none was ever recorded.

With the rebuilding of Glasgow Royal Infirmary, the present department, then named the 'George V Electrical Institute', was opened in 1914.[30] At the outbreak of war the hospital managers placed 150 beds at the disposal of the naval and military authorities. Glasgow soon began to receive trainloads of wounded troops and it was recorded that on each occasion, within the Electrical Department, 'sixty to eighty photographs may be taken in an afternoon of soldiers and sailors suffering from injuries'. In a report written in 1916 Macintyre declared that during the first seven months of the year 7000 radiographs had been taken—a far cry from the modest beginnings of twenty years earlier.

It was a consequence as much of existing social conditions as the nature of the new diagnostic technique that the use of X-rays remained predominantly in the localisation of foreign bodies and visualisation of bone lesions. In addition to the numerous shrapnel and bullet wounds encountered during war time, industrial injuries and skeletal malformation due to dietary deprivation were commonplace.

7. X-rays at other Glasgow hospitals

Within the Western Infirmary, the medical superintendent, Dr Donald Mackintosh, personally experimented with the production of radiographs using the simplest equipment. Initially, he concentrated on those areas in which X-rays could be of immediate clinical value. The culmination of this work was the publication of a 'Skiagraphic Atlas', in 1899.[31] This was a comprehensive atlas containing photographic plates mainly illustrating fractures and dislocations, with brief notes on treatment added by Dr G. H. Edington, then a dispensary surgeon.

Certain of the cases are indicative of the problems inherited by X-ray pioneers from a time when bone injuries could only be assessed by guesswork. One eight-year-old patient had received an injury to the forearm four years previously, but no deformity was observed until three months after the injury. When an X-ray revealed the true nature of the lesion, the following was recommended; 'Treatment-osteotomy and straightening the bone. Partial resection may be required.'

A less serious case was that of a child who took a penny from her sister with whom she was playing and attempted to conceal it in her mouth. It suddenly 'went over'. She at once complained of severe pain in the right side of her neck. The skiagram clearly indicated the position of the coin, which was removed immediately afterwards by means of the 'coin catcher'.

Donald Mackintosh took charge of the Electrical Department until 1907 with help from a sister and nurses only. However, in that year he asked Joseph Goodwin-Tomkinson and Archibald Hay to assist him. On 22 February the managers resolved to officially acknowledge their work and 'unanimously agreed to recommend that Dr Mackintosh be requested to continue to act as Medical Electrician, and that Dr J. Goodwin-Tomkinson, and Dr Archibald Hay be recognised as Assistant Medical Electricians, but that no salary or honorariums be attached to any of the appointments recommended to be made'. The following year Donald Mackintosh was designated Consulting Medical Electrician while Goodwin-Tomkinson, Hay and also William Francis Somerville were each appointed Medical Electrician.

These appointments constituted the start of a properly organised Electrical Department. Expansion followed a similar pattern to that of the Department at the Royal Infirmary, with X-ray work becoming increasingly prevalent. By 1920, the year in which James R. Riddell moved from the Royal Infirmary to become Medical Electrician and University lecturer at the Western Infirmary, the number of X-ray photographs taken during the year was in excess of 6000. Riddell continued to devote himself to Radiology and was one of the earliest specialists. Unfortunately, as a result of his work with X-rays he suffered severe ill health for many years before his death from heart disease in 1935. His name was one of sixteen initially inscribed on the memorial to X-ray martyrs in Hamburg.

John Gilchrist, first Medical Electrician to assist John Macintyre at Glasgow Royal Infirmary, was subsequently appointed Assistant Surgeon and Medical Electrician to the Ophthalmic Institution. This establishment, founded in 1869, was taken over by the managers of the Royal Infirmary on 1 March 1891 and thenceforth served as the hospital ophthalmic department. With Gilchrist on its staff the Institution equipped itself for X-ray diagnosis.

Dr A. Maitland Ramsay, Consulting Surgeon for Disease of the Eye and St Mungo's College Professor of Ophthalmology, published in 1900 in the Glasgow Hospital Reports[32] a description of some early cases entitled, 'Penetrating wounds of the eye, complicated by the presence of a foreign body in the eyeball.' Ramsay pointed out that in every large industrial centre such accidents are of daily occurrence. One successfully treated patient was a twenty-one-year-old quarry stonecutter who was shown, by means of an X-ray photograph, to have a metal splinter in the vitreous chamber of his left eye. With the aid of a powerful electromagnet the particle was dislodged and then easily removed. Another case illustrated the value of Röntgen rays in determining the precise position of a foreign body in the eyeball. Using a modified version of the 'localisation' method first described by McKenzie Davidson, Ramsay was able to ascertain the site of a chip of steel within the left eyeball of a thirty-six-year-old ironworker. An operation resulted in the eye retaining at least partial vision. Although not all cases were so successful, Ramsay was moved to comment that before the magnet and the Röntgen rays were introduced into practice, there was not '. . . so far as I am aware, a single instance on record of a foreign body having been removed from the vitreous chamber, and the sight at the same time saved'.

In 1900, Dr William James Fleming, former Surgeon to Glasgow Royal Infirmary and one of the Royal Infirmary managers appointed by the Royal College of Physicians and Surgeons, offered to present his Röntgen ray apparatus to the Royal Hospital for Sick Children. This was on condition that the apparatus be 'properly cared for by a competent medical man', and he suggested Dr John Gilchrist as such a person. On 14 August the Board of Directors decided to accept Dr Fleming's offer and invited John Gilchrist to act as Honorary Medical Electrician to the hospital. During 1901 the apparatus was installed in the Dispensary at West Graham Street. In conjunction with this the Glasgow Corporation arranged to supply mains electricity to the Dispensary for a nominal fee.

The routine practice was for X-rays to be taken by the Resident Medical Officer, with John Gilchrist in attendance when required. The apparatus appears to have given good service for it was not until 1915 that the purchase of new equipment was considered.

The Victoria Infirmary was last of the major Glasgow hospitals to provide an X-ray diagnostic service. However, a new pavilion opened by Mr A. Cameron Corbett, MP, on 1 January 1902 included rooms set aside for an 'Electrical and Röntgen Rays Department'. All of the apparatus and fittings were paid for by a far-sighted and magnanimous member of the Board of Governors.

The Department carried out routine but valuable work, with an average daily attendance of about twenty patients during the early years. A great deal of gratuitous advice on the organisation of this activity was provided by James Riddell who, in addition to his duties at the Royal Infirmary, was Extra Dispensary Surgeon at the Victoria Infirmary from 1902 until 1904 and then Surgeon to the Bellahouston Dispensary.

8. Radium and radiotherapy

Although from the start X-rays were put to therapeutic use with moderate success, the technology required to produce high energy X-rays suitable for the effective treatment of most malignant disease was not available until quite recently. Marie Curie's discovery of the radioactive element radium in 1898, and four years later its separation from the natural ore pitchblende, provided a new source of radiation. Capsules containing radium (emanation tubes) could if necessary be surgically implanted in the patient, thus obviating the need for radiation that would penetrate considerable depths of tissue.

Whilst the practical potential of radium in treating disease was self-evident, the method invented by Marie and her husband Pierre for purifying pitchblende and isolating its radium content was extremely complicated. Patenting the technique could have made the Curies wealthy. However, like Wilhelm Conrad Röntgen before them, they decided, 'It is impossible, it would be contrary to the scientific spirit.' From that moment they freely provided all information required for development of the radium industry in France and abroad.

Fortunately, financial reward was not long delayed for in December 1903 the Academy of Science of Stockholm announced that the Nobel prize in Physics was to be awarded jointly to the Curies and to Henri Becquerel, the French discoverer of radioactivity. The Curies' second daughter Eve relates that only a month earlier the first of many notable honours bestowed on her parents was the award of the Davy medal by the Royal Institution. In June, Pierre had been invited by the Institution to lecture on radium, and on arriving in London with his wife had been greeted by Lord Kelvin. Marie later fondly recalled that during that visit, 'The illustrious old man made the success of the young couple his personal business, and was as proud of their researches as if they had been his own.'

There was still a great deal to be done both in producing pure radium and investigating its therapeutic use. In 1909 the 'Institute of Radium' was founded in Paris. Marie Curie, alone now after the tragic death of Pierre in a traffic accident, was to have her own laboratory for the study of radioactivity, and the physician Professor Claude Regaud would be in charge of a twin laboratory for biological research and 'Curietherapy'. Five years later, in July 1914, the new buildings were completed.

In the United Kingdom the year 1914 saw the formation of Radium Institutes in London, and in Manchester where the intention was to 'explore the medical uses of radioactive substances'. At the annual meeting of the British Medical Assocation held in Aberdeen, John Macintyre opened discussion on the second day by presenting a paper entitled, 'The comparative value of X-rays and radium in the treatment of malignant growth.'[33] The same year Macintyre was addressing himself to the matter of obtaining an adequate supply of radium for Glasgow.[34] During 1913 representatives from the Royal, Western, and Victoria Infirmaries and the Glasgow Cancer Hospital had already recommended 'that a sum of £6000 might be expended in the first instance, with a view to obtaining a supply of radium for Glasgow'. Those representatives were formed into a Radium Committee whose task it would be to organise an appeal for the funds, and 'to consider the best means of distributing the radium to the four abovementioned hospitals, and also to supply practitioners for private patients who could pay for the employment of this agent'. Previously, small quantities of radium had been obtained and utilised by individual practitioners but rapidly increasing demand was now causing the price of radium to rise dramatically. There existed a feeling that Glasgow was lagging behind in this work. The City of Berlin had spent £12,000 purchasing a supply of radium for use by its municipal hospitals. In the United States the Johns Hopkins University had formed a radium 'bank' later taken over by the Federal Government. The recently opened Radium Institute in London was already making extensive use of radium in treating malignant disease.

The proposal to spend £6000 on radium for Glasgow would have purchased sufficient to treat between 250 and 300 patients continuously. In the event £8000 was raised by 1917 and supplies sent to the major hospitals in Glasgow, thus beginning a new era in the local development of radiology[35] and keeping Glasgow in the van of progress in its application. Largely as a result of the impetus provided by the introduction of radium, Radiotherapeutics was to become a distinct discipline even rivalling Diagnostic Radiology in its importance in modern medicine. Both specialities have undergone a great many changes but still owe much to the pioneering work carried out at the end of the nineteenth and beginning of the twentieth centuries.

Chapter Eight

OLIVE CHECKLAND

Maternal and Child Welfare

1. An intractable problem

When health care first became a matter of public concern in the nineteenth century, the newly appointed Medical Officers of Health sought to introduce measures to bring down the death rate. At this time, fever epidemics were the most obvious cause of high mortality. Fear of these resulted in the provision of services such as a pure water supply, the building of drains and sewers and the removal of middens and cesspools. Later, large authorities, like Glasgow, provided Fever and Isolation hospitals.

It was widely expected that as a result of these measures the community death rate would fall. And so it did. Nevertheless a close examination of the figures revealed that the death rate of babies under the age of one year remained extremely high and many women still died in childbed.

Until a knowledge of hygiene and antiseptics had become widespread little could be done to protect the mother during childbirth. The Lying-in hospitals that existed were regarded as the resort of desperate women often bearing illegitimate children. Because of their circumstances these women had no choice. Almost all other babies were born at home, sometimes with doctors and often with midwives in attendance, but such services did not necessarily improve the mother's chances for both doctor and nurse could carry dangerous infection from patient to patient.

Many babies died in the first weeks of life before their existence came to the knowledge of the authorities. New babies were subjected to many hazards for although most were fed by their mothers, economic imperatives often forced women back into employment where hard work could dry up the milk supply. Once mother's milk failed, babies often suffered poor, dirty and unsuitable food. Diarrhoea and dysentery abounded. Death was accepted philosophically for it occurred so often. Large Victorian families could easily lose several children and in too many cases mothers died leaving large motherless families.

The matter became more urgent because by 1900 there was in Britain a steady fall in the birth rate. This was an ironic turn of events for most of the commentators had feared the real danger of over-population and had sought means of stemming 'the devastating torrent of babies'.[1] Political economists had spent most of the previous century bemoaning, as Alfred Marshall the economist expressed it, 'the spectre of Malthusian sin' which 'cast a gloom over economic speculation'.

In Glasgow itself, from a high peak of 35.5 per 1000 of population in 1876 the birth rate had dropped steadily to 25.5 in 1914. Commentators feared that Britain, like many great empires, including Greece and Rome, might be brought low by 'depopulation by sterility',[2] and recorded that 'declining fertility (was) associated with a high civilization'.

Indeed writers of 1900 already worried, would have been shocked had they known of the impending loss of young men's lives destined to take place in the 1914–18 war which would result in an even lower birth rate in the 1920s.

During the first world war the Carnegie UK Trust financed a major enquiry into the health and welfare of mothers and babies. There were four volumes, two about England and Wales, and one each on Ireland and Scotland.[3] In this invaluable study Mackenzie blamed 'the want of town planning, the overbuilding of areas, the overcrowding of houses, the urgency of the labour demand, the stresses of the labour required, the ill organised food supplies, the sporadic provision for sickness or injury or temporary unfitness—these and the multitude of derivative effects tend, in the aggregate to destroy the life of the child and to make the life of the mother superlatively difficult'.

He also gave three objectives for maternity and child welfare services. These were:

1. Freedom from discomfort and illness during the period of pregnancy.
2. A safe and painless delivery, followed by a rapid and complete convalescence—these are the benefits for the mother; and
3. Healthy growth and normal development of the child before, during and after his birth—this is the gift which it is desired the infant should receive.[4]

As Mackenzie wrote 'the mother and child suffer first and most' and were indeed 'the most delicate and fluid part of the population'. It is proposed here to outline the measures taken in Glasgow from 1900 in response to these objectives.

2. Early public concern

One of the problems facing the authorities in the case of new born infants was the lack of firm information. J. B. Russell, the Glasgow MOH, first revealed the implication of the 'uncertified death' rate in Glasgow in 1876.[5] He showed, among other things, that while few 'uncertified deaths' were registered in wealthy west-end districts of the city (some eight per cent in Kelvinhaugh and Sandyford and some twelve per cent in Blythswood and Laurieston) the proportion increased in the northern and eastern districts until in Bridgegate and the Wynds it was as high as forty per cent and in St Andrew's Square forty-two per cent. These figures were for the years 1872, '73 and '74. Russell enquired further and discovered that there was a relationship between uncertified deaths and illegitimate births.

Russell's own comments are helpful. He explained the table below in the following terms:

> The broad meaning of these facts seems to be that the more dependent and help-less of itself the life is, the less attention it receives from those on whom it depends. When we refine still further, and distinguish between the unwished-for life, which is to those who begot it, while it exists, a badge of disgrace, and the life which springs up in the home where it is expected and in some degree cherished, we can understand in what a hopeless struggle for existence the illegitimate child is entered at its birth. But we also can comprehend how much the circumstances of our poor demand attention, when even their legitimate offspring are allowed to die amid such evidence of neglect as this Return discloses.[6]

TABLE 22

Uncertified deaths in Glasgow in 1874

Groups[1]	Percentage not certified			Percentage uncertified under 1 year		Percentage uncertified 1 & under 5 years	
	Under 1 yr	1–5 yr	Over 5 yr	Legiti-mate	Illegiti-mate	Legiti-mate	Illegiti-mate
I	24.04	14.69	9.81	20.81	47.37	13.65	29.17
II	28.91	17.93	12.52	26.65	46.33	16.85	37.12
III	42.75	26.11	16.61	29.94	57.04	25.23	35.81
IV	59.15	43.54	22.25	56.11	71.86	41.68	58.34
Whole city	37.86	24.86	14.84	34.90	54.95	23.51	41.03

1. The groups referred to the arrangement of the districts of the city. Group I embraced the best areas of the city. Group IV the worst.
Source: J. B. Russell, *Report on uncertified deaths in Glasgow* (Glasgow 1876).

Russell's report on uncertified deaths represents the first Glasgow enquiry into high infant mortality. The plight of the illegitimate infant was known and in part understood, for in 1871 a *Select committee on the Protection of infant life* had reported on the tragic circumstances of many of these pathetic children. The Scottish evidence gave but a small part of the whole picture but it did reveal a distasteful underworld of 'baby farming'. Mothers or fathers of illegitimate babies often paid a sum of £5, £10 or £20 to a 'baby minder' who took complete and permanent charge of the infant. Usually neglect and inadequate food was sufficient to cause death.

Although Russell appreciated the fragility of infant life, he had many other duties and he did not himself start to organise care specifically to protect the new-born. However, others were beginning to look at the needs of mother and child. These were the philanthropists actively supported by Russell and after 1898, by his successor A. K. Chalmers.

3. The Voluntary contribution

There can be few fields where public authorities originally relied more heavily on voluntary initiatives than in that of maternal and child welfare. Indeed to the public health authorities it was sometimes puzzling as to where advances could be made, but philanthropic vigour often indicated possible avenues of progress. These leads were often given by women who operated pragmatically, recognising that illness, debility and death especially among babies, but also among mothers, stemmed from poor or inadequate feeding. The wide variety of social services that they organised therefore involved the supply of good, pure, nourishing food.

These new ventures included Schools for Mothers, Infant Welfare Centres, Dinners for expectant and nursing mothers, Fresh Air Fortnights, Holiday Homes, Milk for babies, Day Nurseries or Creches and Nursery Schools. All were aimed at mothers in need. From the beginning women who cared deeply for their families were involved: these schemes did not exclude but might not be noticed by the less capable who were unaware of what child rearing required. Medical officers of health, whose resources were always over-committed were on the whole appreciative of these initiatives taken by women on behalf of other women.

Several lessons on child care taken up in both England and Scotland, came from France, 'where an unusually low birth-rate has compelled the question of infantile mortality to be regarded as one of national importance.'[7] French doctors began to consider the need for continuous contact with mothers and their children. Work started in 1890 when Professor Herrgott founded *L'Oeuvre de la Maternité* in Nancy. Infants were brought by their mothers at the age of one month where they were examined, and if in satisfactory health the mothers were rewarded with a small payment. As Dr McLeary reported, 'In the years 1890–1900 2,052 women passed through this institution, and 25,382 francs were distributed among them.'[8] In 1892 Professor Budin established the first *Consultation des Nourrissons* at the Charité Hospital, Paris. Through the 'Consultation' mothers were encouraged to bring their babies for advice. The idea soon spread in France, with centres being set up at other hospitals. Later independent centres were organised to which a mother could go regularly with her child. The baby was weighed, enquiries were made about feeding and encouragement was given. Breast feeding was usually recommended. The baby who could not be breast-fed was put at greater risk and the *Gouttes de Lait* were opened to provide other milk properly diluted. This provision was pioneered by Dr Leon Dufour at Fecamp in 1894. The milk was made available on condition that the child was brought in regularly for examination. Later Madame Coullet organised free dinners for nursing mothers in Paris.

On becoming familiar with the various French schemes the Scots soon made arrangements to feed both mothers and children. The Dundee Social Union seems to have been the first in the field, providing two restaurants in 1906. In Glasgow itself, the Cosy Corner Restaurant (at 116 Garscube Road, Cowcaddens) was opened later that year (originally at 36 Milton Lane, Cowcaddens). Here needy pregnant women and nursing mothers could take a free meal and mothers could feed their babies in a room provided. A doctor was also available to examine babies. By 1916 the Corporation of Glasgow was giving a grant of £50 per annum towards the cost of the mothers' dinners. The Cosy Corner restaurant, primarily a 'Mother's Dinner-Table' was also used by many other women who lived and worked in the vicinity.

Feeding the babies proved a more controversial matter for doctors disagreed on the milk to be provided. The only milk readily available was cow's milk and this was sometimes impure, often diluted and sometimes diseased. (see Section 4 below). There were simple ways of improving the milk by boiling (and later by pasteurising or sterilising), but many believed that heat treatment destroyed the nutritional value and that infants so fed suffered from various ailments. Thus the feeding of infants on some form of milk (other than mother's milk) remained a matter for argument. Clinical physicians clashed with laboratory doctors, refusing to accept scientific findings available from new investigative techniques.

Milk depots were introduced in Glasgow from 1904 at Osborne Street, off the Saltmarket, at Anderston and at Cowcaddens.[9] Of course the provision of pure milk for the babies was important but the presence of women volunteers was also invaluable. The Queen Margaret College Settlement was busy in Anderston, the Ladies' Child Welfare Association worked in Cowcaddens, and the British Women's Temperance Society was also active. Women worked freely in the milk depots, helped the mothers and visited them in their homes. They observed ill-looking nursing and expectant mothers and responded by opening feeding centres for these women and their children. A small charge was made for a nourishing meal.

Once established, the objectives broadened. The first infant consultation centre in the city was set up by the Queen Margaret College students at their Settlement in Anderston in October 1906. At the close of 1907 five such voluntary centres were in operation with the approval of the health authorities. The Health Department had also appointed a woman doctor early in

1906 to co-ordinate the various schemes and to undertake infant consultation sessions.

For some years initiative tended to spring from philanthropic sources for the local authority had no money from central government to provide feeding services for mothers and babies. The turning point came during the First World War. By the Notification of Births (Extension) Act of 1915 some fifty per cent of the cost of these feeding schemes could be claimed from central government if the Local Government Board agreed. As a result Glasgow Corporation could begin to supplement the mother and baby services voluntarily provided.

In the 1920s and 1930s the original voluntary schemes were gradually replaced by official provision although the volunteer remained active in the field.

There was another type of work involving children which began and has remained in voluntary hands. This work, for the protection of children, may have altered according to the demands of a changing society but unfortunately still remains essential.

In 1884 the Scottish National Society for the Prevention of Cruelty to Children was founded as a philanthropic venture in Glasgow. (The Edinburgh branch was founded in 1888.) Although the Glasgow Society was a charity it was supported by a grant from the Common Good Fund of the city as well as by some contributions from parishes outside the city. As the annual report explained, 'The Sole object of the Society is to secure to every little child in the land that its life shall be at least endurable.' The inspectors of the Society came 'to exercise a very powerful influence in the localities'. Indeed 'the cruelty' were soon considered as potent as the police. Their work was no doubt valuable and over the years they did undertake a remarkable workload but were powerless to affect the root-injustices of society. The Society's members believed that most of their cases were caused by 'drink'. In 1915 they reported that '7,200 complaints were lodged, involving 22,263 children; 48,730 supervision visits were paid; 407 parents were sent for trial; and 1,328 children were removed from their parents' charge'. There was criticism of the NSPCC as being an agency intent on breaking up the family, but in most cases the families with whom they were concerned were already in serious trouble.

Shelters were set up in Edinburgh, Glasgow, Leith, Dumbarton and Hamilton, to which children were transferred. Elsewhere children removed from home were placed in the poor house. By 1917 Dr Leslie MacKenzie, Medical member of the Local Government Board for Scotland, was expressing reservations at the numbers of children being sent to institutions. For, as he wrote, 'They are at best, a necessary evil. They cure nothing. They are dealing with accomplished facts. They make a certain relatively good life possible; they keep the children for the time in safety; but equally they take the children out of their place in normal society, and, by that fact, tend to unfit them for a return to it.'[10]

The present day 'philanthropist' is still very active in welfare service for mothers and children. Of course the need has changed and statutory services have replaced much that was formerly voluntary, but there are still many 'causes'; 'battered wives' and 'battered babies' are still at risk in society and the volunteer still has a vital role to play.

4. The expectant mother

Direct public commitment to the health of the expectant mother was hindered by what might be regarded today as Victorian prudery. A 'reserve of modesty' ensured that pregnancy itself was kept within the family circle and from public gaze. As Ballantyne later emphasised, 'The care of the mother in the period of her expectance, both for her own sake and for that of her unborn infant, had until recent years been curiously overlooked.'[11]

Women in childbed normally received attention either from a doctor or from the midwife. Those who had their babies in hospital were looked after by the Physician Accoucheur. In Glasgow Professor John M. Pagan (midwifery) claimed in 1860 that the maternal death rate at the Glasgow University Lying-in Hospital (which may only have delivered women in their own homes) was 1 in 233. But Dr Halliday Croom in 1881 at the Edinburgh Royal Maternity calculated a death rate of 1 in 50 maternal deaths. So that wherever childbirth took place it remained dangerous. The use of antiseptics in childbirth was introduced slowly. Curiously, Dr William L. Reid (physician accoucheur to the Western Infirmary) became convinced of the value of antiseptics after a sojourn in Europe in 1880. He recounts in detail antiseptic practices in a hospital in Prague and notes that 'the results, even in circumstances otherwise not particularly favourable, were much better than those obtained in this country'.[12] Dr Halliday Croom in Edinburgh made an even more pointed remark in 1880, 'It is at least twelve years since Bischoff impressed with a visit he made to Lister in Glasgow returned to Basel and set himself to carry out antiseptics in the lying-in hospital there with most gratifying results.'[13] There were many causes of maternal deaths relating to lack of skill as well as dirt diseases. Puerperal fever was especially prevalent: by the Infectious Diseases (Notification) Act of 1890 it became notifiable. But the definition of 'Puerperal morbidity' remained difficult. At some times and in some places, the term puerperal fever was used, others preferred puerperal pyaemia, septicaemia and erysipelas. Clearly this led to difficulties of classification. The problem is well illustrated by Table 23 below. All that can be said with confidence is that over time, notification became more efficient and more accurate (Column 2) and that (even taking into account the larger number of cases notified) mortality rates for those mothers who contracted puerperal sepsis dropped from roughly two-thirds (64.1 per cent) to one quarter (25.3 per cent) between the 1890s and the 1920s (column 3). The apparent increases in maternal deaths (columns 4 and 5) were believed by Dr Chalmers to be caused by a more accurate knowledge of the cases especially by the new schemes for maternal and infant welfare. This Table therefore must be studied with these warnings in mind.

TABLE 23

Maternal deaths in Glasgow 1855–1925

		Puerperal Sepsis			Combined
Year	Maternal deaths per 1000 births	Notifica- tions per 1000 births	Case Mortality per cent	Other causes per 1000 births	maternal deaths per 1000 births
1855–64	1.9				
1865–74	1.9				
1875–84	1.9				
1885–94	2.3				
1891–95	2.05	3.2	64.1	2.83	4.88
1896–1900	2.04	3.3	61.4	2.68	4.72
1901–5	2.36	3.8	64.8	3.21	5.57
1906–10	2.57	4.9	52.3	3.59	6.16
1911–15	2.41	6.4	39.3	3.63	6.04
1916–20	2.3	7.4	31.3	3.70	6.00
1921–5	2.6	10.6	25.3	4.31	6.91

Source: A. K. Chalmers, *The Health of Glasgow 1818–1925 an outline* (Glasgow 1930), p. 258.

All problems relating to mothers and babies were more acute in the poorer areas of the city. In his Annual Report of 1906 (p. 41), Dr A. K. Chalmers, Medical Officer of Health for Glasgow, explained that in Cowcaddens, where infant mortality was extremely high, 22 per cent of mothers had received medical attention, 31 per cent had had service from a midwife 'attached to one or other of the Training Schools then in existence' and 44 per cent had been attended by an unqualified midwife. The existence of a large number of uneducated women who 'by habit and repute' practised midwifery was believed to be a source of trouble. The Midwives Act of 1902 was an English measure and did not extend to Scotland. Almost all districts had as midwife, a 'handy woman' and it was believed that much infection spread from her 'untutored practices'. As Dr Chalmers reports, 'Many of those ("handy women") who were interviewed, carried whatever equipment they might require such as syringes and catheters and such disinfectants as they deemed necessary, in the pocket of their dress, and many, who had bags, misused some of the material they carried in them. For example, 59 carried a Higginson's syringe, but 22 admitted using it impartially for douching or for administering enemata, frequently for the same patient and always without any effort to disinfect the nozzle save by external rubbing. Twenty-two also, carried no thermometer, and were quite unable to satisfy enquiry that they could appreciate the advent of conditions requiring medical assistance or recognise them even when they were fully established.'[14] For this purpose eighty-eight women were interviewed and forty-six of them had no certificate.

The Midwives Act for Scotland was passed in 1915. As a result of this measure the inefficient unqualified midwives were eliminated.

TABLE 24

Number and qualification of midwives in practice, 1917–25

	1917	1918	1919	1920	1921	1922	1923	1924	1925
Midwives in practice	312	310	365	370	364	348	333	310	307
Qualified as under									
(a) in practice December 1914	200	209	210	210	205	185	170	142	131
(b) CMB (Scotland)	52	65	95	108	107	111	111	119	126
(c) other recognised qualification	60	36	60	52	52	52	52	49	50

Source: A. K. Chalmers, *The Health of Glasgow 1818–1925, an outline* (Glasgow 1930), p. 266.

By the authority of the Midwives Act a Central Midwives Board was set up for Scotland. As part of its duties the Board was to institute and organise an examination programme and issue a certificate of competence to those who were successful.

Of course the high incidence of fatality amongst the many cases of puerperal fever occurring in poor districts was by no means dependent only on the incompetence of the untrained midwife. There were many factors which might have had a bearing, including the size and location of the house, the mother's own health and background, the family 'luck of life' as shown by the brothers or sisters living or dead, and the mother's role either as a wage-earner outside the home, or as a worker within it.

5. The new-born infant

At the beginning of the twentieth century the Interdepartmental Committee on Physical Deterioration pointed out that 'the infant mortality in
this country has not decreased materially during the past twenty-five
years, notwithstanding that the general death-rate has fallen considerably'
(see Table 25 below). General measures of sanitary reform had affected
the death rate of all classes of the population except that of young
babies.

TABLE 25

Infant Mortality Rates, Scotland
1855–1938

Annual mean of deaths under age
one per 1000 live births

Period	Rate	Period	Rate
1855–9	118	1900–4	122
1860–4	120	1905–9	114
1865–9	122	1910–14	109
1870–4	125	1915–19	106
1875–9	120	1920–4	92
1880–4	118	1925–9	87
1885–9	118	1930–4	82
1890–4	126	1935–8	77
1895–9	130		

Source: M. W. Flinn, *Scottish Population History,* 1977, p. 386.

Nowhere was this more true than in Glasgow where the Medical Officer
of Health studied the figures produced by his department.

From these figures it can be seen that, although there were grounds for
hope in that fewer babies died between the ages of 6–12 months and
perhaps fewer between 3–6 months, deaths below the age of 3 months
remained extremely high.

Dr Chalmers believed that the chief causes of infant death were 'Im-
maturity, diarrhoea and pneumonia'.[15] Diarrhoeal diseases were defined by
McLeary in London in 1905 as diarrhoea, infective enteritis, dysentery,
enteritis, English cholera, gastro-enteritis, dyspepsia, gastric catarrh and

TABLE 26

Deaths of infants per 1000 births, Glasgow 1870—1902

Period	−3 months	3—6 months	6—12 months	Average infant mortality per 1000
1870−2	72	31	67	170
1880−2	65	25	58	148
1890−2	70	25	54	149
1900−2	72	26	47	145
Reduction per cent 1870−2 1900−2	—	16	30	15

Source: A. K. Chalmers, *The Health of Glasgow 1818—1925, an outline* (Glasgow 1930), p. 198.

other diseases of the stomach.[16] Chalmers also recognised that many children had no chance because of 'improper feeding, germ-laden milk and parental ignorance of child nurture'.[17] There were particular difficulties over milk supply which must have caused many deaths amongst those children not breastfed. But Dr Chalmers' discussion of infant deaths was, in the early years of the century severely limited by a lack of factual information.

The public health authorities were at a serious disadvantage because of the state of the law. Births were to be registered within twenty-one days but this proved to be a major stumbling block, for many babies died during the twenty-one days and so their births and deaths were registered simultaneously. For some years in Glasgow attempts had been made to collect information daily, from midwives, doctors, maternity hospitals, to try to trace the babies at risk but it was a cumbersome and inadequate operation. Glasgow was one of the authorities instrumental in launching the Notification of Births Act which was passed in April 1907. This was an optional Act but applied in Glasgow from 1 January 1908. Under its terms all births had to be registered within thirty-six hours. It was hoped that the Local Authority would be enabled to get 'into closer touch with the causes of infant mortality' by its means.[18]

Throughout these early years the co-operation between the Voluntary sector and the Glasgow Medical Officer of Health should be noted. The Medical Officer of Health often collected and collated facts and figures on which the infant and child welfare schemes were built. Most often early efforts were a combined operation. The role of women in these services, whether official or voluntary is also of prime importance: those seeking a wider more meaningful role in service to the community certainly found many outlets here. Women, many of them unmarried, were attracted to the maternal and child welfare services. The public authorities were not slow to recognise the special skills of women: the first female medical officer was appointed in the spring of 1906.

By 1906 other interesting and important initiatives were in operation in Glasgow giving an indication of the serious efforts being made to grapple with the problems revealed by the appalling infant mortality rates.

These were:

1. The visitation of infants fed on Depot Milk;
2. The visitation of birth intimated under the arrangement with the maternity hospital, and under that applying to births not medically attended;
3. The introduction of a system of weekly consultations and weighing of infants at Queen Margaret Settlement, Anderston; and
4. A special enquiry in Cowcaddens into all births occurring.[19]

It should be noted that Cowcaddens was taken as an example of really bad conditions where need was greatest and that all these services were intended for the very poor. Births which were medically attended (which included most respectable and all middle-class families) were never at this time included in any local authority welfare scheme.

The efforts of the Medical Officer of Health and his assistants continued until and throughout the First World War. Although the budget was small, medical officers from Glasgow were also very active in extending their commitments with others at national and international gatherings concerning infant mortality. Glasgow's problems in this field were indeed acute but efforts to solve them were continuous and searching.

The outbreak of war in August 1914 caused an augmentation of pressures at every level. The one with which we are concerned involves increased official concern with the health of women because so many were undertaking, for the first time, full-time industrial jobs formerly done exclusively by men. It is pertinent to equate governmental concern with the days of national crisis. The linking of the two reflects a recognition of the value of the old continental ideas of medical police, that the state is best served if it ensures high standards of health among its people.

Official concern was turned into positive action with the Notification of Births (Extension) Act 1915. Under this Act much of the voluntary work encouraged by local authorities for the welfare of mothers and infants became obligatory. Not only did the Act require 'local authorities to make provision for expectant and nursing mothers and for children under five years of age', but it also provided a Treasury grant of 50 per cent for such work.

6. Food and nutrition

'That human milk is much the best food for human infants is a conclusion suggested by common sense and amply confirmed by the united testimony of physiology, statistics and clinical evidence. It is the great central fact in infant feeding.'[20] Everyone agreed and others went further, 'From a physiological stand-point, the artificially-fed baby is a premature child, and anything but maternal milk is foreign to its digestive tract'.[21] Chapin also declared that 'anything aside from breast-milk that is put into an infant's stomach is a foreign substance'. But herein lay the problem, for many mothers, ill nurtured all their lives, were unlikely to be able to provide for their infants from their own resources. In addition wealthy mothers foolishly concerned with what they called 'social duties' also sometimes declined to feed their babies because of what they deemed to be other and more important pre-occupations.

For these reasons there was an increasing demand for artificial food for the new-born. It was particularly important that a successful artificial milk was manufactured to provide nourishment for those babies, who if left on the diet provided by their mothers, would die. By 1900 there were various forms of substitute milks. These were either a proprietary food, condensed milk or cow's milk. None of them could be considered satisfactory.

These artificial 'milks' were 'largely vegetable in composition, as nearly all contain wheat flour or other matter of vegetable origin, and many contain unaltered starch, a substance the young infant is quite unable to digest. Generally speaking, these foods are deficient in fat, too rich in carbohydrate, and lack the anti-scorbutic elements'. Nor was condensed milk considered any better, being 'deficient in fat, and contain an excessive amount of cane-sugar, while all lack anti-scorbutic elements'.[22] It was popularly believed that condensed milk was a 'safe' food during hot weather, the 'diarrhoea season', but this was strenuously denied by doctors. Much medical evidence was given to substantiate the view that many babies fed on a mixture of condensed milk and water, did die of summer diarrhoea.

Doctors believed that cow's milk was the best substitute for mother's milk, but there were great dangers. Dr Leslie Mackenzie gave a graphic account: 'To watch the milking of cows is to watch a process of unscientific inoculation of a pure (or almost pure) medium with unknown quantities of unspecified germs. . . . Whoever knows the meaning of aseptic surgery must feel his blood run cold when he watches, even in imagination, the thousand chances of germ inoculation. From cow to cow the milker goes, taking with her (or him) the stale epithelium (cellular tissue covering mucous membrane) of the last cow, the particles of dirt caught from the floor, the hairs, the dust and the germs that adhere to them. . . . Everywhere, throughout the whole process of milking, the perishable, superbly nutrient liquid receives its repeated sowings of germinal and non-germinal dirt. . . . And this in good dairies! What must it be where cows are never groomed, where hands are only by accident all washed, where heads are only occasionally cleaned, where spittings (tobacco or other) are not infrequent, where the milker may be a chance-comer from some filthy slum—where . . . the various dirts of the civilised human, are at every hand reinforced by the inevitable dirts of the domesticated cow? . . . I could name many admirable byres, where these conditions are, in a greater or less degree, normal.'[23]

The dangers and difficulties were only overcome in course of time by a number of disparate efforts. Research work was undertaken which improved our knowledge of nutrition and dietetics resulting in dried and powdered milk more suited to babies. Stringent health tests were imposed upon dairy herds and veterinarian inspection made obligatory.

7. A new beginning: 1915

With the passing in 1915 of the Notification of Births (Extension) Act began a new era in the hopes and expectations of the maternal and infant welfare movement. For the Act stated that 'any Local Authority within the meaning of the Principal Act may make such arrangements as they see fit, and as may be sanctioned by the Local Government Board for Scotland, for attending to the health of expectant mothers and nursing mothers and of children under five years of age within the meaning of Section 7 of the Education Act (Scotland) 1908'.

The Principal Act was the Notification of Births (Scotland) Act of 1907 which had hitherto been adoptive. By the 1915 Act both Acts became obligatory, although it should be noted that the clause given above applied only to Scotland. It was removed from the English Act.

At the same time as these Acts became compulsory central government committed itself to 'make grants to an amount not exceeding one half of the expenditure involved under any scheme of arrangements sanctioned by the Local Government Board in terms of the Act'.

The legal and financial encouragement which local authorities now had, resulted in a quiet revolution. By 1917 thirty-two schemes for maternal and infant welfare had been worked out in Scotland by various small burgh and county authorities in addition to those of the big four burghs, Dundee, Aberdeen, Edinburgh and Glasgow. Most of them were in burghs or more populous counties but the enthusiasm is especially notable in view of the continuing unfavourable circumstances as the war dragged on. It is much to the credit of the Medical Officers of Health and their local committees that so much progress was made.

Notwithstanding the prompt response by Medical Officers of Health seeking to reduce infant and maternal mortality the extent of the problem must not be glossed over. Without doubt it was at its worst in Glasgow. In 1911 Glasgow had 115,519 children under five years of age. This was rather more than one-fifth of the under-five population for the whole of Scotland—532,745. Edinburgh had just less than 30,000 under-fives. But the health support team of nurses, health visitors and doctors (numbering twelve whole-time appointments) was broadly the same for both cities. Edinburgh was therefore in 1917 providing a more comprehensive system of help for mothers and infants than Glasgow, where problems were inevitably exacerbated by low standards in housing, feeding and education.

Notwithstanding the rather discouraging impression bound to be given by the recognition of the magnitude of the Glasgow problem, the plans which its officers drew up in 1917 give a good indication of what they hoped to achieve. The programme of health was to have two main arms, 'infant and child consultation' and 'home visitation of expectant mothers, nursing mothers and children up to age five'. The Infant and Child Welfare Clinics were to become the local administrative bases for home visitation.

There were to be fourteen 'infant and child consultation' centres at:

1. Kinning Park Hall, West Scotland Street
2. 7 Franklin Street
3. Sanitary Chambers
4. 181 Claythorn Street
5. 77 Port Street, Anderston
6. Ruchill United Free Church Hall
7. Town Hall, Merryland Street, Govan
8. 168 Garngad Hill
9. Hill Street Hall, Shettleston
10. 90 Hospital Street, Gorbals
11. 87 Campbellfield Street
12. 15 Peel Street, Partick
13. 46 White Street, Govan
14. 416 Dobbies Loan.

The fourteen centres occupied premises originally supplied by the voluntary movement, although the local authority may have financed them. The purpose-built maternity and child welfare centres were erected later. There were at the time twelve health visitors whose duties were to visit nursing mothers and children. At this period only mothers and children in the poorer districts were on the list, indeed the Glasgow health visitors could only cover a fraction of those in the city. Although it was reported in 1917 that the staff of twelve was 'to be increased as required' reliance for most of the visitations was placed on the volunteers.

A centre and Day Nursery were built in Sister Street (now Orr Street), Bridgeton, opened in October 1925 by Mr Baldwin, the Prime Minister. In 1926 the pace quickened and three centres were built and opened at Maryhill, Springburn and Arklet Road, West Govan. Another centre was opened at Wellshot Road, Shettleston in 1928 (in Tollcross Park). In 1931 slum clearance in Anderston enabled a new building to be opened 'replacing and amplifying' the clinic services formerly provided by Queen Margaret College Settlement nearby.

8. To 1939

During the thirties further progress was made. By the Local Government (Scotland) Act of 1929 the school medical service was transferred to the Corporation. This caused the authority to build multi-purpose centres which could cater for school and pre-school children. Glenbarr Street, Provan

(1935) and Florence Street, Gorbals (1937) were two examples of these centres. Sandy Road, Partick came into use in 1941, although it was hurriedly commissioned as a war-time first aid centre.

The Welfare centres (there were seventeen by 1941) had three main functions, medical, educational and social. The medical officer had a wide-ranging brief when she interviewed mothers and examined babies. She looked at the general condition of the child, advised mothers on feeding and care, recommended milk and or cod liver oil, chose children needing day nursery care or a period in a convalescent home. She usually consulted in co-operation with the health visitor who also dealt with cuts and bruises giving simple treatment and advice. Encouragement was also given to other organisations to provide educational classes in cookery, keep fit, family health care, food and nutrition and many other areas.

The health visitors attached to each centre were the vital personnel bringing their own enthusiasms to their tasks. The 'green ladies', as the health visitors were called in Glasgow, brought to 'the Welfare' a friendly familiarity which was heartening and encouraging. One 'green lady' wrote in 1930 after twenty-five years experience, 'It took a few visits to establish friendship and then the mothers look to you for advice on many subjects. I found that to be a successful visitor you must be interested not only in family but in other household affairs. Health visiting cannot be done in a hurry if you are to be successful in gaining their confidence.'[24]

The numbers of children being brought to the clinics was constantly increasing:

1914	2250
1920	5000
1926	9000
1937	10000

Even so, this really represented a small proportion of the young children in the city.

The Corporation took over the six day nurseries or creches in 1918 from the Glasgow Day Nurseries Association (1883) (see section 3 above). New premises were in some cases provided. The main function was originally to provide food and rest for the children (220 could be accommodated at any one time) but later, nursery schools became part of the educational pro-vision.

There were also convalescent homes for children and their mothers in Garscube, Mount Vernon and Scotstoun. Originally all the residential facilities were really places where children and their mothers could be given rest and a nourishing diet. With the widespread provision of cod liver oil, and later the addition to it of Vitamin D, deficiency diseases like rickets were banished from the city.

The service set up by the corporation was of undoubted value to mothers and babies. None the less infant mortality rates in Glasgow remained high and some felt that of all sections of the community wives and mothers were least cared for. As Margery Spring Rice emphasised in *Working Class*

Wives, published in 1939, men (breadwinners) and children, (the hope of the future) receive the best food, wives and mothers inevitably serving themselves last and least. Thus when the war came in 1939 there was still much to be done. The war proved a blessing in one sense for mothers and their babies for, with the onset of a state of emergency when there was likely to be a serious shortfall in food supplies, positive discrimination was practised. The Ministry of Food, taking overall responsibility for feeding the nation, singled out pregnant women, babies and young children for special issues not only of free concentrated orange juice and cod liver oil but also for priority supplies of other foods. The result of this was an astonishing improvement in maternal and infant health and welfare. After the war when the conscience of the nation demanded a National Health Service it was possible for large resources to be channelled into the care of mothers and their babies.

Chapter Nine

RONA GAFFNEY

Women as doctors and nurses

1. Widening horizons

Militant feminism of the Edwardian era aimed primarily at getting votes for women. Some sections of the movement, however, had wider social goals; through the acquisition of the vote they hoped to gain a variety of ends, chief amongst them were social improvement for women, greater economic rewards for their labour, and equality of opportunity for both sexes in careers. This concern for better career opportunity also motivated many women who were unconnected with militant groups or with any purely political or social considerations. In the latter part of the nineteenth century some women attempted to enter professions from which they had hitherto been barred. Women involved in the nursing and medical professions did achieve some notable success, so that by the end of the First World War nursing was indisputably established as a respected, useful and essential profession, while female doctors qualified from medical schools in increasing numbers. Very few of these developments had any close connection with the activities of the radical women's groups. Instead, changes in the status and acceptability of nurses and female doctors evolved gradually from the 1860s, were furthered by many, though often obscure, individuals, and were strengthened by developments in medical and surgical techniques and in hospital policy which demanded a new approach to women medical workers.

Improvements in nursing and medical training for women were countrywide during the late nineteenth and early twentieth centuries. The changes which took place in the Glasgow medical scene at that time were largely similar to the national trend, though local pressures and personalities influenced the detail and precise timing of events.

2. Women as medical students and doctors

Women who aspired to become doctors in mid-Victorian Britain faced an unsympathetic and, indeed, hostile world. Their ambitions were misunderstood, misrepresented and mocked by large sections of the population, some of the severest criticism coming from other women. The Queen herself expressed much of the feeling of antipathy and horror current in the country, writing in 1870:

> What an *awful* idea this is of allowing *young* girls and men to enter the dissecting room together. . . . To tear away all the barriers which surround a woman and to

propose that they should study with *men* things which could not be named before them, certainly not in a mixed audience, would be to introduce a complete disregard of what must be considered as belonging to the rules and principles of morality. Let woman be what God intended, a helpmate for man, but with totally different duties and vocations.[1]

In spite of the difficulty of dealing with attitudes like these, the Victorian era did see the start of a female medical profession. In 1849 an English girl, Elizabeth Blackwell,[2] graduated in medicine in the USA, and ten years later was placed on the British medical register. In 1865 Elizabeth Garrett qualified in Britain as a medical practitioner when she became a Licentiate of the Society of Apothecaries.[3] In Glasgow the question of female medical education did not become important till the 1890s, and it was very much bound up with the foundation of Queen Margaret College in 1883, the first institution to provide a comprehensive programme of higher education for women in the city. The College intended to fill the gap created by Glasgow University's consistent refusal to admit female students to any of its classes, even after the Universities Act of 1889 removed all remaining legal restraints. In the 1891–2 session the College extended its teaching into the medical field, offering courses in chemistry, botany, physiology, natural philosophy, mathematics, anatomy, materia medica, medicine, surgery, midwifery, gynaecology, medical jurisprudence and pathology.[4] However, like the universities, the College authorities felt that practical work was as important as theoretical lectures and that a term of hospital experience was an essential part of their students' training. It was in this attempt to have women students accepted for hospital work that the greatest problems arose. Among doctors themselves there were few who were definitely enthusiastic and many who were absolutely opposed to the idea. The minutes of one of Glasgow's medical societies give an indication of the range of doctors opinions in the late 1870s:

A professional conversation on the admission of women to the profession followed—the President said that exceptional women of better brain power than the average man might be allowed, and certainly ought not to be hindered from practising. Dr Gairdner concurred in the President's view and thought every liberty ought to be granted to those who were willing to enter medical practice. . . . Dr Ronald said No, they cannot, he believed, attend to their duty properly and they want strength of character. Dr Kelly would not enter into the pros and cons of the question, but the physical difficulties are insuperable, they would fail utterly and completely, there is no duty so inappropriate. . . . Dr Pollock . . . thought medical women would be very useful in obstetric cases, and that men would be relieved of much irksome and poorly paid work.[5]

Queen Margaret College encountered a great deal of resistance when it enquired, in 1890, about clinical facilities in hospital for its women medical students. The College application was refused outright by Glasgow Western Infirmary, shelved by the Victoria Infirmary, and given only very limited approval by the Maternity Hospital. The Royal Infirmary initially gave guarded approval for the attendance of female students, but violent opposition from their male students forced the managers to cancel their agreement. In 1893 they arranged that women students could only be seen and taught in completely separate groups from the men.

The reasons for opposition were varied. Managers often claimed first that their teachers and facilities were already fully taken up by the needs of their male students. This was popular reasoning because it avoided the thorny problem of actually defining why a woman was unacceptable. A further argument was often produced: that hospitals had no physical facilities to cater for females—no cloakrooms, toilets or recreational amenities. This was true to some degree, but the fact that all of them possessed a female nursing staff whose accommodation could perhaps have been shared by the students, indicates that this was a gross exaggeration. It also throws some light on the class-based differences felt to exist between nursing and medical staff; facilities which were suitable for nurses might not come up to the standards acceptable to doctors.

Probably the most significant argument against women students was that their mental capacity, poor standard of education, and the social 'delicacy' of the female sex made them poor material for medical training. This was, however, the least articulated of the reasons. It came to light when the Royal Infirmary's male students complained about the admission of women in 1891. They objected to mixed classes because they claimed that 'their work is being seriously hampered by the presence of females'.[6] This could only reflect on the intellectual adequacy of the fifteen women or on the outlook of the men; but the first women graduated with honours in medicine from the University of Glasgow.[7] If female delicacy caused embarrassment how did male doctors cope in the wards with female nurses? It must be borne in mind, however, that even after the Nightingale changes in nursing, nurses tended to be recruited almost exclusively from the working class. This was not the case for female medical students: the Queen Margaret College fees alone amounted to £80 for four years of training, and the educational standards required at entry to a medical course ensured that only members of the middle-classes could become students. Presumably the feelings attributed to social equals differed from those ascribed to the lower classes. Even though those feelings might be wholly absent from the females in question, they were not absent from the minds of the males whether students, staff or hospital managers.

Women students, and later doctors, found it easier to gain access to the hospitals which dealt with women's or children's diseases. This was hardly surprising, for the 'indelicacy' arguments normally used against them were inoperative. In 1890 Glasgow Sick Children's Hospital admitted female students, and by 1892 it had twelve Queen Margaret College students working in its wards, while only two male students applied in that year. In the 1892–3 session, the Samaritan Hospital for Women actually took two female doctors on to its staff, the first such in any Glasgow hospital. This example was soon followed by the Sick Children's Hospital which in 1893 appointed a woman doctor as a temporary dispensary assistant, and in 1895 appointed Dr Alice McLaren as an extra Honorary Physician to the hospital.

These early successes were repeated much later in the larger and more prestigious hospitals. In Glasgow, as in most other British cities, the big voluntary infirmaries were the hospitals in which the most respected consultants practised, where the most advanced techniques were in use, and where a junior doctor could thus receive the best training. Consequently, competition for house officer jobs and for more permanent posts was fiercest in the voluntary infirmaries, and women's chances of selection much restricted. Glasgow's Royal Infirmary admitted its first female house officers in 1900, and in 1907 appointed women for the first time to slightly more senior posts by employing three women as extra assistant gynaecologist, assistant pathologist, and extra assistant bacteriologist respectively. These changes, though hardly dramatic, occurred at a time when the first women were elected to serve on the boards of management of the Glasgow infirmaries. They were beginning to make their presence felt. The impact of the First World War made little difference to the infirmary's employment of women doctors. Numbers did increase, but even in the stress years of 1917 and 1918 women still held a minority of house officer posts, were employed in very few permanent medical jobs, and held no senior appointments at all. This situation changed very little in the inter-war years. In Glasgow's Victoria Infirmary the position was similar, though it seemed slightly easier for a small number of women to get promoted posts, probably due to the fact that the infirmary was smaller, newer and less academically respected than its rivals. In 1913 the infirmary managers appointed Dr Ivy McKenzie as a medical consultant, the most senior position yet attained by any female in Glasgow medical circles. However, this development, though important, in no way altered the infirmary's general policy, and it remained very much male dominated at all levels of its staff.

Glasgow's other large general hospital, the Western Infirmary, maintained a steadfast resistance against female practitioners and students for many years longer than the others. Apart from one brief six-month lapse in 1903 (when the infirmary took Ivy McKenzie, future consultant at the Victoria, as a house officer) the managers of the Western refused to admit the claims of females to join their medical staff in any capacity until the pressures of the Second World War forced the issue in 1943.[8]

By the beginning of the twentieth century there were eleven medically qualified women[9] practising in Glasgow. One was assisting a well-known doctor in the west end and another her doctor father.

Three of the women held appointments in hospitals or dispensaries which were concerned solely with the health problems of women or children: and where previous experience is recorded, it would seem that adult male patients were not part of it.

Ten years later in 1911 five of the female practitioners were still in Glasgow, three apparently confining themselves to general practice, one having acquired a lecturing post with the Glasgow Education Authority:

and Dr Alice McLaren, one of the London graduates, had improved her position in the hospital hierarchy and was an Assistant Surgeon at the Samaritan.

There were twenty-two recruits to the women's medical group over the decade 1901–11, twenty-one of them graduates: the Triple Qualification, which had been open to women before University degrees, was losing ground, just as it had with male students in the later nineteenth century. Most of them had some kind of appointment outside general practice: but it is doubtful if two of these medical women practised at all, since they were both Research Scholars, involved in scientific investigation, one in Physiology and the other in Pathology.

Again, hospital and dispensary appointments involved women and child patients only: enterprise was evident, for Dr MacLaren and two of the newer group of women doctors were serving in the Glasgow Women's Private Hospital. The avenues which were to provide employment for many qualified women are indicated—Mrs Dr Lily Clarke had been an Assistant Medical Officer of Health in Glasgow, and Dr Kate Fraser was Medical Officer to Govan Parish School Board.

The modest expansion of public health services and the circumstance of the war years of 1914–18 meant that more women doctors found salaried employment; but by 1921 there was a far larger number from which to recruit. There were almost three times as many (seventy-six) registered medical women as in 1911, and almost half (thirty-four) had qualified during the previous three years. With very few exceptions, the whole group was the product of the Glasgow medical school.

Medicine was beginning to provide a satisfying career: eighteen women had practised in Glasgow for at least ten years, and three of those for over twenty years. Hospital work was still a restricted area, and young women who could afford an extra year's time and money were adding a Diploma of Public Health to their degree—a valuable extra qualification for employment in the statutory health services. Marriage, it is worth noting did not appear to be a bar to practice.

The range of women's medical work continued to widen slowly; pioneers had blazed a trail and even in 1921 there were impressive achievements.

Louise McIlroy, a Glasgow graduate of 1898 served with distinction as Surgeon-in-Chief in the United Scottish Women's Hospitals Foreign Service, and was Senior Assistant to the Muirhead Professor of Obstetrics and Gynaecology (University of Glasgow) as well as Assistant Gynaecological Surgeon at the Glasgow Royal Infirmary.

Dr Winifred Ross, a daughter of the manse at Partickhill had been awarded the OBE.

The redoubtable Dr Ivy MacKenzie in addition to her consultancy at the Victoria Infirmary, was Consulting Physician to the Glasgow District Board of Control, and had become the first woman resident Fellow of the Royal Faculty of Physicians and Surgeons of Glasgow.

The position of women was consolidated during the inter-war years; again war-time and the subsequent setting-up of the National Health

Service created more opportunities for them, particularly in hospital work. But progress in academic medicine was much more hardly won—it was not until very recent years that the first woman professor was appointed to the Medical Faculty of Glasgow University.[10]

3. Nursing: the emergence of a profession

Until the mid-nineteenth century nursing was not an activity which demanded either skill or training. Nor did it command respect. As Florence Nightingale put it, nursing was left to those 'who were too old, too weak, too drunken, too dirty, too stupid or too bad to do anything else'.[11] There were many reasons for these views. The intimate body services to be done for the patient were considered to be unseemly or immodest for young, unmarried or well-bred females, especially if the recipient of these services was not a member of the family. The cleaning and feeding of a human body were chores on a par with the other domestic tasks performed by servants.

A second consideration is that before about 1880 the hospital treatment of illness was fairly rare. It is certainly true that the great period of Britain's voluntary hospital foundation had begun in the eighteenth century. Voluntary hospitals were, however, intended by their eighteenth-century founders for the treatment of the poor, to plug the gap left by bad or impoverished home conditions. Where home circumstances were adequate, a sick person spent his illness there attended by his own doctor and nursed either by the females of his family or by his servants. However, from the middle of the nineteenth century, the discovery and application of anaesthetics and antiseptic surgery widened medical technique considerably and made it increasingly popular for patients of all classes to seek medical treatment in hospitals. Later, new private nursing homes catered for many of these better-off patients, but pay beds were introduced into many of the charity hospitals too (in Glasgow, the Victoria Infirmary was built with a special wing for paying patients); and it was not unknown for people to attempt to get free medical care in a charity hospital though they could well afford to pay the cost of private treatment.[12] This new situation required higher standards of nursing to meet the greater demands both of expanding medical therapy and of artisan and middle class patients. From the 1860s onwards, a series of nurses' training schools began to turn out fairly large numbers of educated women who were eagerly accepted by hospital authorities, who in turn found that their medical officers, patients and public opinion in general were insisting on higher levels of nursing skill in the wards.

Undoubtedly the most visible figure in the campaign for nurses' training was Florence Nightingale herself, the Nightingale School for Nurses at St Thomas's Hospital in London being one of the first to offer a training course. Miss Nightingale was not, however, the sole or even the major agent of this change. Her forceful personality, influential contacts and dramatic exploits at Scutari made sure that she remained an authority on all matters connected with nursing. But it was the changing medical requirements of hospital treatment and the middle-classes' conversion to the benefits of hospitals which ensured that the character of nursing in British hospitals changed so completely between 1860 and 1900.

In Glasgow the improvement of nurses' working conditions, training and duties depended very much on the attitudes and aims of the hospital managers. There were three broad types of hospital in the city at the time: voluntary hospitals, which were managed by independent boards of directors and funded from public donations; Poor Law hospitals, which were managed and funded by the local parish Poor Law authorities; and municipal hospitals, which were provided by the Glasgow Local Authority and used entirely for the treatment of infectious disease. Though nursing in all Glasgow hospitals improved during the period, differences of approach and timing were evident in the three groups, and were attributable to varying financial pressures and to differing definitions of hospital functions and aims.

(a) In Local Authority hospitals

The Glasgow Local Authority, the Police Board, opened its first hospital in 1865, at a time when nursing in voluntary and parochial establishments in the city, and indeed in Britain as a whole, was just taking its first tentative steps towards improvement. The Police Board found that its nurses shared all the disadvantages common to most contemporary nurses, where ignorance, drunkenness and inefficiency abounded. They were, perhaps, in an even worse position than the other Glasgow hospitals because they catered exclusively for fever patients. The risks of infection which attached to fever nursing were so great that it was always very difficult to find any women, with character or qualifications sufficient to obtain alternative employment, who were willing to accept the job of fever nurse. The Police Board found itself obliged to take on nurses who were amongst the worst available.[13]

Dr J. B. Russell, then Medical Superintendent of the hospital, expressed himself forcefully:

> As things are, nurses have no organisation as a class, no *morale*. The popular idea, particularly of a hospital nurse, resembles that of a washerwoman— drinking is inseparable from both. The idea is only too true, in fact; and its very existence and truth react against any individual effort to raise the standard of character. Indeed, I often fancy good people are amused while listening to my complaints, and surprised that I have not yet learned to believe that drink and dishonesty are essential properties of a nurse. I admit that at present nursing is the last resource of female adversity. Slatternly widows, runaway wives, servants out of place, women bankrupt of fame or fortune from whatever cause, fall back on

1. *Glasgow Royal Infirmary c.1832.* An artist's impression of the Adam building of 1792—4 and the new block (on left) to be erected for the reception of fever patients who were unduly straining the GRI facilities in the 1820s.

2. *Belvidere Hospital, Glasgow 1891,* showing all the pavilions. Note the variegated brickwork, the hospital chimney and the many factory chimneys beyond.
Photograph by courtesy of Dr Peter Mackenzie.

3. *The Glasgow Asylum for Lunatics.* The domed building, designed by William Stark, was Glasgow's first purpose-built Asylum (1814). Extensions were added after 1843, when the City Parish authorities took over these premises in Parliamentary Road as the nucleus of a new poorhouse.

4. *Glasgow Asylum for Lunatics, Gartnavel c.1915.* 'Milieu therapy' in action—for the wealthy. This opulent accommodation was in the private wing of the hospital's West House.

5. *The dining hall, Gartnavel, prepared for a special occasion, c.1915.* The mural decorations are indicative of piety and milieu therapy, important elements in the contemporary philosophy of the care and treatment of the mentally ill.

6. *William Macewen*, pioneer of the white coat, with his assistants preparing for work in the operating theatre at the Glasgow Royal Infirmary in 1892.

7. *Sir William Macewen*, Regius Professor of Surgery in the University of Glasgow (1892–1924). One of his responsibilities was to deliver a course of formal systematic lectures to medical students.

D   E   C   B   A

Fig. 2.

A—Battery. B—Induction coil. C—Tesla coil. D—Crooke's tube. E Mahogany half plate slide containing sensitive plate and coins on top to be photographed.

8. *Dr John Macintyre's first X-ray apparatus, 1896.*

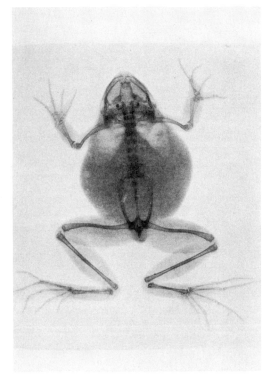

9. *X-ray photograph of a frog.* The photograph, which demonstrates the differentiation of hard and soft tissues, was obtained using Macintyre's first equipment (Plate 8) and required an exposure time of 40 seconds. It was first publicly shown on 5 February 1896.

10. This photograph shows the earliest properly-equipped X-ray room in the Glasgow Royal Infirmary: part of the Lister Ward, it was used temporarily until the purpose-built pavilion was opened in 1902. The room is furnished with wall-mounted control panel, patient couch, and upright tube stand (chest stand, on right). It features several racks of X-ray tubes and an induction coil on the rear wall.

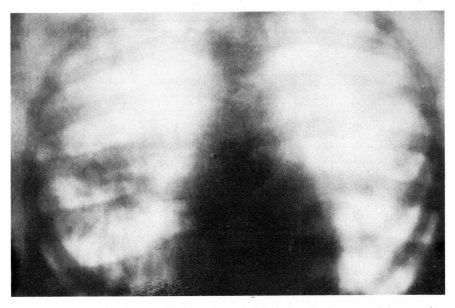

11. *X-ray photograph of lung, c. 1900.* The lesion is indicated by the darker patch between the two lower ribs on the left of the photograph. The X-ray was probably obtained with equipment shown in the Photographic Room (Plate 10).

12. Mothers with infants waiting to be examined at the Milk Depot, 106 Maitland Street, Glasgow (c. 1911).

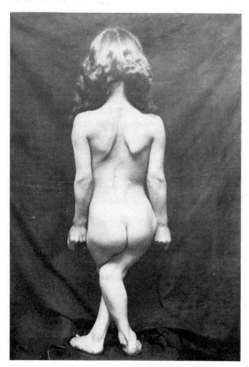

13. This child, suffering from rickets, was photographed at Belvidere Hospital c.1910. The gross physical deformity which could be caused by malnutrition is vividly illustrated.

14. *Scottish Asylum Matrons at Glasgow:* February 1914. Miss Darney, Matron of Glasgow Asylum for Lunatics was hostess (seated centre) and four of her six Assistants (in uniform or hatless) were in attendance. Miss Brodie (in uniform, far left) was soon to join the Army Nursing service and later to be Matron of Glasgow Asylum for Lunatics, 1922–1948.

Miss Brodie, Glasgow R. Asylum	Miss Keay, Kirklands Asylum
Miss Cameron, Glasgow R. Asylum	Miss Lorimer, Glasgow R. Asylum
Miss Christie, Ayr D. Asylum	Miss Lumsden, Murray's R.A. Perth
Miss Darney, Glasgow R. Asylum	Miss Macaulay, Crichton R.I.
Miss Davidson, Edinburgh, D. Asylum	Miss McBean, Govan D. Asylum
Miss Donald, Glasgow D. Asylum (Gartloch)	Miss Maccallum, Renfrew D. Asylum
Miss Finn, Paisley D. Asylum	Miss M'Grigor, Stirling D. Asylum
Mrs. Freer, Govan D. Asylum	Miss Pirie, Lanark D. Asylum
Miss Hearden, Edinburgh R. Asylum	Miss Rae, Glasgow D. Asylum (Woodilee)
Miss Howden, Crichton R. Instn.	Mrs. Salmond, Glasgow R. Asylum

Miss Thyne, R. Edinburgh Asylum.

15. One of the gold medals issued by Glasgow Corporation to nurses in charge of plague patients at Belvidere Hospital 1900—01.

16. *Memorial headstone: Belvidere Nurses.* This imposing headstone was erected by the Lord Provost, Magistrates and Council in Sandymount Cemetery, Glasgow, to honour those dedicated nurses who had either died in the course of duty or who had given a lifetime's service to Belvidere Hospital.

hospital nursing. When on rare occasions a respectable young woman takes to it from choice, her friends most likely repudiate her, her relatives resort to various ways of concealing her whereabouts. . . . For all this we have ourselves to blame. Until our nurses have conferred upon them the dignity and morale of a special education, special organisation, firm and kind moral supervision, with high pay during active service, a home when not actually engaged, and a superannuation fund to look forward to in old age, we shall never have good nurses—or if we have them we don't deserve them.[14]

Russell's far-sighted opinions were borne out by the fact that in the first year of the hospital's operation, eighteen nurses out of the total of thirty-five were dismissed for some form of malpractice.

From the very start, then, medical officers of the Glasgow Police Board were anything but complacent about the standards of their nurses. There was no central authority like the Poor Law Board of Supervision to prod them into making improvements and they had no subscribers or other voluntary contributors of money whose continuing good opinion might have to be bought by evidence of efforts to follow modern trends in nursing. These external spurs were unnecessary when the board's medical officers, and especially Russell himself, took such a keen interest in all the details involved in the provision of an efficient nursing service. The organisation of nurses' working hours, duties, pay and training was done by the medical officers and only brought to the attention of the Police Board for its official sanction.

In the very first year of the hospital's existence, Russell expressed a desire to introduce 'a more systematic means of instruction' for his nurses. In the typhus emergency of that year he found the situation far too distracting and disorganised to attempt anything of such a revolutionary and far-reaching nature, but did introduce a few practical ground rules for the selection and training of nurses. After the initial discouraging experience of bad characters, he decided to refuse any applicant who had been either an inmate of a poorhouse or who had worked in another hospital. This last exception seems odd, but. nursing in other hospitals at the time had little to recommend it, and any such nurse who left or was dismissed from her post was likely to possess serious faults of intellect or character. Russell decided that entire self-reliance was the only answer, and set about selecting applicants of good character and no nursing experience who could be trained to an acceptable level. He had very definite views about the sort of woman who would make the best nurse:

The class who make the best nurses, and who are the most difficult to get, are widows between 30 and 40, with good character, with good plain education, and who, from having reared children and known the personal effects of sickness, are more gentle and sympathising with the sick.[15]

This ideal sounds fairly far from the vision of some reformers seeking to turn nurses into an educated, technical, professional body, but it shows how much the first improvements had to be tied to contemporary needs and realities.

In these early days, training consisted only of reading and of some practical instructions. All nurses were supplied with Florence Nightingale's book and were taught by example by one of the few good nurses whom Russell had encountered. However, as soon as time was available, some further action was taken to ensure more thorough training. Russell persuaded the Police Board to provide a small medical reference library for the fever nurses. This numbered about eighty volumes and consisted mainly of fairly simple, introductory works which could be readily understood by the women without the need for detailed medical background. This kind of educational provision was an innovation as far as Glasgow hospitals were concerned. During the winter session of 1866–7 Russell also embarked on some basic anatomy and physiology demonstrations, using sets of diagrams which had been prepared for public lectures given in previous years.

In 1881 the training of nurses at Police Board hospitals was put on a more formal footing. The board's Hospital Sub-committee agreed that nurses would in future be appointed as full members of staff only after a period of training lasting at least one year. This included, as before, formal lectures, practical demonstrations and working experience but it now ended with an examination consisting of written papers and a *viva voce* test. Candidates who successfully passed this examination were awarded a Certificate of Proficiency in Nursing of the first, second or third class.

Running parallel to these improvements in training were advances in living conditions, wages and working hours. In some of these areas, especially that of working hours, the Police Board was slightly slower to change than were the managers of voluntary hospitals or those of Barony Parish. The original allocation of duties for nurses in 1865 conformed fairly well with accepted practice. Hours were extremely long and free time limited. Fever nurses spent an average of fourteen hours a day on duty and had an afternoon off every fortnight. Though these hours were the equivalent of domestic service, Police Board nurses had an advantage offered to few of their colleagues in that rough domestic chores were excluded from their duties from the beginning.

The situation altered little in the succeeding twenty years, but in 1891 in response to difficulties of attracting permanent staff and, possibly, to the example of reforms at the city's Royal Infirmary, changes in working conditions were introduced. By employing four nurses for each ward instead of three, it was possible to reduce the daily workload of head nurses and day nurses to ten hours and of night nurses to eleven hours. This new schedule compared favourably with the changes being introduced at the Royal and other voluntary hospitals and it was rather better than the situation in most Poor Law hospitals.

As far as accommodation and wages were concerned, the local authority was also able to maintain standards which were equivalent to the best in voluntary institutions. In the early years, nurses' wages ranged between 25s. and 30s. a month, depending on satisfactory conduct and experience. In

1873 Russell recommended an increase in these rates to between 35*s*. and 40*s*., which was accepted by the Police Board. Later, in an attempt to retain the services of their best qualified nurses, the local authority decided that nurses' pay should rise in nine annual increments from the starting salary of £18 until it reached £45 per annum in the tenth year of service.

In terms of education, pay rates and duties the standard of nursing in Glasgow's Police Board hospitals certainly kept pace with the developments in infirmaries and elsewhere. There was never any evidence of neglect or disinterest on the part of board officials, though the emergency nature of their first fever hospitals hampered any systematic action being taken initially.

(b) In Voluntary hospitals

Before the 1870s very little in the way of education, training or expertise was required from the women who acted as nurses in Glasgow's voluntary hospitals. The most valued qualities, where they could be obtained at all, were those of gentleness and respectability. As late as 1867 it is clear that the managers of the city's biggest hospital, the Royal Infirmary, retained these old fashioned ideas and gave little evidence of any aquaintance with the changes in nursing taking place at the London hospitals. In that year, the managers admitted the inadequacy of their own nurses, but far from tackling the problem with extensive educational provision, they merely tried to attract the old valued virtues with a species of bribery. The Infirmary Annual Report for 1866 noted that the managers would give 'prizes to a day and a night nurse in each department for good conduct, kindness to the patients, and cleanliness in their wards'. It is evident that infirmary nursing was still regarded in the light of domestic service, where specialised knowledge or expertise was not considered important.

The first indication of changing views appeared in the appointment by the larger hospitals in the 1870s and 1880s of matrons or lady superintendents who had themselves received a systematic training in nursing. Before this, a matron's duties had been almost exclusively those of housekeeper; for instance, the Royal Infirmary's Regulations of 1867 expected the matron to inspect the hospital premises daily, to attend to the laundry, to supervise the hiring of nurses and female servants, to be responsible for the furniture and utensils, to take personal responsibility for the cooking and serving of meals, to look after the feeding of the resident medical officers, to attend chapel daily, and to allocate housework to all female patients capable of doing any.

With the employment of trained nurses as matrons in the larger hospitals, it became easier to organise systematic training for the nurses under their control. This usually consisted of a course extending over two, and later three, years. The most important part of the training was a kind of apprenticeship—the trainee or probationer carried out routine ward work under the supervision of a sister or staff nurse. Supplementing this practical work were lectures from the medical staff on subjects such as bandaging or the use of common medical instruments. These lectures from doctors began in the Maternity Hospital in 1871, in the Western Infirmary in 1875, in the Royal Infirmary in 1878, and in the Sick Children's Hospital in 1888. Though they became an essential part of the probationer nurse's work, they continued to be given voluntarily and gratis by the doctors.

The hospitals which provided this pattern of education became recognised training schools for nurses, and in Glasgow nursing certificates were issued by the Royal Infirmary, the Western Infirmary, the Victoria Infirmary and the Sick Children's Hospital, and a midwives' certificate was offered by the Maternity Hospital. These qualifications fitted women not only for hospital nursing but for jobs in the growing private or home-nursing associations.

However, in the 1890s several people in Glasgow, the most notable amongst whom was the eminent surgeon, Dr William Macewen, began to suggest that more was required than this simple, basic training if nurses were to respond to medical developments. Dr Macewen believed that a modern nurse needed more than a good liberal education, that she must be given a specific grounding in anatomy, physiology, therapeutics, medicine and surgery 'sufficient to enable her to follow with intelligence the move-ments of the disease and the treatment she was entrusted to carry out'.[16] The implementation of such calls for far-reaching improvement in training began first in Glasgow's Royal Infirmary, and were very much due to the energy and determination of the Infirmary's Matron, Mrs Rebecca Strong. The Infirmary's new Regulations, which came into operation in 1893, required reasonable evidence of educational attainment before nursing applicants could be accepted. Candidates had to take a preliminary formal examination or produce Leaving Certificates from the Scottish Education Department. Once accepted into the training school, probationer nurses received a much more thorough and technical education than that which was currently offered even in the most respected of British hospitals. It involved two courses in the theory of anatomy, physiology and hygiene and two on practical nursing. All the lecture courses were accompanied by oral or written examinations and a class certificate was given at the end of each set. This more rigorous and theoretical approach was quickly adopted by other British hospitals around the turn of the century.

Parallel with the new training schemes were corresponding changes in financial reward and other indicators of status. In the 1860s the wages of nurses at the Royal Infirmary had been from 15s. to 17s. 6d. a month and no meals were provided for these women in hospital. Twenty years later, wage scales in the Glasgow voluntary hospitals increased to average rates of between £20 and £30 a year,[17] while it was possible for head nurses or sisters to earn up to £40 a year in the 1890s.

Further evidence of changing status appeared with the construction by most of the larger hospitals of special 'homes' which usually provided indi-vidual bedrooms for the nurses and communal sitting or dining rooms. Extra facilities, such as pianos or libraries, were frequently donated by supporters of the institutions. The Glasgow Eye Infirmary provided 'comfortable apartments' for its nurses in 1886, while the three general infirmaries embarked on the building of special separate accommodation. These buildings were completed by the Royal in 1888, by the Western in 1892, and by the Victoria in 1894.

As well as these improvements, nurses' hours decreased from an average of fifteen hours a day in the 1870s to an average of eleven in the 1890s, and the nature of their duties changed considerably. By the end of the century most hospitals ended or limited the purely domestic chores which had formerly taken up a high proportion of a nurse's day, and she could now concentrate almost exclusively on patient care.

Therefore, by the end of the century the situation in Glasgow's voluntary hospitals had greatly changed. Beginning in the 1870s as the first signs of what might be termed the 'Nightingale Revolution' filtered through, Glasgow hospitals took the initiative in sponsoring greater improvements so that by the 1880s and 1890s the emphasis shifted entirely towards selecting a respectable type of applicant who was attracted to nursing by the certainty of receiving a useful professional qualification at the end of an instructive period of training.

(c) In Poor Law hospitals

Nursing in Scottish poorhouses in the mid-nineteenth century was almost entirely done by the inmates themselves. These people were unpaid, unsuitable and completely untrained for their task. This unsatisfactory, though traditional, system eventually provoked attention from the central Poor Law authority in Scotland, the Board of Supervision, and between 1875 and 1896 the Board issued numerous circulars to local parish authorities urging them to introduce paid, trained nurses to their poorhouse hospitals. In an effort to strengthen these pleas, the Board of Supervision in 1885 organised a register of trained nurses who would be acceptable to them for parochial employment. In order to become registered with the Board, a nurse had to satisfy requirements on age and qualifications, but the real incentive of the registration plan lay in a decision to allow parishes to benefit from a money reward if they co-operated. A poorhouse hospital which employed the recommended number of registered nurses for its size was allowed to charge part of the cost of these nurses to the government's annual medical relief grant. The Board allowed that:

> The amount to be allocated from the grant will be at the rate of one half of the actual salary of each nurse for which satisfactory vouchers are obtained, together with an allowance of 3/- per week in respect of the cost of rations, lodging and uniform.[18]

One of the first parishes in the country to adopt the Board of Supervision's recommendations was Barony in Glasgow, and as far as the trained-nurse scheme was concerned it remained a shining example of advanced thinking amongst Scottish poorhouses (though Scottish Poor Law nursing always lagged considerably behind developments in England). Barony's Parochial Board had examined the problems of pauper nursing some time before the Board of Supervision issued its first circular on the matter. On several occasions in the 1860s and 1870s, the parish poorhouse medical officer suggested the necessity of introducing some sort of paid nursing system.[19] Finally in 1880, after long consideration, the Barony Board decided to experiment with employing five paid nurses and a lady superintendent. In April of that year, from the thirty applications for the superintendent's post which they received, the board selected Miss Augusta Pigott of Guy's Hospital, London.

The nursing regime which was established in Barony was one which met with the Board of Supervision's full approval and was subsequently copied by many other poorhouse hospitals. Drawing on the experience of the older voluntary hospitals and of the English workhouse infirmaries, Barony Parochial Board drew up comprehensive regulations to govern the duties, timetables, and even the food allocated to its trained nurses. The hospital was not physically separated from the main part of the poorhouse, but was autonomous in terms of organisation. The lady superintendent controlled all household matters concerning the hospital, though real medical authority still lay with the medical officer. The nursing staff was divided into three categories:

(1) *Staff nurses* (day and night), who were the only trained staff. Their duties included making beds, bathing patients, giving out food, looking after the ventilation and medicines in the wards, and reporting any change in the condition of patients to the doctors. Their salary was £20 a year initially, rising to £28 after several years' service. Their working day was an average of eleven-and-a-half hours and they were allowed one day off per month.

(2) *Probationers*. These were nurses in training for full registration. From the beginning of the scheme, Barony organised a training school for nurses with a course lasting two years. Applicants were taken on for a trial period of one month after which, if satisfactory, they received a salary of £10 in the first year and £15 in the second. At the end of their training these nurses were acceptable in general hospitals or to private nursing associations. Their duties were roughly similar to those of staff nurses, and there never seems to have been any shortage of applicants.

(3) *Pauper assistants*. There was at least one of these for each hospital ward and they were on duty from 6.30 a.m. till 8 p.m. Their job was to do the cleaning of the ward, bathroom and utensils. While they could watch and report on patients, they were absolutely forbidden to give medicines or to wash or to apply dressings to patients except under nursing supervision.

In the ensuing five years the Barony Parochial Board did not regret its decision, though occasional worries about increased poorhouse costs were sometimes voiced at meetings. By 1885 they employed fourteen trained nurses including a lady superintendent, nine untrained nurses (probationers), and twenty-seven assistant menials and servants.

The training school at Barony continued to be very important. Proba-tioners had to take written and oral examinations before being accredited as trained nurses, and though an Inspector from the Board of Supervision made the wry comment that the value of these examinations 'would be materially increased if the examinations were conducted by medical men unconnected with the Parochial staff,[20] standards stayed quite high. The resident medical officer (Dr Core) always took a close interest in the progress of nurses in training at Barony. He inaugurated a short course of lectures for nurses in 1885, which in the succeeding ten years developed into regular, twice-weekly lectures for two periods of six months each. That Barony's training school was well thought of is seen by the application of several other nursing establishments in Britain to have their nurses trained there.[21]

However, Barony was unusual and its policy on nursing cannot be con-sidered an accurate representation of the general state of affairs in the other Glasgow or Scottish Poor Law hospitals. In the other two Glasgow parishes progress in nursing was much slower and much less enthusiastically accepted by board members. Govan Combination Parish only began to introduce paid nurses after 1888, and never became a training centre itself. Glasgow City Parish resisted repeated efforts at persuasion by the Board of Supervision until 1890. After frequently protesting its inability to change because of financial difficulties and accommodation shortages, the parish finally bowed to the inevitable and began to end its reliance on pauper staff. A lady superintendent was appointed in April 1891 and by the following spring the parish possessed a fully trained staff. This rapid advance was apparently effected by two main factors. First of all, City Parish was in-fluenced by its loss of the monetary aid which the Board of Supervision gave towards nursing costs. Secondly, from the mid 1880s it had a poor-house medical officer (Dr Buchan—MO 1884–92) who shared the same kind of concern for progress and improvement which Barony medical officers had always shown, and who repeatedly asked his board to consider changing the old system of pauper nursing.

The experience of Glasgow's three parishes in the introduction of trained nurses to their hospitals shows that though very different opinions were held by the various boards and different rates of progress were achieved, the late nineteenth century saw a more enlightened approach being followed by all of them.

4. Men and women, partners in medicine?

This short survey of the position of women in medicine in the late nineteenth and early twentieth centuries reveals that this was the critical period in which they first managed to become accepted and necessary partners with men in hospital health care. The Glasgow case was in no way unusual in British hospital development, changes being neither very far in advance nor far behind the country-wide trend. However, though women achieved professional status as nurses and began to invade the preserves of male doctors, they attained nothing approaching full equality. Even the new, highly trained nurses of the 1890s remained entirely subordinate to doctors, while the number of women entering the medical profession was always small.[22] The highest ranks of the profession were out of reach of the great majority. In all hospital work women's career chances were completely under the control of male hospital administrations.[23] Hospital managers certainly did inaugurate important new schemes which led to improvements in the status of female medical workers, but these schemes were never undertaken altruistically. The position of women as doctors and nurses improved mainly for practical reasons. Nursing changed because medical techniques became more sophisticated and demanded more highly-trained assistants. Female students and doctors became accepted grudgingly because they offered the financial advantage of a new source of fees and because subscriber opinion influenced management decisions.

Chapter Ten

THOMAS SCOTT WILSON

The National Health Service 1948–1980

1. 1948 and after, the National Health Service

The National Health (Scotland) Act of 1947 became operational in 1948 and gave everyone in the country access to comprehensive medical care. Each person could register with a general practitioner of his choice and through him be admitted to hospital or have any other type of medical care covered by the scheme. The service was paid for by various national insurance schemes and by taxation. Unlike the systems elsewhere, where the patient first pays for the services he has received and then claims for his out-goings against his insurances, the British system was intended to be 'free' to all.

The health services which a patient could obtain depended largely on the facilities available fairly near his home. GPs often referred patients to the nearest hospitals although in Glasgow, as elsewhere, the prestigious teaching hospitals could always attract patients from afar. The Poor Law hospitals had become a part of municipal provision in 1929 (see Chapter Three above) and after 1948 they became an important feature of the National Health Service. They were often well-known (being sited in heavily populated areas) but due to historical circumstances they required a good deal of investment to bring them up to standard. Their earlier history as 'pauper' institutions was the more readily forgotten when, as in the case of the Southern General in Glasgow, specialist units (Neurology) were established thus effectively blotting out the earlier image of the Govan Poor Law Hospital.

The Act of 1947 planned a type of community health service focused upon Health Centres, with GPs, health visitors, social workers and nursing staff providing a comprehensive service to the people living nearby. Very few Health Centres were built although the general practitioner group practice has acted as a focus for other medical and socio-medical services.

After 1948 the organisation of the Health Service was on a tri-partite basis:

1. Hospital Boards, which took over voluntary and municipal Hospitals.
2. The Local Executive Council which was responsible for General Practitioners (hereafter GPs) dental, pharmaceutical and ophthalmic services.
3. The Local Authority (apart from its duties under the Public Health Acts) continued to provide services for mothers and young children, school children, health visiting and gradually took over the hitherto voluntary District Nursing Service.

The task undertaken by all these bodies was formidable. The system seemed to work reasonably well although the medical profession and some others were dissatisfied with what was still seen as a piecemeal structure. As a result of the Porritt committee's enquiries and later government white papers, the National Health Service (Scotland) Act of 1972 was passed.

In 1974 Health Boards took over GP, hospital and local authority personal health services. The post of Medical Officer of Health was abolished, leaving no doctors in the employ of local government. The public health duties of the 'Sanitary Department' were re-organised as the Environmental Health Department, and its control by a sanitary expert has re-established the importance of the sanitarian in local government.

The non-sanitary duties of the MOH were assumed by the Health Board which set up appropriate mechanisms for their execution along with all other medical matters.

The medical presence remains with the Health Board from which the Environmental Health Department can request advice: close liaison is maintained by joint committees of the two bodies at both administrative and executive level.

2. Health and the environment

(a) Housing

Despite the efforts of the City Improvement Trust from 1866 to clear the most congested housing sites in the city there was little progress in re-housing the people. Only after the First World War when Addison's Housing Act was passed in 1919 were financial inducements offered by central government to local authorities who wished to build subsidised housing. Glasgow completed some council estates between the wars but the great expansion came in the post-1945 period when large peripheral housing schemes such as Drumchapel, Castlemilk and Pollok were built. There were virtually no social facilities provided. For some years children were taken by bus to school in older parts of the city: later tenement schools were developed and eventually neighbourhood schools were built. Finally shopping centres and community facilities were provided.

In the 1960s partly in order to help solve the acute housing problem new towns were launched in green field sites in central Scotland. The Glasgow Municipal Authority had an official overspill scheme designed to decant Glasgow citizens into the new towns and by the mid 1960s a loss of 200,000 citizens was planned over a 20 year period. Unfortunately the movement of people from the city gained momentum and the 200,000 were lost over a period of 10 years. The New Towns themselves, such as East Kilbride, Cumbernauld and Livingstone can be considered successful. They often attracted active young families keen to make new lives for themselves. New industries were established with generous government grants which attracted foreign companies.

Some 70% of housing in Glasgow is publicly owned. The swing to municipally owned houses reflects not only the earlier housing problems of Glasgow but also the view that housing ought to be a social service. Paradoxically with the falling population council houses are left empty, and yet people still remain on the housing list in urgent need of accommodation. Vandalism is serious and prevents the letting of houses in recognisably poor areas.

At the present time the planning authorities have delineated deprived areas in publicly-owned housing schemes where there is often serious overcrowding. The main problem categories—large families, with the breadwinners frequently unemployed, and the old—are found there. The East End of Glasgow has been declared a special case, and many millions of pounds of government money have been advanced to finance the Glasgow Eastern Area Rehabilitation Scheme (GEAR). New housing is being erected, private housing is being encouraged, new industrial estates are being built (with many small factory units), open spaces are being provided and the whole area is being landscaped. It is of interest to note that the Greater Glasgow Health Board is one of the organisations involved in this important project because medical support is essential to its success.

(b) Smoke control

Since 1900 the city has been active in the field of smoke control. Marine engineers were appointed to the staff of the Public Health Department and advice was given to manufacturers on boiler operation. In the industrial sphere great progress was made but the domestic chimney continued to pollute the atmosphere. Following 'the great smog' in London in 1953 the Beaver Committee recommended more positive action. The Clean Air Act of 1956 gave the Glasgow authorities the opportunity to undertake campaigns for Clean Air Zones. By now some seventy per cent of all houses in the city have, with financial assistance, been converted. The change has been remarkable. Prior to the Clean Air Campaigns it was said that from the University tower at Gilmorehill, Goat Fell, on the island of Arran, could be seen only during the Glasgow Fair fortnight in July each year. Now visibility is much better.

Glasgow takes part in the National Monitoring scheme for clean air and observation stations are maintained in various parts of the city. There is also the five-town scheme to monitor grit emission and gases, such as sulphur dioxide. The results of the work done by the clean air station in Hope Street, Glasgow, are collated in England at the Warren Springs Laboratory.

(c) Water supplies

Since the Loch Katrine water project was successfully completed in 1859 (see Chapter One above) Glasgow has had no great problems regarding the quantity of water brought into the city. But the quality has led to difficulties. The water is pure and acid (the pH being 6.3) the total hardness is

WESTERN REGIONAL HOSPITAL BOARD

1948 — 1974

Map showing the area in which the Western Regional Hospital Board was responsible for the provision of in- and out-patient hospital services: 1948–1974.

Map showing the area over which the Greater Glasgow Health Board has controlled community medical services since 1974.

merely ten parts per million and only 0.1 parts per million of fluoride is present naturally. The fluoride content of water can provide an effective defence against dental decay: in view of the insignificant natural fluoride in Loch Katrine water, positive measures to augment it have been under consideration for some years by the various authorities involved. Though generally supported as a valuable element in preventive medicine, opposition on other grounds has delayed any action.

Until recently almost all Glasgow water pipes were made of lead; acid water, such as that from Loch Katrine, reacts with the metal and a considerable uptake of lead in solution can occur. Of recent years the relationship between lead in water and heart disease has caused concern. Professor Goldberg of the Regius Chair of Medicine in the University of Glasgow has developed research on these problems. From 1967, with the formation of the then Lower Clyde Water Board, lead pipes were prohibited in all new house building. Since then a massive slum clearance programme (removing some 60,000 houses) has cleared much of the lead piping. Since 1973 the municipal authority has, while rehabilitating its own housing stock, removed lead from a further 16,000 houses. Nevertheless many lead pipes and lead dietetic water tanks remain especially in older owner-occupied houses, for no grants are available to the private owner for this replacement work. Lime has been added to the water at Milngavie Reservoir making the water more alkaline in an attempt to reduce the uptake of lead. Chlorine was introduced into the water, in 1939 as an anti-bacteriological warfare measure, but nowadays it is needed to counteract the pollution caused by the seagulls which live there.

(d) Food

The local authority has had widespread responsibility for ensuring pure food supplies. As early as 1890, Dr Russell then MOH sought powers to control milk and meat supply (see Chapters One and Six above). The vulnerability of the people to impurities in food must always be a factor in maintaining the utmost public vigilance. Over the years standards have risen, precautions once considered controversial are now routine. This is very much the case with regulations concerning a basic food, milk.

From 1983 in Scotland all milk will have to be pasteurised, to prevent it acting as a transmission agent for bacterial diseases such as Salmonellosis. Meat too faces stringent tests, for a variety of bacteria but especially Salmonella. Strict regulation has also been necessary in the case of new battery farming, where feeding systems involving recycling could lead to the spread of disease. The effectiveness of control is somewhat offset by deep-freeze processing of poultry for retail sale; extra care is essential in dealing with this type of food. Chickens kept thus must be carefully tested and checked before the housewife buys them. The final responsibility for eliminating the risk of salmonella poisoning must rest with the cook.

(e) Epidemic disease

Public health came into being as a result of fever epidemics which so ravaged urban populations in nineteenth-century Glasgow (see Chapter One above). The first nationwide programme was vaccination against smallpox following the Vaccination Act of 1863. As Professor Ferguson explained, 'From 1864 to 1906 the proportion of infants born in Scotland who were "successfully vaccinated" never fell below 90%.' Over the years, the initiatives of the Medical Officer of Health resulted in the eradication of many diseases, although most would agree that better diet and better housing also played an important part in the process of control.

In recent years most epidemics have affected children who, unless protected, are the more vulnerable section of the community. Some diseases disappeared or ceased to be virulent but diphtheria remained a dangerous infection. As recently as 1940, nearly 6000 cases of diphtheria occurred in the city: of these there were 163 deaths. Glasgow adopted the National Diphtheria Immunisation Scheme in 1940. There have been no cases of diphtheria in the city for twenty-five years. Whooping cough and tetanus immunisation have also been given although the remote possibility of brain damage as a result of whooping cough immunisation has alarmed parents and caused the campaign to falter. Poliomyelitis, a crippling and killing disease was eventually eliminated after 1956 with the introduction of the Salk vaccine and later the Sabin oral vaccine. Vaccination against measles also proved successful. Although it is British policy to let rubella (German measles) take its course among boys and men, special immunisation (which is estimated to be over 90 per cent effective) exists for twelve- and thirteen-year-old girls and all women in the reproductive age group.

It is a curious reflection that with the overwhelming success of campaigns against so many infections the great infectious diseases hospitals have now outlived their usefulness. The tremendous efforts which W. T. Gairdner and J. B. Russell made to open the city's infectious diseases hospitals have achieved the ultimate success in that such hospitals are no longer needed. The progress which has been made in this field would have amazed them.

Ruchill Hospital provides the only remaining infectious diseases unit in the city, for bacteriological and virological investigation now provide detailed information formerly unavailable.

Tuberculosis was another disease which was indeed infectious and was treated in the infectious diseases hospital or more usually in sanitoria where isolation and rest and good food could be procured. TB was sometimes caused by drinking infected milk (see Chapter Six above). Again it was the discovery of new drugs which completely altered the expectations of TB patients. Antibiotic and chemotherapeutic agents, including Streptomycin revolutionised the treatment.

BCG vaccination was introduced in Glasgow in 1953 for contacts of cases with TB and for all school children aged thirteen years. New born infants were also vaccinated. During the campaign it was found that the majority of children were tuberculin positive as a result of environmental factors but nowadays the picture has radically changed and under 10 per cent are positive.

Finally in 1957 the city gave the *coup de grace* to TB. They took the lead in the National X-ray campaign and during a period of five weeks some three-quarters of a million people were X-rayed and several thousand fresh cases were discovered. At this time about 2300 new cases were discovered in Glasgow every year; now the figure is about 250 and involves mostly the elderly.

(f) Sexually transmitted disease

Civic authorities have been vexed over the centuries by the ever present problem of venereal disease. In Glasgow the solution for women was the Lock Hospital, founded in 1805 in Rottenrow and which remained in continuous existence until the Second World War.

The disease was for long associated with prostitution and was particularly prevalent at major sea-ports. During the First World War large scale naval use of the Clyde prompted the establishment of *ad hoc* VD clinics some of which were in Glasgow. In 1917 the Venereal Diseases Act formalised procedures for identification, treatment and limitation of infection.

Changing social mores, aetiological research and modern drugs have contributed to the modification of attitudes towards this type of disease. To face up to the changed picture and to avoid the stigma of the term VD, Genito-urinary medicine is the name now often used. It is becoming established policy to site clinic facilities for these patients in the ordinary out-patient department of the general hospital. Unfortunately it is believed that with more casual sexual relationships there is a greater incidence of these diseases especially among young adults.

3. Glasgow's current health problems

The health problems of the city stem from the social mix of the population. In general terms health and social problems are exacerbated in a city of falling population as the younger, more active people move away. This tends to leave, in the broadest sense, the less able people behind. The result is that Glasgow is a city of marked contrasts. Among the better-off population, standards are high and health statistics compare favourably with similar ones anywhere in the world. Among the rest of the population (mostly Social Classes IV and V) matters are very different.

Glasgow has serious problems of addiction with large numbers of cases of lung cancer and various heart diseases. Smoking is still widely acceptable, although attitudes are changing. School children start to smoke at a very early age despite active advertising campaigns to discourage them.

Alcoholism is another major health problem which affects Scotland in general and Glasgow in particular. Drugs and glue sniffng have also increased in recent years. The prevalence of alcoholic psychosis makes its impact on the hospitals where the psychiatric units are under constant pressure. Over the past twenty years figures for admission of such patients show a six-fold increase for men and a ten-fold increase for women.

It is a sign of the success of social provision that Glasgow has an ageing population kept in good health by effective medical treatment and nurtured by good food. This has put strain on the resources of the Health Boards now faced with a rapidly increasing demand for long stay beds in geriatric wards. For the past fifteen years efforts have been made to increase the number of beds for the old. The University of Glasgow recognising the problem established in 1964 the David Cargill Chair of Geriatric Medicine under Professor (later Sir) W. Ferguson Anderson. Housing authorities too now recognise the need for sheltered housing. This also involves the Social Work Department who maintain many residential homes and undertake much support work, including the provision of home helps.

The health authorities in Glasgow have faced an intractable problem in bringing down the infant mortality rate. After the First World War the rate was some 106 per 1000 live births. This has been successfully reduced to some twelve per 1000 live births, still high by standards achieved by most advanced countries. The Montgomery Report (1959) which was approved by the Scottish Home and Health Department recommended that eight ante natal beds per 1000 births per annum should be provided. At that time in the 1960s, lying in beds were provided to cover 75 per cent of all births, on a calculation then that one bed would accommodate twenty-six patients a year. This produced a total need of 980 beds. In more recent years, it has been decided to provide hospital facilities for as near as possible to 100 per cent of all births, although the time spent in hospital by new mothers has been reduced from the traditional two weeks to a matter of three or four days.

The University of Glasgow in co-operation with the Municipal Health Authority and the Scottish Home and Health Department has been active in attempting to solve some of the problems of infant health through the Paediatric Research Group (later the Social Paediatric and Obstetric Research Unit).

It is indicative of the constant vigilance required in child health problems to remember that rickets, endemic in Glasgow eighty years ago, had virtually disappeared with the regular free issue of orange juice and cod liver oil (since 1940). Now in Indian and Pakistani children cases of rickets have reappeared.

All the authorities whether the Corporation of Glasgow, before 1948 or the Western Regional Health Board (1948—74) and now the Greater Glasgow Health Board (from 1974) have always exerted themselves to respond effectively to the ever changing demands made upon them. Their tasks remains a formidable one, exacerbated now by a declining population for with each drop of 15,000 people in Glasgow the Health Board loses some £3,000,000 of revenue each year.

For further reading on this subject see Notes pp. 204—206.

Chapter Eleven

DEREK DOW

The archives of the Greater Glasgow Health Board

1. Historical background

In 1946 a leading American medical historian drew attention to the part played by Charles Daremberg, a mid-nineteenth-century predecessor, in promoting the importance of the history of medicine. Central to Daremberg's belief was the concept that:[1]

> Medicine, based as it was on the experiences and observations of many generations, could not do without its archive.

A similar, though less publicised, stance had been adopted in the West of Scotland in the early years of last century. In 1810, William Speirs, a director of the newly-established Greenock Infirmary, proposed that an iron chest should be purchased to hold the minute book, which currently lay on the table where 'an accident might happen to it'.[2] Speirs implied that his fellow-director, William Dingwall, should have dealt with this, a remark which brought an immediate and somewhat testy reply. Since Messrs Watt, Ritchie and Baine had not attended to this, a task remitted to them in May 1809, Dingwall himself would now provide a chest 'for the preservation of the books and papers of the institution'.[3] Twenty years later, Dr Moses Buchanan gave a practical demonstration of the benefits to be gained from careful preservation of hospital records, in what he immodestly described as 'the first essay . . . on Hospital statistics which has appeared in this country'.[4] Although Glasgow Royal Infirmary had been founded less than forty years prior to this, Buchanan was appalled to discover that many of the records were already widely dispersed, and some had disappeared entirely.[5]

> Some of them I discovered, after a laborious search, in the Hospital, others in the office of the Treasurer, and the rest in that of the Secretary. Would it not be of advantage to have the whole concentrated in the office of the Secretary, who should be *enjoined*, to secure them in a *fire-proof safe*? . . . Surely the Directors will see it a duty hereafter, to *file* a few copies of these unique records.

Buchanan's impassioned and manifestly sensible plea is equally relevant a century and a half later.

Despite Buchanan's pioneering work in Glasgow, the initiative in Scottish medical history was seized by Edinburgh during the next hundred years. In the 1850s and 1860s James Warburton Begbie, a lecturer in medicine in the extra-mural school in that city, presented a short annual lecture course on the history of medicine.[6] After the demise of this venture the practice apparently lapsed until 1927, when it was revived on a new and enhanced footing. In that year J. D. Comrie was appointed lecturer in the history of medicine, a post which remained unique to Edinburgh among UK medical schools throughout Comrie's thirty-year tenure, during which time he delivered a series of twenty lectures per annum.[7] The tradition founded by Begbie and brought to maturity by Comrie was further consolidated in 1956 with the endowment of the Douglas Guthrie Lectureship in the History of Medicine.[8]

Parallel with the groundswell of interest in medical history as a separate and important discipline, a process begun in America in the 1930s and nurtured in Britain by men like Douglas Guthrie and Edwin Clarke,[9] there emerged a growing demand for better and more readily available sources in this field. Professor Rosenberg of the University of Pennsylvania has drawn attention to the importance of hospital archives in the provision of data for the study of therapeutics and aetiology, stressing the fact that 'the compilation of a guide to such archival materials would certainly increase the likelihood of their being consulted in the future'.[10] In Britain, efforts to catalogue hospital records have been both slow and sporadic. A natural starting point might have been the inception of the National Health Service in 1948, one result of which was the classification of NHS records as public records.[11] The first real advance, however, did not occur until almost a decade later. In the summer of 1957 a letter appeared in *The Times* expressing alarm at the proposed destruction of King's College Hospital case notes dating from 1839. The collection was saved by the efforts of the Royal College of Physicians, and the incident prompted the British Records Association to undertake a survey to assess the range and compass of surviving medical records. The early response was disappointing, and the Association concluded that the majority of hospitals had little or no material which pre-dated the twentieth century.[12] Contemporaneously with this, the Department of Health for Scotland, with the assistance of the Scottish Record Office, issued a circular (SHM58/60) specifying, in general terms, those classes of hospital records which ought to be preserved. Three years later a similar circular (HM(61)73) was issued by the DHSS in England. In Scotland, the initial reaction to SHM58/60 was disappointing: few members of staff achieved more than a nodding acquaintance with its provisions, and responsibility for its implementation was seldom assumed. The first tangible response came only in the late 1960s, with the appointment by Edinburgh Royal Infirmary of a hospital archivist. The first attempt to establish an archive service on a regional basis did not take place until 1975, spurred on by the reorganisation of the Health Service in the previous year. The five Regional Hospital Boards, containing some seventy-six individual Boards of Management, were replaced by fifteen Area Health Boards, the largest of which was that of Greater Glasgow. Although smallest of all in terms of area, Greater Glasgow Health Board became responsible for the medical welfare of one quarter of the entire population of Scotland. With the integration of hospital, general practice and local authority health services under the control of the new body, the potential range of valuable documentary evidence was felt to be considerable. In September 1975, therefore, in co-operation with the University of Glasgow, the GGHB appointed an archivist to locate and list records of historical interest in the care of the Board.

2. The Greater Glasgow Health Board Archives

In a lively and thought-provoking article written to commemorate the coming-of-age of the NHS Sir John Brotherston described the hospital as 'the success story of the history of modern medical care' and the 'power house of the health services'.[13] In terms of record creation and survival hospitals far outweigh any of the other component parts of the NHS. Paradoxically, less serious research has been undertaken using this source material than has been the case with the records of individual practitioners, or with those relating to local authority involvement in health and environmental care. Improvements in the accessibility of hospital records in the future, and an increased awareness of their value as sources, will undoubtedly redress the balance.

In an unpublished PhD thesis relating to Glasgow hospitals in the second half of the nineteenth century, Dr Gaffney listed seventeen inpatient hospitals established in the city between 1794 and 1890.[14] Of these seventeen, records from no less than fourteen are held by the GGHB archives. In some instances these consist only of one or two isolated items: in others the collections contain several hundred pieces covering the entire spectrum of the hospital's activities since foundation. Broadly speaking, these records fall into one of two classes, administrative and clinical. Central to the first category are the minute books, annual reports, and financial papers which detail the structure and management of each institution. Those pre-dating 1948 relate mainly to the voluntary hospital movement and provide a comprehensive picture of the evolution of charitable health care in Glasgow. Minute books from nineteen different hospitals, dating from the opening of Glasgow Royal Infirmary in 1794, are well-represented. Although most of the series are complete there are some unfortunate gaps, where volumes have been lost or destroyed at some point in the past. Printed annual reports, particularly those dating from the nineteenth century, often contain a wealth of information which supplements that inscribed in the minutes. Current holdings include reports from approximately thirty hospitals and allied institutions. While there are some unbroken runs spanning a century or more, notably for Glasgow Royal Infirmary and Glasgow Asylum for Lunatics (Gartnavel) (see Chapter Four above), other series survive in a much more fragmented form. In some instances these can be supplemented from the equally incomplete series retained in the Mitchell Library and that of the Royal College of Physicians and Surgeons of Glasgow. Financial records, by and large, lack the popular appeal of both minute books—with their sometimes controversial and acrimonious accounts of things past—and of annual reports, which are often sumptuously bound and easily stored on a book-shelf in someone's office. Bulky ledgers and cash books frequently have been the first items to be discarded when some rationalisation of storage space is necessitated by the proliferation of current paperwork. This selectivity is reflected in the relatively poor survival rate of such records. Fortunately, details of annual accounts, capital expenditure and salary structure are generally contained in minute books and annual reports. Where fuller records survive, a clearer picture can be obtained of the complexities of hospital administration in the voluntary era. In one or two instances this structure can be examined further through the existence of correspondence files and letter books.

From 1948 onwards the principal administrative unit was the Board of Management, responsible for a single hospital or for a series of smaller units. Board minutes provide the main source of information for this period, and the majority of these have survived intact. Overall policy can be discerned from the Western Regional Hospital Board minutes and annual reports. A standardised accounting system, and a multitude of statistical returns (contained in printed WRHB and Board of Management annual accounts and statistics) will permit a more direct comparison between units.[15] Implementation of policy on a day-to-day basis can be examined through the correspondence files of both the Regional and Hospital Boards. In order to accommodate the sheer volume of these files, a rigorous selection process must be applied to ensure that important files are not destroyed when space is at a premium. In this way it is hoped to avoid the perils of piecemeal and wholesale destruction which occurred with many of the pre-1948 records, and thus ensure the survival of a balanced and adequate body of evidence for future historians of the NHS.

The pessimism of the British Records Association over the survival of clinicial records in 1958 is, happily, largely unfounded with regard to Glasgow. As early as the 1830s the Royal Infirmary was described as treating a range of cases unequalled in any other hospital in the world, due to its monopoly of hospital provision in an 'extensive and diversified' manufacturing centre.[16] Although this monopoly was broken in the latter half of the century, the same general principle held true for the city. It was with an uncomfortable blend of pride and shame, however, that Alex Robertson, Consulting Physician at the City Parochial Board Hospital and Asylum, wrote in 1888 that:[17]

It is clear that where there is such an immense mass of disease, with a large mortality, there must be an excellent field for clinical and pathological research.

In terms of medical provision Glasgow has always served a catchment area extending far beyond the city boundaries. Throughout the years this has added an extra dimension to the practice of medicine in Glasgow hospitals, a point eloquently taken up by Dr. J. Walker Downie. A distinguished aurist, Downie explained that he and his colleagues encountered:[18]

> . . . at all times in the large general hospitals of Glasgow a greater variety of industrial disease and diseases associated with advanced life in country people, than can be seen in any other city in the Kingdom.

Although a certain degree of chauvinism is attached to such statements, they convincingly demonstrate Glasgow's claim to a prominent place in the forefront of hospital care in Britain since the Industrial Revolution.

The survival of extensive collections of ward journals owes much to the labyrinthine structures of Victorian hospital buildings in Glasgow, with their more than ample attic and cellar storage areas, many of which remained undisturbed for decades. On receiving an appointment as a resident at Glasgow Royal Infirmary in 1913 Dr O. H. Mavor (better known as the dramatist, James Bridie) obtained a master key and set off to explore his new surroundings.[19]

> With this key I opened the little, low, dark worm-eaten door and found an enormous heap of ward journals deep in dust and festooned with cobwebs.

Almost 3500 of these books, dating from 1804–1948, have withstood the ravages of time and are now housed in the archives. Although the vast bulk of these relate to the early twentieth century, no fewer than one hundred contain records of patients admitted before 1850.[20] By the 1870s the Western Infirmary had joined the Royal in providing acute general hospital medical care. More than 2000 ward journals for the period 1874–1940 have been preserved, 700 of them relating to the nineteenth century. Although there are occasional gaps, the series is remarkably complete and affords a comprehensive picture of the establishment and development of a teaching hospital. A similar situation applies with regard to the third great voluntary hospital in Glasgow, the Victoria Infirmary, opened in 1890. More than 500 journals, covering the years 1890 to 1948 have been retained. The parallel retention of the majority of admissions and other registers complements— and sometimes helpfully abbreviates—this information.

Specialist and psychiatric care in Glasgow is equally well documented. The ward journals of the Royal Hospital for Sick Children from the opening in 1883 until the outbreak of war in 1914 exist in the original, and those for the later period in microfilm. The clinical records of Infectious Diseases are preserved for a number of hospitals, and include fever ward journals from the Royal Infirmary and a full series of registers of tuberculosis patients treated in Robroyston Hospital from 1919 to 1964. Maternity records—mainly in register form—also exist in significant numbers. Second only to those of the general hospitals in volume, are the asylum and mental hospital records. In many respects these contain a range of information unmatched in any other series. Two of the local authority asylums, Woodilee and Gartloch, have maintained case notes dating from

1875 and 1896 respectively. In this sphere pride of place undoubtedly must go to Glasgow Asylum for Lunatics, with a superabundance of case notes in a virtually unbroken sequence from 1814 until the 1960s.[21] In 1806 D. D. Davis completed a translation of Pinel's *Treatise on Insanity*, which emphasised the necessity of good history taking and of keeping detailed entries in house journals.[22] In Glasgow's premier asylum the injunction was followed conscientiously, and the notes are a model of clarity and concise reporting, often verbatim. Their quality was sufficient to draw the following praise from Dr Yellowlees, Physician Superintendent, in 1888:[23]

. . . in its oldest records it is striking and instructive to find all the best treatment of today foreshadowed and approved.

The recording and interpretation of clinical notes, particularly in the field of psychiatric medicine, can be a highly subjective matter. It is fortunate for modern scholars, however, that not all nineteenth-century doctors were like Thomas Reid, who 'was a man of wide learning with a phenomenal memory and never took notes on cases'.[24]

3. Using the records

Partly as a result of the demise of the voluntary hospital system in 1948, and partly as a result of the growing number of hospitals celebrating centenaries or jubilees, the last twenty years have seen a marked rise in the number of hospital histories published. Many of these have been classified as 'so thin and lacking in critical framework as to be of almost no use to succeeding scholars'[25] and criticism has been focused on the 'elderly, successful practitioner regarding history as intrinsically simple,'[26] and on the 'stream of consciousness' technique[27] so common in such works. In a talk delivered to the Scottish Society of the History of Medicine in 1970, Dr Allan C. Tait frankly and succinctly pinpointed the essential problem.[28]

I am not expert in medical history; like any other consultant, I know only something about my own speciality, and about my own hospital.

The results of amateur writing in the field of medical history are not without merit. A review of Dr A. M. Wright Thomson's *The Glasgow Eye Infirmary, 1824–1962* in the *Scottish Historical Review* (1964) paid credit to the information which it contained on Glasgow medicine, 'the traditional financial problems of the early voluntary hospitals and, incidentally, about the growth of social conscience in the city'. There is, nevertheless, a clamant need for a collective and non-partisan examination of the development of Glasgow hospitals since the late eighteenth century. Some useful and interesting studies have appeared already, but many important areas remain relatively uncharted. There is, for instance, a paucity of works relating the growth of the hospital movement more closely to other social, political, economic and religious factors which can be identified in Glasgow during this period. Too few sources have, as yet, been utilised in tackling this problem.

Dr Gaffney has provided an admirably lucid account of some changes and developments which occurred during the last three decades of the nineteenth century. Many of these had their roots much earlier, and the repercussions continued much later. Management structures in Victorian Glasgow, for example, deserve much fuller study. Even while the Royal Infirmary stood alone, matters were sometimes exceedingly complicated, with an ostensibly democratic body subject to both 'the self-election system' and to 'tyrannical, intriguing medical monopoly'.[29] At the opposite end of the spectrum, Richard Crossman, sometime Secretary of State for Social Services, was equally critical of the method of appointment to the Regional and Hospital Boards after 1948.[30] In the intervening period the pattern of interlocking directorates is a fascinating one. No hospital could develop or expand in isolation, and occasional clashes of interest took place. Robert Gourlay, a director of the Royal Hospital for Sick Children, felt constrained to resign in 1906 because the RHSC appeal for funds for a new hospital led to a conflict of interest with his position as deputy chairman of the Maternity Hospital, concurrently appealing for funds. Many prominent Glasgow doctors were elected to serve as directors, in many cases while they still held senior medical appointments at other hospitals. The increased role of women, rising from the organisation of Ladies' Auxiliaries and Samaritan Societies to become full directors by the closing years of the century, encouraged other indirect links. A considerable number were married to men who held similar posts, sometimes on different hospital boards. Such informal connections may have led to a concealed infrastructure for hospital and other charitable bodies, but the need for examination goes further than this.

One major study of Victorian society in Glasgow has suggested the existence of a homogeneous Glasgow élite, founded on secondary business pursuits involving directorates of local banks, railways and insurance companies.[31] Changing economic patterns after 1900 reduced the interdependence of this élite,[32] and it would be instructive to determine whether this is reflected in hospital management. A second theme which has not been adequately explored is that of the impact of religious denominationalism. A number of hospital directors were active at both Presbytery and Assembly level, often serving on the influential mission and temperance committees. A comparison of these and hospital committee representation gives a much clearer guide to evangelical interest than Dr Gaffney's assessment of simple church connection.[33] On occasion, denominational rivalry was displayed overtly. In 1877 allegations were made that the Royal Infirmary favoured Roman Catholic applicants for nursing and other posts, an accusation vigorously denied.[34] In 1893, denominational support for the Royal and Western Infirmaries was cited to counteract accusations that Established churchmen were comparatively illiberal.[35] For some individuals, including

J. R. Wolfe, founder of the Ophthalmic Institution, denominational allegiance and support were regarded as the sole basis of success.[36] In addition to political and religious bonds there is a potential influence through geographical and social groupings, although these are less readily quantifiable. A study of support for Scottish Church foreign mission work within Perth Presbytery has revealed that certain areas, even streets, showed a high density of supporters.[37] Comparison of the composition of the management teams of hospital, local authority, church and other charitable bodies in Glasgow would probably reveal similar concentrations not immediately apparent.

The ability of the voluntary hospitals to survive and expand to meet the increasing medical expectations of the population was dependent on their success in persuading the general public to subscribe to their funds. By the 1920s this system was clearly unable to cope satisfactorily with the demands made upon it, and the establishment of a National Health Service was a logical development. Throughout the nineteenth century, fund raising was a central concern of the managers, and detailed lists of subscribers and donors were included in the published annual reports. This practice was common to most philanthropic[38] and religious bodies,[39] yet little has been done to evaluate the various movements in relation to one another. To study the finances of each hospital entirely in isolation, as frequently happens in histories of individual institutions, is to ignore cyclical and other factors affecting the level of donations. Not surprisingly, perhaps, the managers of the Royal Infirmary tended to resent any intrusion into their sources of income. Opposition to the foundation of the Glasgow Hospital for Sick Children centred on a belief that this would siphon-off funds previously given to the Infirmary. This theme was reiterated in 1878, when the Lord Provost, William Collins, attributed the reduction of the Royal Infirmary's ordinary income to the transfer of subscriptions to the Western Infirmary.[40] It is not unreasonable, however, to assume that the failure of the City of Glasgow Bank in the same year had played a not insignificant part. Comparison with other fund-raising organisations would give a clearer indication of the validity of Collins' claims. Thomas Chalmers, doyen of social reformers in nineteenth-century Scotland, had convincingly argued that congregational giving worked by a process of fermentation, not exhaustion.[41] Briefly stated, any increase in the number of charities could be expected to tap fresh sources of income. Once subscribers acquired the habit of giving, older charities were also likely to benefit from this new-found liberality. Close scrutiny of subscribers' lists, though not entirely conclusive, could be used to test the validity of this theory. These comparative techniques might be employed in relation to the theme of deficit budgeting, increasingly common in the hospital movement in the latter part of the century.[42] Similar problems beset church missionary societies at this period,[43] and the varying responses to this dilemma require fuller examination. The topic of hospital finance is one for which evidence abounds, though hitherto little research has been attempted.

Allied to the question of hospital expenditure is that of hospital building in the nineteenth century. Here again, a number of avenues of exploration readily suggest themselves. Was the location of hospitals, for example, ever subject to any kind of coherent policy? By the 1860s the Royal Infirmary was situated in a remote part of the city[44] as a result of boundary and population changes. Attempts to respond to these and other stimuli, such as the re-location of the University in the 1870s, were usually unsuccessful.[45] In other cases the development of facilities depended on the provision of underground or suburban railway networks.[46] To some extent, hospital building in the city reflected local styles and concepts.[47] Architects such as J. J. Burnett and John Carrick were engaged on numerous building and extension projects, and a further degree of homogeneity was encouraged by the repeated services of medical men such as Dr J. B. Russell and D. J. Mackintosh, as advisers on design and equipment. Although no integrated policy was ever formally adopted, it is conceivable that men of this stamp may have worked unobtrusively towards this end. Certainly, their standards were high, and careful consideration was given to contemporary developments elsewhere in the UK and abroad.[48] Minute books, annual reports, letter books and various collections of plans contain a wealth of information on this aspect of Glasgow hospitals which still awaits adequate analysis.[49]

Clinical records (including case notes, registers and statistical information found in annual reports) are a rich and currently under-utilised source. Although specific directions on the keeping of medical records were included in the Rules and Regulations adopted by the hospitals, and managers took a keen interest in monitoring this work,[50] the results as presented in tabular form are often unsatisfactory. Moses Buchanan's methodology, for example, is exceedingly suspect.[51] 'Perfect fidelity'[52] in compiling tables from the case records was by no means universal. On numerous occasions tabulators appear to have succumbed to the temptation to manipulate figures in order to prove a theory, or to impress subscribers. Figures abstracted from Gartnavel case volumes, purporting to show the causes of insanity, do not tally with the returns printed in the annual reports. While a certain degree of caution is required before accepting statistical information, the extremely detailed nature of individual case notes makes them an invaluable aid for the medical and historical researcher. It has been noted on more than one occasion that these notes constitute the record of actual medical practice, and not merely of theoretical descriptions of what should be done. For the astute clinician, case notes can provide relevant clinical and therapeutic observations, albeit stated in unfamiliar terms. Epidemiologists in particular can make use of ward journals to clothe the bones of the statistical models presented by A. K. Chalmers[53] and his colleagues, and to re-interpret the diagnostic evidence collected by their predecessors.[54]

Sociologists have argued that in past generations the lower classes have been under-represented in written records,[55] yet patients' records sometimes rectify this in vivid detail.[56] In May 1815 Margaret Bruce was admitted to the Glasgow Asylum for Lunatics. Extant correspondence and other admission documents[57] reveal that she had lived in the village of New Lanark for thirteen years, where she was employed to pick cotton and 'sew occasionally' in her own home. Her husband, a former militia-man who had enlisted in the Regular Army, was currently somewhere in England with his regiment. His absence, and perhaps concern that he might be sent to France, had apparently had a detrimental effect upon her sanity. The firm of Robert Owen and Co., managed by the famous cotton spinner, guaranteed to meet the cost of boarding her in the Asylum, demonstrating Owen's practical concern for the welfare of his workforce. An Irishwoman, Margaret Bruce had no relations in the vicinity and A. C. Pack—one of those who corresponded officially from New Lanark—even offered to accept responsibility for her four infant children.

In addition to furnishing the historian with information about specific individuals the scrutiny of medical records can be highly rewarding in the study of broader themes. The formal opening of the new and enlarged Asylum at Gartnavel in June 1843, less than a month after the Disruption which sundered the Church of Scotland, was undoubtedly no more than coincidence. The impact of this schism, and of later religious revival movements in the 1850s and 1870s, has been examined in depth using church and newspaper reports, both official and unofficial, and personal papers. A new and important perspective might be achieved by examination of the case notes of those unfortunates who could not withstand the religious fervours of nineteenth-century Scotland, and were admitted to one or other of the Scottish Asylums.[58] Fresh enlightenment as to the results—perhaps even the causes—of trade depression and business failure might be achieved in the same manner.

Hospital records are an especially prolific, but largely neglected, source for the history of the Temperance Movement. No attempt has been made to study these systematically, although Brian Harrison's monumental work on the subject, *Drink and The Victorians* (London, 1971), contains interesting references to such themes as the attitudes of medical practitioners, the decline in the use of alcohol as a medicine, and the recognition of alcoholism as a disease rather than a crime. Numerous illustrations of these and other aspects of the movement can be found in the records of Glasgow hospitals. Policy decisions regularly appear in the minutes[59] and in hospital regulations.[60] Changing views on the prescribing of alcohol can be traced through medical and annual reports, diet sheets, ledgers and cash books, and individual case notes.[61] Many of the early temperance reformers in the medical profession were asylum doctors, some of whom became almost obsessive in their attempts to prove a causal link between drunkenness and insanity.[62] The opinions of W. A. F. Browne, J. M. Pagan[63] and others were based as firmly on moral as on medical conviction,[64] yet by virtue of their professional status Browne and his colleagues may have had a disproportionate influence on the deliberations which led to early and controversial anti-drink legislation like the Forbes-Mackenzie Act of 1853. On occasion their theories were substantiated by recourse to very dubious statistical evidence.[65] In the 1960s, after a career in psychiatric medicine spanning nearly half a century, D. K. Henderson reflected upon:[66]

. . . a too facile tendency, particularly in former years, to class as alcoholic psychoses those conditions of pre-existing nervous or mental illness or defect of which alcoholism was a symptom rather than a cause.

In the light of Henderson's comments there is an obvious need for some re-evaluation of these findings, using the primary source material. In addition to delineating a more objective relationship between drink and mental illness than that contained in the published comments of the medical profession the original case notes probably act as a more accurate barometer of Victorian social and moral attitudes towards drink.

4. Future developments

While the past five years have seen a considerable advance in the establishment of medical archives in the West of Scotland, much remains to be done in the spheres of collection and preservation. Medical historians in the past have been accused on occasion of presenting an imbalanced picture of medical development by concentrating solely on its more successful side. It is envisaged that the retention of hospital and other health records of an entire region can go some way towards redressing this situation, especially by allowing historians of a future generation to select their own themes from the full range of current practice. The NHS reorganisation in 1974 devolved the responsibilities of the former Western Regional Hospital Board, encompassing sixty per cent of the population of Scotland, to six Area Health Boards—Ayrshire and Arran, Argyll and Clyde, Lanarkshire, Forth Valley, Dumfries and Galloway, and Greater Glasgow. Since 1979, when the first approach was made to the other five boards, extensive record surveys have been conducted on behalf of the first three Boards on the above list, and a preliminary survey undertaken within Forth Valley. The ultimate aim of this project must be the provision of an integrated archive service covering the West of Scotland Health Boards.

Less readily soluble is the problem of the records of general practitioners. These form a crucial element in the history of health care,[67] but there is often great reluctance on the part of practitioners to consider depositing confidential material of this type. The recent appointment of an Honorary Archivist by the Royal College of General Practitioners suggests that this situation may improve considerably in the future. Although relatively few collections of pre-NHS general practice records have survived intact, other sources do exist. As James Bridie explained in his autobiography, appointment as an honorary consultant in a voluntary hospital was frequently the life-line which enabled the general practitioner to survive, and these appointments are well documented. Among Public Record Office holdings in London are records of legal cases, bankruptcies, apprenticeships, and imports of drugs, all involving doctors and all awaiting systematic use.[68] In

Scotland an equally untapped source exists in the form of sequestration records retained in the Scottish Record Office. In the area of collective responsibility, the records of the Royal College of Physicians and Surgeons of Glasgow (recently catalogued) are a principal source for the era prior to the 1858 Medical Act. The Glasgow and West of Scotland Branch of the British Medical Association was brought into being in 1875, with an initial membership approaching two hundred, and has maintained records of its transactions to the present day. The introduction of the Burgh Insurance Committee in the early twentieth century brought a more formal structure to general practice, evolving into the Executive Council in 1948. Many of the records of these two bodies are extant, though the confidential nature of the information which they hold ensures that the bulk will remain closed to the eyes of historians until sometime next century.

Despite restrictions of this nature, medical history has a vital role to play in modern times. In addition to maintaining contact with the humanities and social sciences it may act increasingly as a synthesis for the greatly increased specialisation which has seen the emergence of a host of distinct branches of medicine over the past hundred years. Secondly, there is a constant need for the re-assessment of received wisdom, to combat the 'fossilization of evidence'[69] in the light of fresh discoveries. Thirdly, an awareness of the past can be crucial to our understanding of the present. The benefit of this historical perspective was central to the inception of the NHS, and was unequivocally demonstrated in the 1944 Goodenough Report on Medical Education in the UK[70] and in the 1945–6 Survey of Scottish Hospitals. In 1927, J. D. Comrie's presidential address to the History of Medicine Section which attended the BMA Annual Meeting in Edinburgh was entitled 'A Vindication of the Section'.[71] It is to be hoped and anticipated that no such apology will be required in the future.

Chapter Twelve

SYDNEY CHECKLAND

British urban health in general and in a single city

1. The phasing of British urban health

Britain's response to the challenge of health care as posed by industrialisation came from the 1830s onward.[1] It can be roughly divided into four phases: from 1830 to 1900, from 1900 to 1948, from 1948 to 1975, and from 1975 to the present. Over all four of these the response had two principal aspects. There was the effort to improve the conditions of public health by various forms of preventative action by public authorities, and there was the increased provision and improvement of the means of therapy by the medical men. But the nature of these responses, and their interactions, showed a striking pattern over time.

The essays in this book are mainly concerned with the first of these periods, as is the present contribution, though some of them try to construct certain bridges over to the present. By the accident of scholarship it is in the 1830–1900 period that most of the monographical work has been done. In this first phase there was relatively little interference by authority with individuals and the family; intervention was largely a matter of providing a new infrastructure in the form of sanitation and water supply. Certainly the Medical Officers of Health sought to enforce standards of cleanliness and to control overcrowding. But such intervention in working class lives, though it has attracted a fair amount of attention, was minimal, being largely confined in its operations to the very worst end of the scale.

But from 1900, partly under the impetus of improved medical techniques, but mainly because of the discovery of a particular set of casualties (namely the victims of a gross infant mortality rate), prevention by the public authorities became more intrusive. It moved from mainly infrastructural provision of sanitation and water supply into the field of maternity and child care, involving feeding and medical inspection.[2] From there it spread to a more general dietary concern, beginning with school meals. More or less at the same time attention turned to what was perhaps the greatest damager and destroyer of life, namely tuberculosis: the discovery of this disease hanging over the national life inspired a programme which involved the direct manipulation of patients and their families. The first great step by the state in providing a generalised health service came with the National Insurance Act of 1911; its drafters encountered the complex problem of how to provide the financial means in such a manner as to limit state liability (using the insurance principle), not offend the susceptibilities of the doctors or the Friendly Societies, and still maintain the notion of self-help. Infrastructural provision, and *ad hoc* intervention in family life were thus joined by an attempt at generalised state provision. But the need to prescribe the conditions of eligibility for the latter made necessary a yet further extension of state interference.

This trend towards surveillance of the individual and the family was much accelerated after the beginning of the National Health Service in 1948. The insistence by the Labour Party that the Service be free to all was an attempt to limit the interventionist element by removing any consideration of personal or family means. The infrastructural problems seemed to be largely solved (though much of the sanitation and water plant of the Victorian age, thought by its builders to be their memorial for all time coming, was secretly becoming decayed and obsolescent, with a consequent vast accumulation of hidden costs). Meanwhile, a new range of illnesses and accidents (especially by road) had been generated by society.

For all illnesses the state accepted responsibility through the NHS. Indeed there was an increasing trend for people to try to surrender large parts of their lives to their NHS doctors, or to other parts of the welfare state. At the same time the medical profession suddenly produced a further vast range of therapies, which the public demanded should be made generally available, and at zero or negligible cost to the individual. Some of these therapies have proved to be inconsistent with others, or have produced adverse side-effects, giving rise to the expression 'iatrogenic', or doctor-induced illnesses and injury; this perverse outcome is reminiscent of that of cross-infection in hospitals a century earlier. The resources to sustain the growing Health Service burden could be found without too much difficulty while the economy of the country performed at a reasonably high level.

When it failed to do so in the later 1970s, the strain on governmental finance and the consequent contribution to inflationary pressure provoked an attempt to reduce health costs. Moreover, some cities, fast losing population, were required to cut back their medical provision more than proportionately. They were also required to make very difficult adjustments in the location and nature of the health services provided. The convergence of the need for economy and efficiency (in a context of declining national productivity), with the indictment of iatrogenic medicine, has provoked profound questioning of the entire system of health care.

Health is one of the most intractable aspects of urban social experience. To begin with, there is the data problem. Medical statistics are notoriously difficult, involving as they do so many problems of diagnosis and categorisation, variations in age composition of the population being observed, and the spatial definitions that are necessary in tracing the geographical (and thus the social) incidence of disease and death. And yet statistics are the only basis on which a general diagnosis of the health state of a community can rest. With a data base that is often lacking in robustness, the next step, that of causal analysis, is even more difficult. So many factors operate upon community health as to make it exceedingly difficult to assess the success rate of particular attempts at improvement. Much of what has been done in terms of health policy, indeed, has rested upon a kind of *a priori* confidence in this line of action or that.

All these difficulties of data and diagnosis increase more than proportionately as we look further back in time. For these reasons health history has tended to be a collection of fragments. The present volume of essays is no exception. Each contribution represents a particular sighting on the problem of urban health, and is offered as such. There would seem, in the present state of health studies, to be no other way of proceeding. But it is hoped that the study of the evolution of health care will be extended so that the gaps in the earlier part of the story may be filled, and the three later periods more fully investigated. Only then will it be possible to attempt a real synthetised account.

Health history is one of the great strands of urban history, and of the evolution of society generally. Mortality and morbidity (illness and the failure to achieve a reasonable level of physical and mental performance) are both indicators and determinants of the performance of a society, reflecting its economic achievement, its class and income configuration, its political structure and its value systems.

2. The Glasgow case

Such matters have been approached by a number of scholars at the national level. Here are encountered the great figures of Chadwick, Farr, Simon and others, together with the ambience of national policy in which they operated. At the level of particular cities the investigation of the response to the health challenge has been largely confined to London, with some more or less passing references to health in the case of other cities. Even here the approach has been a limited one. It has been concerned with one or other particular aspects, or a group of them, rather than with the general response of a city and its region to the health problem, taking account of the many facets of public health and therapy. Partly this failure to investigate the city region as such in terms of health has been due to the difficulty of so doing. The study of the development of health care through the locality must be based on a set of monographs, prepared by those propelled by a compulsion to see how one or other of these complex matters worked themselves out in the city-region context.

The Glasgow case now provides an opportunity to go a step beyond the monographic approach, bringing together the recent work of a range of scholars, with a range of ages and interests, all centred upon what has been done in the city in pursuit of a better health performance. Glasgow, proudly proclaiming itself as the second city of the Empire through the nineteenth century, and with a Faculty of Physicians and Surgeons chartered by King James VI in 1599, and with some of the most notable names in medical history, demands attention in its own right. Moreover, it offers a leading case in the gallery of British cities struggling with one of the most intractable of urban problems. It can be inspected over a period of a century and a half, during which time it went through a great cycle of expansion and contraction, its population rising to over a million by 1921, and losing a quarter of a million in the past fifteen years.[3] It did so under the compulsion of economic forces, acting without regard to the health problems they were generating.

The study of a particular city such as Glasgow must be conducted within the perspective of British cities generally. The challenges (both emergency and long term), and opportunities for effective action will be different; so too will the responses and the degrees of success. There will be differences too in the form of persistence of the local medical tradition, with the nature of medical politics and in the structure of the profession, all three of which are closely related. Similarly, localities will perform differently in terms of the operation of the voluntarist principle, and in their response to the challenge of the National Health Service. It is time that there be a disaggregation of the national picture, not only in terms of statistics,[4] but in terms of regional challenge and responses. It is true in this, as in other matters, that the significance of regions has diminished with the growth of centralisation. But it is as well to know how this came about and what the losses of comprehension and effectiveness, standardisation and averaging have involved.

3. The challenge of prevention, 1830–1900: water supply, sanitation and inspection of homes and food

Preventive action after 1830 demanded the intervention of the state, both central and local, for the problems it posed were outside the scope of the market economy and its auxiliary, philanthropic action. Only the state, at these two levels, could provide the three great necessary facilities, namely an adequate water supply, together with a system of sanitation based upon water-borné sewage, and a regime of health inspection embracing homes and food. Prevention and therapy were, of course, related in the sense that the provision of a better environment for living made it possible to produce healthier bodies, more resistant to disease and more responsive to therapy.

But behind prevention there lurked two further great limiting determinants, namely the level of working-class incomes and the availability of cheap housing. With a considerable proportion of the population in British industrial cities below the poverty line, living in conditions of overcrowding (some of it appallingly bad), the potential for raising the level of public health was limited. Poverty and overcrowding, in turn, interacted, through the inability of many families to make the best of such income as they had, particularly in improving housing standards; the family budgeting problem was often confounded by drink, causing a waste of family resources both directly and indirectly, together with a weakening of the physical constitution. Neither incomes nor housing were, however, capable of improvement by philanthropic action, except to a very minor degree. Nor was the state prepared to act upon either of these circumstances, until under the Addison Act of 1919 it finally embarked upon large-scale subsidised public sector housing.

Public health regulation and provision, and the improvement of therapy in kind and availability, were both subject to further serious constraints. Among these cost was the greatest; every proposed improvement that involved a charge on the public purse (in most cases, until after 1948, on the local rates), was resisted by those upon whom the burden might fall.

Thus it was that, though the effort to improve the level of health was a sustained one in terms both of certain aspects of environment and of therapy, it was subject throughout the nineteenth century to two great limitations. The first of these was the fearful drag-chain of low incomes as affecting a significant proportion of the population. The second was the unwillingness of the better-off in Glasgow as elsewhere to accept additional tax burdens, fighting them off through local politics, using the argument that local taxes beyond a very modest level would damage the ability of the local economy to generate jobs and incomes.

Because health was so deeply involved with the general question of the distribution of incomes and wealth, to which the politics of the nineteenth century did not respond, and because of the inability of sections of the working classes to make the most of what they did receive, a large part of the health system was locked in a self-confirming syndrome, constituting a barrier against efforts to improve the health of society.

It is with attempts to operate on those aspects of the situation that did hold some prospect of success that we are concerned here. In particular it is the Glasgow response that provides the clinical case.

How did a fast-growing industrial urban community like Glasgow act against the health hazards it was itself creating? In general the challenge confronting nineteenth-century British cities was that of prevention: public health was largely a matter, on the one hand, of attempting to remove the causes of contagion, and on the other of improving the resistance of the population to it. The former of these two lines of endeavour, that of prevention by the attempted removal of causes arising from the urban environment, was by far the dominant one. It could be pursued by three means. The first of these was to acquire from parliament, powers of local intervention (in Scotland the Police Acts). These could then be used to enforce standards of cleanliness (watering, sweeping and cleansing of closes; emptying of middens; disinfecting of premises); they could also be employed in the attempt to limit overcrowding by enforcing standards of occupancy at the very bottom end of the income and housing scale. Secondly, the city could acquire power to borrow money to carry out public works associated with sewage and water supply, and then proceed to make the necessary provision. Thirdly, the city could appoint a Medical Officer of Health, and charge him with general surveillance.[5]

Public inspection and public works were thus the two great elements of a civic health policy. But their respective politics were very different.

Inspection involved the setting up of an organisation, and the embodying in it of powers of scrutiny and interference on an altogether new scale. Moreover, a strong class element was involved: members of the middle classes inspected and disciplined members of the working classes. Sometimes this was done without sufficient consideration of the implications, as when in Glasgow overcrowding was tackled through the ticketing system without the provision of somewhere else to go. But such action was often powered by a strong sense of dedication, driving middle class men and women into the slums in the hope of redeeming them, at least to some degree.

In terms of proportionalities, however, the number of working class families thus made subject to sanitary and overcrowding discipline was small. The staffs provided by the Corporation were tiny; for good or ill the working classes largely escaped this part of the preventive programme. The Sanitary Department of Glasgow had only ninety members in 1886, though there was a considerable acceleration as the city moved from some 750,000 population to over a million: by 1914 the sanitary staff was 401.[6] On the other hand the successive MOHs and their staffs, by inspection of facilities like abattoirs and milk supply, could do much to improve health without intruding into the family.

The politics of public works for health purposes scarcely involved the working classes at all. Water supply and sewage were, first of all, an engineering matter.[7] This was so especially in terms of the indivisibility involved in carrying water at great distances by pipe line and reservoirs. Secondly there was the question of raising and servicing the necessary capital: a proposition consistent with the responses of the money market, and with the revenues of the local authority, had to be designed.[8] Thus public works were, in large measure, an operation on the city from above, whereas public inspection brought a class interaction, though in a one-way direction only.

Both forms of health action required that leadership be present. The inspection system, leading to the appointment of the Medical Officer of Health, generated a cadre of men, many of them drawn from the medical profession, who soon sought to constitute themselves the guardians of the social interest in this respect, developing their own ideas as to what should be done, and fighting for them. In this they were often at odds with their employers, the magnates of the city council, who, of course, largely represented the ratepayer interest at least until the later nineteenth century. Moreover, Medical Officers of Health could disagree among themselves as to the correct line of policy. Public relations was thus a very important condition of success: advocacy could be as important as analysis. Public works, as in the case of the Loch Katrine Water Scheme for Glasgow (1859) and the Improvement Commissioners (after 1866) involved the high politics of the city, where powerful personalities could assert themselves and clash with one another, each with a supporting following.

For this reason an air of the fortuitous hangs over the way in which cities, including Glasgow, attacked their health problems. If the story is made to focus on the dominant personalities, there will be a tendency to imply that if such men had not been present, nothing would have happened. This is clearly not the case: the need for action was becoming cumulatively pressing, while at the same time many of the conditions for a successful response were being generated. On the other hand there is no reason gratuitously to assume that social problems have only to reach a certain threshold of seriousness for effective action to be taken. In any case, the condition of life of the generation living through any given phase is greatly affected by the matter of timing. The responses themselves can bear a widely ranging relationship to need: the system of inspection was never more than the merest palliative, one of its principal roles being to reassure the middle classes. The Loch Katrine water scheme and the sewerage system on the other hand, provided facilities that would serve excellently for generations ahead. The sewer system of what is now inner Glasgow consisted of some 6 miles in 1818, 40 in 1850 and 100 by 1890; thereafter, as the city expanded, the sewers did the same, though at a much faster rate, reaching 800 miles by 1948.[9] With them came a new problem, namely the health of the sewer men.

The great names in the Glasgow public health story in the nineteenth century were those of two holders of the office of MOH, Gairdner and Russell; among civic politicians the great exemplars were John Ure and Provost Blackie. Gairdner, though a notable man, was much less successful than Russell. There were a number of reasons for this, but many of them centred upon Gairdner's zeal and directness, which caused him to make enemies and frighten the politicians representing the ratepayers' interest.[10] The dilemma lay in the fact that whereas for action to be taken need had to be demonstrated, there was always the danger of overstating the case and provoking crippling opposition. Russell was much more successful in this regard, following a policy of what might be called optimal provocation. He was the most effective kind of propagandist, working patiently to generate the necessary favourable opinion over a wide range of the middle classes. Moreover, Russell had the advantage that by the time he was appointed in 1872 the city corporation had accepted the need for a full-time MOH.

This acceptance owed a good deal to the activities and advocacy of John Ure. He stands as the great exemplar of a civic politician who seized upon the challenge of health, and who made it a life mission to work for effective action against Glasgow's living conditions and death rate. But Ure, in spite of his dedication, had to work to a necessary sequence. The first step was to obtain the necessary Police Acts, which embodied a growing acceptance of the need for data and action based upon it, accompanied by the realisation that the city would not cleanse itself automatically, but had to be operated upon by public authority. Ure could thus follow a policy of incrementalism, and so fragment the challenge he was presenting to society, offering it bit by bit. With Provost Blackie the case was different. His Improvement Commission was intended to carry out a surgical operation on the slum housing in the centre of Glasgow. But whereas the Loch Katrine water scheme could succeed triumphantly as a great indivisibility, an attack on the housing problem on a comparable scale as proposed by Blackie caused him to be removed from the office of Lord Provost. And yet, because the need was so pressing, a modified scheme was carried through.

4. The challenge of prevention: diet, incomes and education

From the 1830s, if not earlier, certain Glasgow doctors had been concerned about the diet of the working classes. They were well aware of the fact that the capacity to resist illness and to recover from disability was very much a matter of nutrition. They had, too, general ideas concerning food intake, as was reflected in their prescriptions for their better-off clients. They knew, also, of course, that a lowering diet could be used to induce quiescence in those with mental disorders or in long-term prisoners.

This intuitive and observational knowledge caused a number of them to make the link between the level of working class incomes (which also affected their access to decent housing) and health. The individual doctor and his professional organisations were thus left with a three-part choice. They could retreat from the matter, leaving it as unresolvable in the prevailing state of the economy and society. Secondly they could adopt what could be a professionally dangerous stance of arguing for a political programme that would bring about a significant redistribution of incomes (together perhaps with educational or other provision that would lead to better spending patterns). Thirdly they could seek a programme of strategically selective dietary supports, such that no significant operation upon incomes would be necessary.

A few doctors were radical enough to make flat statements about the level of the lower working class incomes, and the life chances these determined. But by and large the Glasgow medical profession was not radicalised by what it saw in the slums, though many of its members did what they could personally, as well as being active in charity organisations. The third possibility, that of selective dietary reinforcement, did not present itself until there had been progress in physiology, dietary knowledge, pharmacy and the provision of food essences.

In physiology and dietary knowledge, which were the direct responsibility of the medical profession, there was little progress before 1900. When it did come Glasgow played an important part. In essence the attraction of dietary inquiry was scientific, but it inevitably acquired social and political overtones, especially in a context such as Glasgow, where diseases such as rickets were so obvious.

Noel Paton, professor of physiology in the University of Glasgow from 1906 to 1928, began to interest himself scientifically in the relationship between health and nutritional inputs.[11] Edward Provan Cathcart (who succeeded Paton in the chair, holding it from 1928 to 1947), pursued this line of inquiry. A pupil, Dr Dorothy Lindsay, adopted a pioneering social survey approach, as did A. M. T. Tulley and E. M. Urie.[12] They sought, by careful study of a range of statistically standardised families, using carefully designed dietary sheets, to ascertain the relationship between food consumed and physiological development. This work made much more precise the dependence of health standards on feeding habits. It also high-lighted social differences within the working classes: there was evidence that, of two mothers with the same income one could feed her family well, and the other not. This confirmed the view that there should be more teaching of domestic science in schools, so that girls could approach family budgeting and food preparation more effectively. Lord Boyd Orr, another Glasgow graduate, founder of the Food and Agriculture Organisation, carried the challenge of nutrition to an even wider stage.

The range of problems presented by the relationship between the many elements of food intake and general health was so complex that it proved difficult to establish firm ground on which to base a programme. Vitamin D was identified in 1918. This was of course beneficial, though the lesson had to be learned that Vitamin D used against rickets could be given in excess, resulting in the hypercalcemic brain-damaged child.[13]

Moreover, as inquiries extended, there arose the problem of specifiying diet over the whole range of food intake, so that, in terms of the quantity and balance of its components, it would be possible to define the cost in-volved to the family. When this was done, it would then become possible to set the prevailing income pattern against the dietary needs of the poorest part of the population. This meant, of course, difficulties of calculation on the food pattern side, the prices side as affecting food purchases, and on the income side.

Nevertheless the results, affecting a considerable proportion of Glas-gow's population, were such as to establish a serious dietary shortfall. Boyd Orr produced dramatic figures in the attempt to demonstrate this.[14] Indeed it is true to say that he was radicalised by his inquiries. But the notion of selective dietary reinforcement did not reach implementation until the Second World War, with the issue of free orange juice and cod liver oil.

It is not surprising that those concerned with health promotion through positive action in the nineteenth century were baffled by the challenge of prevention, especially in terms of diet, incomes and education. For in addi-tion to the resistances society might put in the way, there was the problem of the state of knowledge and theory as they related to health promotion, disease prevention and health education. The same situation obtains today. Among doctors, academics, administrators and politicians there continues to be great uncertainty about the conditions of health and of illness-related behaviour. The calling in of aid in recent years from the social sciences has not greatly altered this picture. Little of a systematic nature is known of the value systems and beliefs that lie behind attitudes and policies, either in respect to health in general or with regard to particular aspects of it. The few studies that have been carried out seem to show a wide range of attitudes, depending upon occupational groups, incomes, age, regional residence and other factors. The same is true about the choice of modes of intervention. How far are sources of health behaviour rooted in social and economic structure, and are therefore in large measure impervious to attempts to change them through education? There would seem to be a compelling case for study in social science terms of these matters: the historical context may help in the provision of clues.

5. The challenge of cure, 1830–1900: the physician, the surgeon and the psychologist

The therapy aspect, like that of prevention, has also had three great components, namely the medical profession and its evolving techniques, the initiatives of the philanthropists, and provision through the public sector. The latter came first in the form of the poor law since Stuart times, and finally in the form of the National Health Service after 1948. Glasgow was one of the principal scenes of the therapeutic endeavour, both nationally and on a world scale.

By the 1880s Lister's method of antiseptic surgery, developed in Glasgow Royal Infirmary, had been routinised in Glasgow's hospitals; the improved success rate greatly increased the number and range of operations.[15] The stiff battle against opposition by conservative colleagues in control of access to the wards had been won. On this Macewen built, carrying Glasgow Royal Infirmary and the world into the age of aseptic surgery, with its great symbol, the white coat. He further increased the range of operations by his pioneering efforts, extending the surgeon's ability to intervene in the human body to the treatment of new conditions. By 1900 a whole set of new surgical techniques had been opened up. Anaesthetics, though available from 1847, came into general use only when aseptic procedures had drastically lowered the dangers of infection. One further great nineteenth-century advance in surgical techniques was made. Scarcely had Röntgen announced his new marvel of X-rays in 1895, when the Glasgow men, with Kelvin at their head, took it up; in 1896 John Macintyre achieved at the Royal the 'first X-ray cinematograph ever taken'; a supply of radium for cancer treatment was obtained; by 1902 the Royal had its 'electrical pavilion', that was to be so useful in locating pieces of metal in soldiers' bodies after 1914. Thus could the surgeons make great advances. But before 1900 or 1914, their value lay in their potential for the future rather than in their application.

With the physicians there was no such dramatic achievement in treatment. The advances in physiological repair work by the surgeons, made possible by 1900, had no parallel on the side of medicine. The discovery of the aetiology of tuberculosis in 1882 produced no effective treatment until 1944. Nor did any of the other ancient curses of mankind yield to science. The age of the wonder drug had not begun; aspirin as its harbinger came into widespread use only with the new century.

It was similar with the treatment of lunacy.[16] Some of the Glasgow physician superintendents of asylums earnestly sought an improved theory of mental illness in their desire to use it as a basis for better treatment. But in the face of a general world failure to make progress with the theory of madness, they could do little else down to 1900 but follow tradition. This meant, with the milder cases, using 'milieu treatment', namely feeding, and providing productive work in the garden or workshop. The more seriously disturbed could be subjected to barbarous devices going back to the eighteenth century and earlier, with their combination of shock and debilitation.

So it was that the nineteenth century ended with the surgeons, physicians and psychiatrists still not yet ready to make their great attack on illness, injury and the death rate.

But there were important indirect effects, especially through the sanitation movement. The isolation of the TB bacillus, together with other developments in the field of bacterial studies, gave sanitation a further great impetus after 1899, carrying it into new fields of inspection having to do with food supply, especially milk and meat. The Medical Officers of Health thus found their sphere of operations greatly extended, from homes to shops and food handling premises.

6. Group achievement, motivation, career structure and status pattern

In assessing the functioning of the medical responses of a city and its region, two aspects seem to stand out. One is that of achievement, together with the cumulative ethos and the medical perspective thus generated; the other has to do with the more general pattern of motivation, training, career structure and status.

As to achievement, just as Glasgow's greatest days in the social sciences lay in the second half of the eighteenth century, with Francis Hutcheson, Adam Smith and John Miller, so her greatest days in medicine lay in the second half of the nineteenth century. It is true that the eighteenth century produced Cullen, Hunter and Black, but the nineteenth century, with Lister and Macewen and others, made a larger impact on the world. Both eighteenth- and nineteenth-century Glasgow medicos were in the tradition of the renaissance and the enlightenment; they were sets of men who were part of the relentless scientific investigation of nature upon which European man had embarked, and which by the last quarter of the nineteenth century was irresistible: its embodiment at this time in Glasgow was the splendid Kelvin, falling just short of the greatness of Newton.

Lister, Macewen, Macintyre and the physiologists with their concern for diet, did not, of course, exhaust the Glasgow medical achievement. There was a notable second echelon of men who led in their particular fields. Of these James Nicoll was an example. He used his great surgical skills and inventiveness in aid of children who had been victims of malnutrition and disease both before and after birth. Living in Glasgow he knew better than anyone the root causes of the damage to the bodies and minds of children by malnutrition, rickets, infestations, infections, particularly infections such as tuberculosis. Though he could do little by way of prevention, he devoted his life, especially in the years 1890 to 1921 to trying, by surgical means, to repair the damage. He was the first, for example, to perform the operation of pyloromyotomy for obstruction of the lower end of the stomach. Others, not medicos themselves, also made their contributions. Glasgow Royal Infirmary had owed its foundation in 1794 to the community feeling of George Jardine the University's Professor of Logic. Kelvin's predecessor in the chair of natural philosophy at Glasgow University, William Meikleham, made no great discoveries in natural science, but as a manager of Glasgow Royal Infirmary in the early 1800s he was the first to attempt to apply scientific principles to hospital management by trying to introduce a system of financial accounting.[17]

What was it that produced the local ambience necessary for such achievement? Is it possible to identify the conditions that had to be met, and to trace how they came about? Can such conditions be induced by policy, or are they wholly fortuitous? It would seem to be reasonable to suppose that, at least within a moderate time span, they are cumulative, with success generating confidence and inquiry, thus generating further success. Moreover, a rapidly growing city, like Glasgow, with more than its share of violence producing broken heads and bodies, and with more than the average level of dietary and sanitation problems, is presumably a favourable place for medical advance.

But the starting conditions for great and sustained achievement are very subtle; so too are those necessary for its continuance, in the face of the danger that success and prestige may generate complacency and deference to authoritative opinion. They include the presence of a range of ills of mortality and morbidity that are severe, not to say appalling. These must penetrate the consciousness of the medical profession, endowing it with a sense of urgency. This, moreover, must be accompanied by plenty of cases upon which to develop doctoral skills and insights. This would seem to suggest a minimal size of city for an effective medical community (in the sense of participating in forwarding the art and science of healing), and one with a considerable concentration on heavy industry, with a large component of unskilled labour and low incomes, with intensive slums, plenty of deformity and a high incidence of accidents and violence to provide casualties. Simultaneously any local group of medicos must be open to the influence of new ideas, either in the scientific mainstream, or generated among their own number.

Finally the structure of the profession must combine leadership and authority with opportunity and the encouragement of new men. The system of training, qualification, organisation, status and functioning of doctors and nurses in Glasgow evolved a pattern of power, politics and prestige that was of great importance for the working and evolution of the system.[18]

The new surgical skills greatly altered the level and distribution of medical prestige in Glasgow. They did so by causing a concentration of function:

the surgeons became specialists operating and teaching in the environment of a hospital, thus drawing away from their former peers, the general practitioners.[19] Indeed Mr Gladstone delivering his rectorial address to the University of Glasgow in 1879 warmly congratulated the surgical fraternity on their recent progress in operations, and on their consequential advance in social standing, gaining 'equality with the other cultivated or leisured classes'.[20] This was so even though their equipment was simple: apart from the operating table their gear, well into the inter-war years, could be locked away when not in use in small cupboards set in the walls: physics, chemistry and electricity had not yet generated sophisticated medical machinery.[21]

In all of this the infirmaries were the fundamental basis of hospital provision in Glasgow as in Scotland generally. They were the foundation of the Scottish medical schools, and the principal setting in which Scottish doctors made their contribution to medical knowledge. They had immense achievements to their credit. But there was an obverse side to this. So powerful did the infirmaries become in Glasgow that they were, throughout Victorian times, openly and persistently hostile to rival, innovative institutions, as in the case of the specialist hospitals. They embodied a powerful centralising influence arising from their own convenience and values, a tendency which was under more or less continuous challenge from those whose thinking started from the needs of patients.

The monolithic dominance of the Glasgow Royal Infirmary had become very strong in 1870. The existence in the city and its region of a single powerful professional guild in the form of the Faculty of Physicians and Surgeons enabled the medical establishment in the city to make the Royal an extension of itself, and to safeguard its position of dominance. A doctor who was or had been president of the Faculty and a physician in the Infirmary was in a most powerful position. The Glasgow professors in the University, on the other hand, had no access as of right to hospital beds for clinical teaching.

The contrast with Edinburgh in this regard is instructive. Glasgow had the advantage of being cheaper (with lower fees), but Edinburgh was in many ways more progressive. The University there was not only in command of the degree structure, but its professors had control of the wards of the Infirmary. This was the case because in Edinburgh, because there were two medical professional bodies (The Royal College of Physicians and the Royal College of Surgeons), the medical men of the town could not present a single front to those of the gown, thus allowing the University, in effect to preside over the city's medicine. Glasgow's academics were, by contrast, inhibited in their access to wards, a factor contributing to Lister's return to Edinburgh.

The Glasgow situation was radically altered by the founding of the Western Infirmary, opened in 1874. Glasgow was growing rapidly, so that for it to be necessary for all patients and doctors to converge on the Royal became increasingly unreasonable. The new Infirmary was set up in Glasgow's West end, next to the University, near which new concentrations of workers were building up.

Irrespective of location, however, there was by this time a real need for a second such institution. The Royal had become very large, and somewhat set in its ways. It was chronically in arrears of Glasgow's needs. It had a virtual monopoly of clinical medical teaching. The only way in which to get a really major new injection of resources into the infirmary system was to make an appeal on behalf of a new institution. The Royal had continued for two generations to rely on subscriptions, together with workers' contributions, without any major attempt to raise capital funds. There had been an extension of the surgical wing in the 1860s and a nurses' home was built in the 1880s, but these were fairly modest additions. A detonating circumstance was needed to create a new situation.

This was supplied by the movement of the University in 1870 from its foundation site in the heart of the old town and near the Royal Infirmary to its new location at Gilmorehill in the West End. The Royal was asked to build and run the new Infirmary; it declined the first suggestion, but said it was willing to operate the hospital when built. But the result of setting up a new University fund-raising and planning committee was to create a separate initiative that acquired its own momentum. The final break came over the insistence by the Royal that it have a veto on appointments to both infirmaries, a suggestion unacceptable to the University. The degree students at the Royal moved in a body to the Western Infirmary in 1874, largely depriving the Royal of its teaching function. Its response was to reorganise its own medical school, setting up St Mungo's College where students were prepared for the triple qualification of the Faculty in Glasgow and the two Colleges in Edinburgh. But St Mungo's, with no connection with the University, did not prosper.

Medicine in Glasgow was, therefore, split at its core for thirty-six years. This came about not by reason of circumstances directly affecting the Royal Infirmary, which continued on its traditional site (by now the centre of working class concentration), but because the University, fearful for the moral welfare of its students, was extruded by the terrible deterioration of the old core of Glasgow. The University had, quite naturally, headed up west, taking the medical initiative with it. The Glasgow system had thus decentralised almost by accident. At the same time the academic component was much strengthened.

No supervisory state authority regulated what was happening, attempted to produce an integrated system, or even to repair the damage. In Edinburgh no such separation took place: although the Royal Infirmary itself removed to a new site it continued to be the great focus of the city's medical service and the sole seat of its medical school, with the University professors in a powerful position. Edinburgh was not growing so rapidly as Glasgow, and its University made no move from its old site.

The general centralisation of medical facilities under the Scottish infirmary system had of course a profound effect upon the power structure of the profession. Those who became potent in the infirmaries, with their personal wards and their influence with the boards of management, stood at the centre of the system: they enjoyed emoluments, prestige and the control of staff and resources. The circumstances that their patients were working class people, and that the careers of other doctors and of students were largely in their hands, could only confirm their self-esteem. To them the poor law doctors felt distinctly inferior. The medical officers of health were perhaps the only doctors of independent status, with their own source of authority, men like, in Edinburgh Henry Littlejohn (first MOH in Scotland, appointed 1862), and, in Glasgow Gairdner, Russell and Chalmers.

The career of William Macewen perhaps throws some light on the problems of entry and promotion. He was a boy from Bute, with no status within the Glasgow medical establishment, having no connection with the locally dominant families of the profession like the Cowans and Rainys. He thus stood little chance of a surgery appointment at the Royal, then at the peak of its prestige. Instead he served in humbler roles, first as Assistant Surgeon at the Town's Hospital, later as resident doctor at Belvidere Hospital and then as a Casualty Surgeon for the Central Police Division of Glasgow. His chance came when the Royal was stripped of the University professors and students by the migration of the University to Gilmorehill. The Royal in its extremity, in 1874, appointed him to its junior staff. Macewen was undoubtedly one of the great men of his age, but it seems likely that his early rise to a position of power within a hierarchical profession owed something at least to the newly fluid Glasgow situation of the 1870s.

As to the doctors, in general, it can be argued that every British city with half a million to a million population has had its own medical tradition in terms of its philosophy of medicine, its structure and its interplay of personalities.

7. The medicos and the *demos*

While the medical profession was thus achieving great things on the surgical side, and simultaneously was evolving a career structure and status pattern, the working classes (the principal element in the population, and those principally in need of care), were also altering their attitudes and responses.

Down until the 1880s they seem to have been largely passive acceptors of what was offered to them in terms of health provision. Indeed so fatalistic did they seem to Gairdner that he was provoked to strong utterance. Speaking of Glasgow he said, 'the facts we come across daily show the deplorable apathy that exists concerning the perishing offspring of the poor. Almost every medical man knows of cases in which parents of a family of 10, 12 or 14 children have lost all but one or two and yet have actually come to think that it is the ordinary course of God's providence, or at all events that, it was an almost inevitable misfortune.'[22] Gairdner did not enter into the sources of this fatalism (to which a Calvinistic Church may have contributed), or into its social role as a means of inducing acceptance and passivity, or into its function of reconciling mothers to heavy loss of infant life without inducing in them a devaluation of life itself. But he pointed out how such an attitude was self-confirming, being itself a large part of the cause of the tragedy of infant mortality. He called upon the middle classes to respond to the need to attack this passivity, as part of an attack on the problem of infant mortality. Such an attitude, he urged, 'must quicken all our feelings as to the best way in which a new and better state of mind may be brought about'. Thus Gairdner repudiated any notion of social Darwinism, with its implication that a selective process working through high infant mortality was a good thing for the race; instead he emphasised the elements of suffering and waste.

From the 1880s there are signs of an ending of working-class docility in the matter of medicine, as in other respects. The working classes gained greatly in both political and industrial power, and in articulateness, through the extension of the parliamentary and local franchises, and through the growth of trade unions and the removal of constraints on their actions. Through the new school boards (in Scotland after 1872), and as poor law guardians, the working-class presence on policy-making bodies grew. But their influence remained indirect, for though they were gaining status in these important directions, they continued to have few rights as hospital patients, being still largely treated as objects by busy surgeons and physicians.

Meanwhile there were notable improvements in what could be provided, embodied in both a surgical and a nursing revolution. Though there was less progress in medicine, the adoption of the Compulsory Vaccination Act (Scotland) of 1863 marked a new beginning in the treatment of the masses, with Glasgow opening its vaccination station in 1864. These gains meant that whereas the shortfall in medical services provoked little response among the working classes when such services had relatively little efficacy, the surgical and nursing revolutions 'created' a shortfall of facilities of which the working classes would eventually become conscious.

From the 1880s, therefore, the attractions to the working classes of health provision notably increased. The old function of the philanthropists as providing the basis of finance (and to some degree of management), continued to be important, and was not overthrown until 1948.[23] But thereafter the establishment of a generalised state system was, of course, the consummation of the trend toward popular political power, to which the medical profession has had to learn to accommodate itself.

The consequent enormous flow of public funds into health care from the later 1940s, and the subsequent attempt to curtail it from the later 1970s, has made necessary a search for objective criteria by means of which to establish the health share of GNP, and to allocate it between claimants. Procedures of resource allocation have thus been sought, in the hope that scientific criteria would take the matter of health provision out of politics. But the search for objective principles has caused the debate to push through to much greater depths, namely those where philosophic values and religion rule. So we learn that the allocation of resources as between competing human needs is ultimately not reducible to science (though science can indeed be a partial guide by defining the implications of the choices to be made).

The responses of the *demos* to the provision of health care has received relatively little attention. It would make an intriguing chapter of social history, to be put alongside the popular responses to factory conditions, the poor law, and indeed all aspects of the evolution of working class consciousness.

8. Judging a nation's health performance

Historians of medicine may perhaps be charged with overmuch concern with the development of medical theories and practices, leaving two areas largely undiscussed.[24] These are the general relations between medicine and the mass of the people as the principal source of ill-health, and, as a facet of this, the differential performance as between cities in their attack on the problem of health as reflected in their respective degrees of success through the voluntarist period of the nineteenth century and the state provision era from the mid-twentieth.

Judging the national performance in an aggregative way is difficult enough. There must be measurement of the degree of success that has accompanied medical effort. This has involved attempts to measure the trend of improvement in mortality and in morbidity. There can be no doubt that in both cases since the 1830s the trend has been downward: a national death rate in the range of 30–35 per 1000 in the 1830s has fallen to 13 per 1000 in the 1970s. An impressive list of diseases has shown striking decline (though others have asserted themselves).

Five principal explanations are on offer for these downward trends. There is the view that they have owed much to the provision of medical services, both those of the surgeon and the physician, made available in a wide range of hospitals and other institutions. Secondly it is argued that mortality and morbidity have declined as a consequence of society learning to dispose of its excreta, effluvia and wastes, so that the self-generated toxicity of the cities that came with industrialisation has been largely purged. Thirdly, there is the argument that the improvement in life expectancy and health during it have been due mainly to better nutrition, which in turn has been the consequence of rising family incomes and of governmental actions in stabilising or lowering the cost of food. Fourthly, and also related to incomes, there was the question of housing: how far was the health problem due to overcrowding, and hence subject to improvement in consequence of pulling down of slums and a generally better supply? Fifthly there is the argument that some diseases, at least, live their own autonomous lives, erupting into human societies according to laws operative in their own universe; that is to say they are, in effect, exogenous forces.

All of the first four causes seem to have been at work in Britain; the fifth is in the present state of knowledge too elusive to comment upon, though it has its advocates. The interesting questions are, of course, in what proportions did these influences work and in what patterns of interaction over time? These are also the questions that lie behind the problem of policy: if resources for health promotion are to be most effectively used, it is necessary, in given situations, to attempt to assign degrees of efficacity to contending programmes.

In all of this, social and political value judgments inevitably intrude. Those who are hostile to medical professionalism, charging its practitioners with exclusiveness, authoritarianism and manipulation, with intruding into physical and mental processes with insufficient knowledge of what they are doing, and with inducing dependency and loss of character among their patients, discount the medical contribution. Among them is a strong naturist and mild anarchistic tendency: those with such perspectives see health as a self-adjusting system, which has been to some degree at least perverted by the professionals. Those who regard diseases, or certain of them as exogenous to society, tend to share the non-interventionist view. Antithetical to this set of attitudes is that which says that, while the perfect society is delayed in its arrival, it is right to try to operate at once on immediate suffering, and to be grateful to the medical profession for so doing.

Those who see the greatest potential for social improvement as lying through political action are likely to espouse the environmental, income and housing theses of health improvement: good communal health is seen as a beneficent by-product of sound social organisation. The anti-medical and the pro-environment and income attitudes can, of course, come together in the same pattern of advocacy. Both regard health, like happiness, as something which if pursued directly by treating individuals, will prove elusive, its professionalism being self-defeating; health, indeed is seen as a residual— get the doctors out of the way and pursue correct social policies and good health will appear spontaneously.

Because of the necessity to penetrate beyond generalised value judgments of this kind, it is important to continue the effort to establish the true nature of the phenomena involved. This is not only an historical question of great fascination, but one of practical and political significance. For example, there is little point in a huge expansion of ante-natal and child clinics if malnutrition or tobacco or alcohol abuse among mothers is the problem. Health budgets have proved to be one of the greatest charges on the welfare state: far from diminishing with preventive medicine bringing improved health, as Aneurin Bevan had hoped, they have become an almost open-ended commitment.

Among those who have attempted the historical view from 1830 in British terms there has been a tendency, stated perhaps most strongly by Professor Thomas McKeown,[25] to discount the contribution of the medical profession, arguing that it was insufficient in its impact (except in the case of smallpox) to account until recently for more than a slight proportion of the general improvement. The approach in terms of diseases as being exogenous to man and his societies has been argued mainly in terms of particular diseases; certainly it would seem highly improbable that diseases in general should go into a concerted phase of decline over the period.

Having disposed of the medical profession and the autonomous theory of diseases, we are left with environment and standards of living. At this point the argument becomes very difficult. As to environment, in the phase 1830–1900 in Britain there was both improvement and deterioration: water supply and sanitation were improved, together with a certain amount of slum clearance, but the cities grew continuously, incarcerating at their cores populations subject to very bad conditions including increasing atmospheric pollution. As for incomes, while there was a tendency for them to rise among the better-off artisans, standards of living among the less skilled, the unskilled and the unemployed showed little improvement, and in some phases and places indeed they deteriorated.

If we take the British story up to about 1830, in the phase when the forces of industrialisation had far outrun those of amelioration, producing terrible mortality and morbidity, with the medical profession in a primitive state, with little scientific dietary knowledge, and with incomes and housing left to market forces, it would seem that the first really effective line of action lay through an operation on the environment through water supply and sewerage. This had the additional advantage of minimising direct governmental interference in the economy and society. Even here, however, controversy over the sources of illness could impede effective action. Moreover, it was necessary to learn to think in terms of age-specific death rates (made possible by vital registration from 1855), especially as affecting infant mortality, before the attack on this enormous wastage could begin. (A country industrialising now will know this lesson from the outset.) As to the greatest of lessons, that having to do with malnutrition, incomes and housing, perceptive doctors, though they had arrived at this conviction by the 1830s, found it hopeless to argue that the nation should undertake a major redistribution of incomes: indeed some doctors may have felt that the side effects of such a radical economic policy might have proved as bad as the disease.

With the passage of time, in the British case, the pattern of relationship between these many circumstances affecting health changed. That is why a phasing approach to the problem, as discussed at the beginning of this essay, is necessary.

But how far does such a phasing represent a universal experience and necessity? Or do we need a health theory for each form and stage of society? For example, in a less developed country, where advanced medicine can be implanted from outside, is the pattern of mortality and morbidity greatly changed thereby? Clearly medicine, whatever its net efficacity, cannot operate in a vacuum—no amount of medical facilities would make Calcutta a healthy place. On the other hand medicine represents immediate provision of a kind that can be made (through foreign aid) long before effective action on environment and incomes: it attracts humanitarian support and it can be provided with minimal political involvement. But its effects can only in the aggregate be superficial if it operates alone. Environmental action, though not entirely neutral from a political point of view, is much less radical in its implications for society than action upon incomes; moreover, it is likely to produce quicker results. Incomes lead to the heart of the society and polity and hence are most contentious and intransigent. Hence, on this reasoning, the pattern of pursuit of health in a less developed country is likely to follow that of Britain, namely environmental action first, to be followed by incomes policy. And yet, with the democratic, participatory philosophy available from the outset of change in less developed countries, rather than following from industrialisation, as in the British case, pressures for an operation on incomes may come first.

9. Health in the city

Retreating now from grand comparisons between countries, the question arises, how valid is it to approach health history on a national basis, using aggregates and averages?

This has been the obvious way to begin, both for the historian and the health policy maker in the Ministry of Health. For the historian an aggregative, averaging attack on the problem came first, because this was the direction in which demography, in its primitive state, led. After all, it seemed sensible to see how national birth and death rates performed, in order to be able to say something about society as a whole, and perhaps to compare it with other societies. Similarly for the health administrator, national averaging had its charms, for it meant that the really bad aspects, with their possible political repercussions, disappeared from view. But there were those from at least the 1930s who, as Charles Webster has pointed out,[26] challenged the use of national averages, charging, as did Major Greenwood, that they were 'an arithmetical veil', obscuring the real phenomena.[27] For example, Scotland was more than ten years behind England and Wales in its control of infant mortality. Not only were there large variations between regions, the same was true within them. This was not merely a geographical phenomenon, it was a class one as well, for the correlation of the worst geographical results with social classes IV and V was striking.

Disaggregation on a regional and class basis had, of course, long been practiced by Medical Officers of Health and others within particular cities. This was done, partly at least, in order to see what pattern of causation as affecting health really operated, as a preliminary to the setting out of a more effective pattern of policy.

Can the exercise of disaggregation usefully take the form of an approach through the city? This could be done in two ways.

A single city might be taken, and the trend of its mortality and morbidity traced, so that the city's performance is seen in terms of its own past. If there is improvement (as was in general the case from the 1830s or 1860s), the causal questions can then be put. Ideally, at this point the attempt should be made, at the level of the city, to consider the resources devoted to medical provision, to water supply and sanitation, and to dietary and other social provision, the pattern of their timing, and their respective contributions to improvement: this would give guidance on the cost-effectiveness of the three lines of attack. This, as we have seen, is very difficult to do. But perhaps clues might be found by studying the phenomena at this level.

The second approach, to set alongside that of the single city, over time, is to take another city of a like kind, or indeed a 'family' of such cities, making a comparison of performances, as indeed some MOHs did. This, of course, would require careful inquiry into the comparability of the general urban situations. The governing criteria for such a 'standardisation' would probably be population size and product mix, with the accompanying employment composition and incomes pattern. If two or more cities thus approached produced the same general health performance over time, then it would seem reasonable to conclude that urban health is determined by causes operating universally in the economy and society, and does not derive from the distinctive characteristics of different cities. Such an outcome would also seem to suggest that the three sets of causal factors operate in more or less the same proportions as between cities, with roughly the same timing. If, of course, the performance between similarly situated cities is significantly different as to mortality and morbidity, then the notion of universality of health phenomena must be modified.

The pursuit of the problems of health performance in the context of a single city and in comparative terms would add much to the understanding of that city, as well as bringing health and life expectancy to the fore in the writing of urban biography. For the city is the place of the masses, where their lives are lengthened or shortened, where they are made more or less efficient as producers, and where they find varying degrees of fulfilment.

Notes

Chapter One *Local government and the health environment*

1 These included University professors, Dr Robert Graham, Botany, 1818, Dr Robert Cowan, Medical Jurisprudence, 1837 and 1840; various Commissioners, J. C. Symons, Handloom Weavers, 1838, Dr Neil Arnott and Mr Chadwick, 1842; magistrates, Henry Paul 1839; the Chief Constable, Captain Miller, 1840; District Surgeons, 1843 and Dr Sutherland of the General Board of Health, 1849.

2 Russell, J. B., *The evolution of the function of Public Health Administration* (Glasgow, 1895), p. 21, report of Dr Sutherland, 'General Board of Health'.

3 Duncan, Eben., MD, Lecturer on Forensic Medicine and Public Health, Western Medical School, Glasgow. 'Sanitary Legislation and the duties of the medical profession in relation to public health', *GMJ*, n.s. **17**, (1882).

4 William IV, c.11 (1832).

5 Longmate, N., *King Cholera* (1966).

6 *Glasgow Past and Present* (Glasgow, 1884), vol. 1, ch. 1, pp. 1-240.

7 Russell, J. B. (1895), 24.

8 See 'The Sanitary Aspect of the Sewage Question', Dr Fergus, *GMJ*, **1** (1868), 115-20. 'Sanitary hints for domestic drainage', Dr Fergus, *GMJ*, **7** (1875), 552-61. 'Sewage gases and typhoid fever', *GMJ*, **16** (1882), 296. J. B. Russell, 'Sewage question in Glasgow', *BMJ* (25 August 1888), 404-6.

9 See 'The main drainage of Glasgow' and other articles, various authors, *Minutes of Proceedings of the Institution of Civil Engineers,* vol. clxxxix, (1912), pp. 167-291.

10 Special Committee, Minutes (26 January 1860) SRA, under chairmanship of John Ure made fifteen recommendations all designed to improve sanitary conditions. These included recommendations regarding the size of houses and arrangements of streets, 'ample ash pit and water closet or privy accommodation', 'a sufficient apparatus for water supply', the appointment of a competent medical officer, regulating the maximum number of inmates, 'to prevent the occupation of sunk floors and garrets', whitewashing of houses, both inside and outside, to prevent drainage from chemical works, distilleries and gas works, from entering sewers or drains, smoke abatement, acquisition by the city of ownership of 'soil and ashes' and that the city 'shall be required to remove the same', baths and wash-houses to be built, a sanitary committee to be set up.

11 Russell, J. B. (1895), 35.

12 Originally in 1864 Gairdner intended to use the 960 enumeration districts (as the Registrar General had done in the 1861 census) but in 1865 he adopted a 54 district scheme. This was scrapped in 1869. In 1871 the 24 district scheme was adopted and remained until 1903 when the enlargement of the city's boundaries caused a further re-drawing of the sanitary districts.

13 See Gairdner, W. T., *Sanitary Visitation Movement* (Glasgow, 1867).

14 Glasgow Corporation Health Committee Minutes, SRA, 25 November 1872.

15 For further details of the Gairdner affair see Glasgow Corporation Health Committee Minutes and Police Board Minutes, SRA, as well as *BMJ* (20 Apr. 1872-21 Sept. 1872).

16 In 1895 when Sir W. T. Gairdner, by then a distinguished professor of medicine of world-wide renown, was invited to write a preface to *Public Health Administration in Glasgow,* (Glasgow, 1895), he referred to Russell as having 'clearness of insight, steadiness of aim, and the conciliatory temper which alone could achieve success in such an enterprise'. Preface V.

17 For a list of Russell's lectures and writings which were published see Bibliography.

18 Russell was persuaded in 1898 to go as medical member of the Local Government Board in Edinburgh but his great contribution to the health environment was in Glasgow and it was at the Necropolis by Glasgow Cathedral that he was buried when he died in 1904.

19 Mackenzie, P., WRHB, *Regional Review* (Winter 1970-1), 24-6.

20 Russell, J. B., (1905), 84.

21 Russell, J. B., (1905), 66.

22 Mackenzie, P., WRHB, *Regional Review* (Winter 1970-1), 24-6.

23 *RC on the Poor Laws and relief of distress. Report on Scotland.* Cd. 4922 (1909), 282.
24 Harris, José. *William Beveridge: a biography* (Oxford 1977), 413.

Chapter Two   *The medical profession*

1 The Faculty of Physicians and Surgeons of Glasgow, founded under Charter of James VI in 1599 regulated medical practice in the city and over a wide area of western Scotland: Dumbarton and the counties of Ayr, Lanark and Renfrew. Apart from being the obvious, recognised authority on medical matters, the Faculty, along with the Church and the Faculty of Procurators was represented in more general matters connected with community life (e.g., on the board of Directors of Stirling's Library).The author wishes to thank the RCPSG for allowing access to its records.
2 Anon, 'The Social position of the Profession', *GMJ*, **9**, (1861-2), 444.
3 The designation 'Town Licentiate' denoted academic equivalence with 'Member' of the Faculty, but involved a smaller financial burden (20 guineas) and Licentiates were barred from participation in Faculty rights and privileges.
4 Charles Badham, a London physician, held the Chair of Medicine at Glasgow University from 1827-41 but did not become a Member of Faculty: he was an exception.
5 In Britain, the Medical licensing bodies stipulated that the teachers of their examinees should be either university graduates in Medicine or Fellows or Members of a Medical Corporation. There were, apart from the FPSG, the Royal Colleges of Physicians and of Surgeons, Edinburgh (RCPEd and RCSEd), the Royal College of Physicians of London (RCPL), the Royal College of Surgeons of London (in 1843, of England: RCSL or RCSE), the London Society of Apothecaries (LSA).
6. Membership was expensive (it could amount to over £100, in the 1840s), mainly because of an insurance scheme (the Widow's Fund) which was financed, on a sliding scale of annual contributions and benefits, by the entrants to the Faculty. At mid-century the scheme was re-organised, entrance fees were cut to £50 and the Members were redesignated 'Fellows'. Licentiates (the term 'Town' was abolished in 1832) remained as the 'lower grade'.
7 The ballot box and the stipulation that Fellows should not engage in trade in 1855.
8 Anderson, J. W. (Glasgow, 1916), p. 14.
9 Minutes, 7 October 1872, FPSG. He was in a better financial position in 1876, and then became FFPSG.
10 *See GMJ*, **3** (1834), 117-19, 153, 187.
11 Christison, R. (Edinburgh, 1885), 361.
12 It is interesting to note that a number of well-established non-graduate doctors took the MD at this period.

e.g. Rainy	1834	MFPSG 1815	J. Burns	1828	MFPSG 1796
J. Armour	1827	MFPSG 1816	W. Mackenzie	1833	MFPSG 1819
C. Ritchie	1839	MFPSG 1827			

13 The idea of a hospital on the south side of the Clyde was floated at a meeting of the Glasgow Southern Medical Society as early as 1866, but it was not seriously considered until 1878, following a paper read to the Society in 1878 by Dr Ebenezer Watson. He chaired a Committee which organised the building and opening of the Victoria Infirmary in 1890.
14 Dr Elizabeth Pace was appointed to the Infirmary's Bellahouston Dispensary as specialist in the Diseases of Women. See also Chapter Nine.
15 See Chapter Five and AR, GRI (1875).
16 Mr Cuthbertson, the Trades House representative on the GRI Board of Directors, was involved in canvassing support for a lying-in hospital. Faculty reaction was distinctly cool. Minutes FPSG 4 Nov. 1805.
17 See Checkland, E.O.A. (1980), ch. 10.
18 Two previous 'Superintendents', non-graduates and not physicians left the GAL to set up their own private establishments for the reception of paying lunatic patients—providing 'depositories' for the unfortunates of wealthy families. See also Chapter Four.
19 Lectures in Mental Disorders were given at the GRI School by 1881: a lectureship in the subject was instituted at Glasgow University in 1880.

20 Two Assistant Medical Officers in the service were J. B. Russell and William Macewen (see below and Chapters One and Five).

21 The buildings at Parliamentary Road were used for short periods as an 'overflow' for the GRI, GWI and the Maternity Hospital between 1878 and 1881. Chalmers, A. K. (1930), 155.

22 The openings for women did not occur until later in the twentieth century.

23 Checkland, E. O. A. (1980), ch. 11.

24 This dispensary is recorded as being run by James Watt, MFPS. Denholm, James (1804), 384.

25 CUS, University of Glasgow (London, 1837). Professor Towers (11 October 1827), 200.

26 The title 'Glasgow University Lying-in Hospital and Dispensary' continued to be used. Pagan was succeeded in 1868 by William Leishman.

27 Two in Gorbals, one in Anderston and one in Gordon Street.

28 The Anderson's Institution of 1796 became Anderson's University in 1828 and Anderson's College in 1877.

In 1886, a reorganisation of that College and the College of Science and Arts resulted in the emergence of the Glasgow and West of Scotland Technical College and Anderson's College Medical School; the latter acquired new buildings at Gilmorehill adjacent to Glasgow University.

See also n. 32.

29 GMJ **26** (1886), 395.

30 A Chair of Medicine founded in 1637 had lapsed in 1646. Although it was revived in 1712 and a Chair of Anatomy and Botany founded under Crown patronage in 1818, the positions were regarded as sinecures.

31 Muir on Midwifery in 1759; Morris on Medicine, Irvine on Botany in the 1760s.

32 John Anderson, Professor of Natural Philosophy in Glasgow University; under his will of 1796, Anderson's University was to be set up as a rival to Glasgow University, but finance was available for the establishment of only one of the proposed medical Chairs, that of Surgery.

33 By 1830, there were also professors of Botany, Anatomy, Midwifery, Medicine, Materia Medica, Chemistry.

34 These were, in Glasgow: 1807—Natural History (later Zoology), 1815—Surgery, 1815—Midwifery (there was a Waltonian Lectureship in Midwifery 1790-1815), 1817—Chemistry (Lectureship from 1747), 1818—Botany (separated from the conjoint foundation with Anatomy of 1718. Previous lectureship 1704-18).

35 Anderson's University provided medical teaching but no medical qualification: students took the Licence of one of the Medical Corporations (often that of the FPSG).

36 The foundation of University College in London in 1828 to offset the religious discrimination of the Universities of Oxford and Cambridge quickly led to the establishment of a Medical School and University College Hospital; similar developments occurred with the establishment of King's College (1829). After 1836, the new University of London was organising a degree qualification in medicine: this was in addition to the revitalisation of medical teaching in the long-established charitable hospitals in London (St Bartholomew's, St Thomas's, etc.).

37 John Burns, the first Professor at Anderson's Institution, became first Professor of Surgery at Glasgow University in 1815. Among later transfers were James Lawrie (Surgery) in 1850, Andrew Buchanan (Materia Medica to Institutes of Medicine) in 1839, John Easton (Materia Medica) in 1855, G. H. B. Macleod (Surgery) in 1869.

38 Mackie, J. D. (1954), 265.

39 CUS 1876, vol. 3 (Returns), 166. An interesting point is made by the Commissioners: 'Where the chair is not of a character to enable the holder to supplement his income by practice outside the University, we think that . . . the emoluments of a Professor should not be under £600 a year' (CUS 1876, vol. 1 (Report), 97).

40 Comrie, J. D. (1932), 661.

41 As far as can be judged, this did not ever fall below 50 per cent; more reliably, during the second half of the nineteenth century it was normally over 70 per cent.

42 One of the rarities, Lister, came from the south, via Edinburgh.

43 From the sixteenth century the Town Council had appointed a 'Surgeon to the poor' and, at times, a 'stone-cutter' (who removed bladder calculi).

44 One of the District Surgeons was often simultaneously Surgeon to the Town's Hospital. The number of districts increased as follows:

1816—4   1818—6   1831—12   1842—16 + 1 'extra'.

45 Examples were: J. Dick, MFPS, 1804; M. Davidson, LRCSEd 1816, MD 1825, MFPS 1828. In 1827 two of the District Surgeons were: John MacFarlane, MFPS 1819, later Professor of Medicine, Glasgow University (1852); Andrew Buchanan, MD 1824, MFPS 1824, later Professor of the Institute of Medicine, Glasgow University (1839). In 1840 two well-known names occur: J. A. Fleming, MD 1830, MFPS 1833, Surgeon to GRI 1846 and to GAL; John Easton, MD 1828, MFPS, later Professor of Materia Medica, Glasgow University (1855).

46 'The Town's Hospital of Glasgow' Regulations 1831, and 'Report to the Quarterly Meeting of Directors (of the Weekly Committee of Directors of the Town's Hospital), 15 May 1832'.

47 Minutes, 6 June 1850, City Parish Medical and Sanitary Committee SRA DHEW 1/5, vol. 1.

48 For example:

J. Lothian—LRCSEd 1849. MD (Aberdeen) 1858). In 1871 was a Parochial Medical Officer, City parish: by 1881 he had moved westward from the city end of Sauchiehall Street to Newton Terrace and was Surgeon at the GRI Dispensary and at the Public Dispensary.

W. Reid—MB, CM 1866, MD 1869. In 1871 was a PMO, Barony parish, and by 1881 had moved from Dumbarton Road to Royal Crescent, had become FFPSG in 1877, had been outdoor accoucheur to the GMH and was, at that time, Outdoor Physician for Diseases of Women at the GWI.

49 Poor Law Medical Officers' Association, 1868.

50 James Barras, LFPS 1860, MD (St Andrews) 1862. Lived in Govan and was, in 1881, PMO, Police Surgeon and Medical Officer of Health for the area. His first salaried appointment was as PMO by 1871.

D. Dewar, MB, CM, 1886, was PMO City Parish in 1891. By 1901 he had moved from Stirling Road to West Princes Street and, in addition to his parochial duties, he was Assistant Surgeon at the GRI.

G. Halket, MB, CM, 1873. Was PMO Barony Parish in 1881. By 1891, he had taken the MD degree (1882) and become FFPSG in 1884 and was still PMO and also Physician at the Samaritan Hospital. He had moved from Anderston to Royal Crescent.

51 Examples of salaries for public medical appointments.

MOH Glasgow	1872—£600 per annum ⎫ full-time 1901—£700 per annum ⎭
MOH Govanhill	1880—£12 per annum part-time
MOH Govan	1901—£100 per annum part-time
Prison MO	1816—£20 per annum part-time
Police Surgeon	pre 1865—£20-£50 per annum—part-time later £30-£100 per annum—part-time In 1871 Dr McGill serving as Surgeon to the largest police district (Central) and as Surgeon to the Police Force, was paid £400 per annum (part-time).
Casualty Surgeon	1871—£60 per annum, part-time.

52 He does not appear in the Glasgow Post Office Directory 1851, or the Scottish Medical Directory 1852.

53 Charitable institutions combining medicine and religion took the form of medical missions; but in Glasgow the number of doctors involved was small—perhaps eight at any given period, after the foundation of the Glasgow Medical Missionary Society in 1868. See Checkland, EOA (1980), 82-4.

54 For example:

1871—J. G. Wilson, Professor of Midwifery, (Andersonian) was medical officer to the Caledonian Insurance Co. and the Scottish Provident Institution. Professor W. T. Gairdner was MO to the Scottish Fire & Life Insurance Co. Professor G. H. B. MacLeod was MO to the Reliance Mutual Life Assurance Society, London.

1891—Professor I. McCall Anderson was MO to the Scottish Imperial Insurance Co.

55 Some Trade groups in Glasgow: Master Bakers' Association, Boilermakers' Association, Scottish Clerks' Association.

56 Barras, J., 'Medical aspects of Friendly Societies', *GMJ*, 5 (1872-3), 283.

57 1881—James Dunlop, MD, FFPS, Surgeon to GRI and Surgeon to Lock Hospital.

58 George Buchanan, MD, FFPS, Surgeon to GWI and Consultant Surgeon to Eye Infirmary and GMH.

59 1881—J. Wallace Anderson, MD, FFPS, Assistant Physician GRI Dispensary and Assistant Physician/Accoucheur, GMH.

60 Discussion on Medical Aid Associations, *BMJ*, (1894), 831.

61 The FPSG became 'Royal' in 1909.

Chapter Three *Poor Law hospitals 1845—1914*

1 The system was slightly altered by the Local Government Act of 1894 which replaced the Board of Supervision with the Scottish Local Government Board and local parochial boards with parish councils. These administrative changes made little difference.

2 An Act for the Better Administration of the Laws Relating to the Relief of the Poor in Scotland, 4 Aug. 1845. 8 and 9 Vict. c. lxxxiii.

3 Springburn, Maryhill and Hillhead became part of Glasgow in 1891.

4 Parochial Board income: an assessment (poor rate) was imposed in all the Glasgow parishes from which they derived well over 80 per cent of their income. Parishes could also get some income from loans raised on the security of their annual assessment, money from the government annual medical grant, from voluntary contributions, from church collections, and from mortifications, usually pre-1845.

5 Board of Supervision circulars on less eligibility: especially 'Circular as to Poorhouses, 2nd February 1850'. In *Appendix* of *5th Annual Report of the Board of Supervision*.

6 See Chapter Five and Lister, J., 'On the Effects of the Antiseptic System of Treatment on the Salubriety of a Surgical Hospital', *Lancet,* I (1870); Bastion, H. C., 'The Bearing of Experimental Evidence upon the Germ Theory of Disease', *GMJ* (12 Jan. 1878), 49; and Messenger Bradley S., 'Antiseptic Surgery', *GMJ* (23 Feb. 1878), 256.

7 Minutes of the City Parish Medical Committee, 8 Apr. 1879.

8 Medical Officer's Half-yearly Report, in Minutes of Barony Parish House Committee, 25 July 1884.

9 Report of Malcolm McNeil, Visiting Officer, of visit made on 14 August 1880. In Minutes of City Parish House Committee, 24 Sept. 1880.

10 Report of Malcolm McNeil, Visiting Officer, in Minutes of Barony Parish House Committee, 1 May 1884.

11 Medical Officer's Report, in Minutes of Barony Parish House Committee, 14 Apr. 1886.

12 Minutes of City Parochial Board, 24 Oct. 1882.

13 Minutes of Barony Parish House Committee, 12 Mar. 1883.

14 Report on the Sanitary Conditions of the Glasgow Poorhouse, by Dr Littlejohn. The visit was made on Saturday, 16 Dec. 1882. In Minutes of City Parochial Board, 6 Feb. 1883.

15 Medical Officer's Report, in Minutes of Barony Parish House Committee, 25 July 1884.

16 Medical Officer's letter, in Minutes of Barony Parish House Committee, 14 Mar. 1886.

17 Voluntary hospital building and extension in nineteenth-century Glasgow:

1816 Royal Infirmary extension (hospital originally opened in 1794). The new wing added 72 beds to the original 136.

1824 The Eye Infirmary was established. No inpatients at first.

1832 The Royal Infirmary's new fever block added an extra 220 beds.

1834 The Maternity Hospital was opened.

1835 The Eye Infirmary moved to College Street.

1852 The Eye Infirmary moved to Charlotte Street with around 20 beds by mid-1860s.

1861 The Royal Infirmary's surgical wing was completed, adding 144 beds.
1868 The Ophthalmic Institution was established in a house in Bath Street.
1869 The Ophthalmic Institution moved to West Regent Street. It now had 12 beds.
1872 The Ophthalmic Insitution moved to 126 West Regent Street. It now had 20 beds.
1874 The Eye Infirmary opened a branch at Berkeley Street and transferred its resident cases
     there. 40 beds.
1875 The Western Infirmary opened. When building was completed in 1883, the infirmary had
     346 beds.
1876 The Eye Infirmary now had 60 beds.
1880 The Ear Hospital opened in Buchanan Street with 15 beds.
1881 The Maternity Hospital moved to new buildings in Rottenrow.
1883 The Sick Children's Hospital was established at 45 Scott Street. It had around 70 beds.
1884 The Ear Hospital moved to Elmbank Street.
1885 The Eye Infirmary at Berkeley Street was extended, giving 104 beds in all.
1886 The Samaritan Hospital for Women opened at South Cumberland Street with 3 beds.
1887 The Sick Children's Hospital acquired the adjacent house, giving a new ward of 12 beds,
     an operating theatre and more domestic accommodation.
1890 The Cancer Hospital opened at 163 Hill Street, with 20 beds.
     The Samaritan Hospital moved to Kingston House, which gave room for 20 patients.
     The Victoria Infirmary opened. Built on a pavilion plan. The central block was
     completed first, the others were finished during the next 8 years. The infirmary opened
     with 84 beds, by 1893 it had 160, and by 1906 it had 260 beds.
1896 The Cancer Hospital moved to larger premises at 132 Hill Street. It could now accommo-
     date 30 inpatients.
     The new Samaritan Hospital building was opened at Coplaw Street with space for 28
     inpatients.
1912 Complete reconstruction of the Royal Infirmary was finished. The new buildings on the
     site of the old hospital now gave 48 wards with around 790 beds in all.
     18 Reasons for merger: see especially 'Special Meeting to consider the Amalgamation with
City Parish' in Minutes of Barony Parish Council, 9 February 1897.
     19 See pp. 55 and 56 on types of patients treated in parish hospitals.
     20 There were some exceptions to this trend. For instance, the development of a system of
trained nursing in Barony Parish hospital was almost entirely due to the energy and persistence
of its Medical Officer, William Core (see Chapter Nine).
     21 Minutes of Barony Parish House Committee, 20 Dec. 1893.
     22 Minutes of City Parish Medical Committee, 20 Aug. 1880.
     23 Board of Supervision Circular as to the Unemployed. In *34th Annual Report of the Board
of Supervision*.
     24 City Parish Medical and Sanitary Committee Minutes, 6 March 1876 insists that 'the
practice of this Board, if it has erred at all, has erred on the side of liberality in the interpretation of the law'.
     25 Minutes of City Parish Relief Committee, 18 Aug. 1896.
     26 Letter from Local Government Board, dated 27 Aug. 1896, in Minutes of City Parish
Council, 1 Sept. 1896.
     27 Minority Report on Scotland, **260**, *RC on Poor Laws Report on Scotland,* Cd **4922** (1909).

Chapter Four   *Care and treatment of the mentally ill*

1 The Glasgow Asylum for Lunatics (abbreviation throughout GAL) opened in 1814. In
1825 it received a Royal Charter and became Glasgow Royal Asylum for Lunatics. In 1931 it
was renamed Glasgow Royal Mental Hospital, early in the 1960s it was renamed Gartnavel
Royal Hospital.
     2 Alexander, F. and Selesrick, S. T. (1967).
     3 Rosen, G. (1968).
     4 Szasz, T. (1971).

5 Quoted in Parry-Jones, W. (1972).

6 Parry-Jones (1972), 11.

7 Foucault, M. (1967).

8 Scull, A. T. (1979), 21, 46, 84.

9 Akerknecht, E. (1959), 38.

10 GH, 19 December 1914.

11 It is difficult to be certain about the extent of private service in Glasgow at this time, but looking ahead, RCLAS, 1857, cited four private madhouses as then existing in the city environs at Rutherglen, Garngad, Springbank, and Bothwell.

12 Gourlay, J., *A Glasgow Miscellany, The Tobacco Period, in Glasgow* 1707-1775, n.d., 2. Robert McNair belonged to an old Glasgow family which had prospered in sugar, but he was to preside over the family's greatest success and failure. He became a burgess and guild brother in 1790 and in 1791 purchased extensive lands in the east of the city. But he lost his fortune in 1812, and he returned to Leith where he was appointed customs inspector in 1812.

13 *Report of the General Committee appointed to carry into effect the proposal for a Lunatic Asylum at Glasgow* (1814, 15). The disparate financial resources can be illustrated from this source. For example, the synod of Glasgow and Ayr appointed a collection in all its parishes, the Marquess of Douglas and Earl of Breadalbane gave a total of £80 between them, colonial gentlemen in Demarara gave £250 and a circus troupe gave £19 9s. 5d.

14 *GH,* 19 Dec. 1914.

15 At Montrose, Dundee, Aberdeen, Edinburgh, Perth and Dumfries: the only Royal Asylum to receive public funds was that at Edinburgh.

16 In 1855, for example, this stood at 8s. 6d. p.a. for Glasgow City Paupers and those of 'contributing' parishes, 9s. for those of 'non-contributing' parishes, and 9s., 15s., £1 1s. 0d., £1 11s. 6d., £2 5s. 0d., £3 3s. 0d., £4 4s. 0d. and £6 6s. 0d. for private patients.

17 The old building was sold to the directors of the Town's Hospital for a sum of £17,732 10s. 0d.

18 *Report of the Royal Commission appointed to enquire into the state of lunatic asylums in Scotland and the existing law in reference to lunatics and lunatic asylums in Scotland* (Edinburgh, 1857).

19 AR GAL, no. **30**, 1844, 44-5.

20 ibid. 44-5.

21 RCLAS, 1857, Appendix 82.

22 RCLAS, 82.

23 RCLAS, 79-80.

24 AR, GAL, no **26** (1840), 10-12.

25 AR, GAL, no **3** (1817), 4.

26 AR, GAL, no **25** (1838), 9.

27 RCLAS, 1857 Appendix, 40.

28 AR, GAL, no **26** (1840), 9.

29 AR, Edinburgh Royal Asylum, no. **4** (1844).

30 AR, GAL, no **47** (1860), 23.

31 Fish, F., 'David Skae,' *MH* (1965), 38.

32 Fish, F., 'David Skae,' *MH* (1965), 38.

33 AR, GAL, nos **16-56,** (1830-70) appendices.

34 See p. 68 above.

35 GAL, Patient case notes (H.B. 13/5/11, 1838), 63.

36 GAL, Patient case notes (H.B. 13/5/12, 1839), 45.

37 GAL, Patient case notes (H.B. 13/5/14, 1841), 21.

38 AR, GAL, no **20** (1833), 5.

39 GAL, Patient case notes (H.B. 13/5/10, 1831), 11.

40 ibid. 11.

41 ibid. 30.

42 ibid. 29.

43 GAL, Patient case notes (H.B. 13/4/10, 1831), 44.

44 ibid. (HB 13/5/90, 1864), 204.

45 ibid. (HB 13/5/90, 1864), 208.

46 ibid. 232.

47 ibid. (HB 13/5/12), 27.
48 ibid. (HB 13/5/43), 47.
49 AR, GAL, no **48** (1861), 28-9.
50 ibid. 28-9.
51 GAL, Patient case notes, op. cit. (HB 13/5/11), 63.
52 ibid. (HB 13/5/15), 28.
53 ibid. (HB 13/5/43, 1847), 56.
54 GAL, Patient case notes (HB 13/5/11), 60.
55 GAL, Patient case notes (HB 13/5/15, 1846), 41.
56 ibid. (HB 13/5/11, 1838), 25.
57 GAL, Patient case notes (HB 13/5/12, 1839), 45.
58 ibid. 65.
59 ibid. (HB 13/5/13, 1840), 63.
60 ibid. (HB 13/5/14, 1841), 21.
61 Fish, F. (1965), 40.
62 Skultans, V. (1979), 137.
63 AR, GAL, no **28** (1841), 41-3.
64 GAL, Patient case notes, op. cit. (HB 13/5/10, 1830-6), 19.
65 ibid. 22.
66 ibid. 29.
67 ibid. (HB 13/5/11, 1830-8), 25.
68 ibid. (HB 13/5/52, 1852-4), 36.
69 ibid. (HB 13/5/51, 1851-2), 12.
70 GAL, Patient case notes (HB 13/5/51, 1851-2), 17.
71 ibid. (HB 13/5/52, 1852-4), 195.
72 ibid. (HB 13/5/10, 1830-6), 30.
73 ibid. (HB 13/5/10), 44.
74 ibid. (HB 13/5/13, 1840), 35.
75 ibid. (HB 13/5/36, 1851-2), 19.
76 ibid. 140.
77 ibid. (HB 13/5/55), 364.
78 GAL, Patient case notes (HB 13/5/11), 21.
79 GAL, Patient case notes (HB 13/5/43, 1846-8), 56.
80 ibid. (HB 13/5/43, 1846-8), 67.
81 RCLAS, 1857, 84.
82 AR, GAL, no **28** (1841), 39-40.
83 AR, GAL, no **28** (1841), 39-40.
84 GAL, Patient case notes (HB 13/5/55), 38.
85 ibid. (HB 13/5/43), 64.
86 ibid. 67.

Chapter Five   *Surgeons and surgery*

1 Unless otherwise stated, the information in the text comes from the Annual Reports of the Glasgow Royal Infirmary. Each year the *GMJ* often added a short commentary after publication of each report.

2 For early descriptions of heroic surgery in the home or lodging houses see *GMJ* **1**, 4 and **2**, 76. Lister, later took private patients into his own home for surgery.

3 In 1831 there were 12 surgeons to the Royal Infirmary, 6 'District Surgeons' attending the official poor (paupers), and they and up to 200 other qualified men may have done surgical work in Glasgow. Fees charged varied with social class—see *Prices fixed by the Physicians and Surgeons of Glasgow for Medicines and Attendance* (Glasgow, 1799).

4 Details of a controversial consultation are given in Pattison, F.M.L., 'The Pattison-Miller Quarrel', *SMJ*, **25** (1980), 234-40.

5 The decline and disappearance of the 'pure' physician is described in *GMJ* (1832), **5**, 403 and in Buchanan, M.S. (1832), 24.

6 James Watson was surgeon to the Infirmary from 1813-14, and physician during 1838-41. A. D. Anderson had similar appointments starting in 1823.

7 Flinn, M. W. (1977), 27.

8 Checkland, O. (1980), 162.

9 The arrival of ether anaesthesia in Glasgow is described in Richardson, B. W., *Vita Medica* (London, 1897), 83. The failure of the introduction of anaesthesia to affect surgical practice is noted by Greene, N. M. (1979), 'Anaesthesia and the development of surgery (1846-1896)', *Anaesthesia and Analgesia,* **58,** 5-12.

10 Carbolic acid had been used in Carlisle as a disinfectant to reduce the smell from the sewers.

11 Lister does appear to have used undiluted carbolic acid on his earliest cases but later modified this to a mixture of carbolic acid, linseed oil and chalk.

12 Buchanan, G., 'Report on Surgical cases at the GRI', *GMJ,* **10** (1862), 300.

13 Lister, J., 'On a new method of treating compound fractures, abscesses etc. with observations on the Conditions of Suppuration', *Lancet,* **1,** (1867), 2.

14 The Infirmary surgeons responsible for reported cases were: George Buchanan (also Professor of Anatomy, Anderson's University); Ebenezer Watson (also Professor of Institutes of Medicine, Anderson's University); Donald Dewar; G. H. B. Macleod (also Professor of Surgery, Anderson's University); Alex. Patterson (Dispensary Surgeon).

15 Watson, Ebenezer, Cases of Amputation of the Foot, *GMJ* (1868), 113.

16 Buchanan, G., Clinical Surgical Report, *GMJ,* **3** (1870), 191.

17 Watson, E., Clinical Surgical Report, *GMJ,* **3** (1870), 309

18 Buchanan, G., Clinical Surgical Report, GRI, *GMJ,* **3** (1870), 4

19 Buchanan, G., Compound Fractures treated in GRI, *GMJ,* **3** (1870), 524

20 Dewar, D., Cases of Compound Fracture treated antiseptically, *GMJ,* **5** (1872), 125.

21 MacLeod, G. H. B., Clinical Surgical Report, *GMJ,* **5** (1872), 338.

22 Morton, J., Clinical Surgical Report for year ending 31 October 1872, *GMJ,* 5, (1872), 211.

23 Some of them were already using carbolic acid in private surgical practice and midwifery in 1868.

24 Sir William Macewen (1848-1924) MB, CM, (1869, Glasgow University), was Medical Superintendent, Fever Hospital, Belvidere 1870-1, then District Medical Officer and Surgeon to Central Police Division 1871-4; appointed Surgeon in Charge of Wards, Glasgow Royal Infirmary 1876 and Regius Professor of Surgery in 1892, working at the Western Infirmary. For Macewen's approach to asepsis, see A. K. Bowman, *The Life and Teaching of Sir William Macewen* (Glasgow, 1942), 33. Macewen's contributions are analysed in Bowman, James, C. D. T. 'Sir William Macewen', *Proceedings of the Royal Society of Medicine,* **67,** 1974, 237-42 and 'Great Teachers of the Past' *British Journal of Surgery,* **54,** 1-7. His contributions to neurosurgery are analysed in B. Jennett 'Sir William Macewen 1848-1924', *Surgical Neurology,* **6,** (1976), 57-60.

25 Clark, H. E., 'On the changes in surgical theory and practice in the past twenty-five years', *GMJ,* vol. **5** (1899), 306, 321. An amusing account of the rising popularity of appendicectomy is given by Clark.

26 The dramatic accounts of the start of the antiseptic era given by earlier biographers are repeated without modification in Fisher, R. B. *Joseph Lister 1827-1912* (London, 1977). So unchanging are these accounts that the unhealthiness of Lister's wards is still blamed on a pre-Listerian 'miasma' from the graves beneath; graveyards are not health hazards.

27 A colleague of Lister pointed to the spontaneous improvement in the results at the time Morton J., 'Carbolic Acid', *Lancet,* **1** (1870), 155-7.

28 Lister's results with carbolic acid are summarised in Fisher and the effect on amputations is given in Lister, J., 'The effects of the antiseptic system . . .', *Lancet,* **1** (1870), 4-6 and 40-1.

29 The good results at Kilmarnock, which also improved with time and without antisepsis are described in McVail, J. C., 'Dr John Borland', *GMJ,* **99** (1923), 1-22. See also the discussion on antisepsis in *GMJ,* 1880, **14,** 65-71.

30 This view of the improving results of surgery is similar to the re-appraisal of the role of medical care in the decline in tuberculosis—(Chapter Six), and Pennington, C. I., 'Mortality and medical care in nineteenth-century Glasgow', *MH,* **23,**442-50.

Chapter Six   *Tuberculosis*

1 McKeown, T., and Brown, R. G. 'Medical evidence related to English population change in the eighteenth century', *Population Studies,* 9 (1955). For an alternative view see Sigsworth, E. M. 'Gateways to death? Medicine, hospitals and mortality, 1700-1850', in *Science and Society, 1600-1900,* ed. by P. Mathias (Cambridge, 1970), 97; Woodward, J., *To Do The Sick No Harm,* (London, 1974); and Cherry, S. 'The role of a provincial hospital: the Norfolk and Norwich Hospital, 1771-1880', *Population Studies,* (1972), 26.

2 McKeown, T. and Record, R. G., 'Reasons for the decline of mortality in England and Wales during the nineteenth century', *Population Studies,* 16 (1962).

3 Pennington, C. I., 'Mortality and medical care in nineteenth-century Glasgow', *MH,* 23 (Oct., 1979), 442-50.

4 Gairdner, W. T. *AR of the Health of the City,* (Glasgow, 1871), 5-6.

5 Russell, J. B. *Lectures on the Theory and General Prevention and Control of Infectious Diseases* (Glasgow, 1879), 37.

6 Gairdner was using cod liver oil as his treatment of choice in the 1860s. Gairdner, W. T., *Clinical Medicine* (Edinburgh, 1862), 6.

7 Soon after the infectious nature of pulmonary TB had been established a bizarre antiseptic treatment was tried, see Coates, J., and Gairdner, W. T., *Lecturers to Practitioners* (London, 1886), 210.

8 Philip, R., 'Present-day outlook on tuberculosis', *EMJ* 20, (1918), 289.

9 ibid.

10 In March, April and May 1889, including one by Professor E. Klein, 'On tuberculosis with regard to diseased meat and infectious disease', reprinted in SJ xiii (1889), 130.

11 *SJ,* xiii, (1889), 244.

12 Russell, J. B., *Public Health Administration in Glasgow* (Glasgow, 1905), 603-8.

13 *Topley and Wilson's Principles of Bacteriology, Virology and Immunity,* ed. by G. S. Wilson and A. Miles, (London, 1975), 1725.

14 Russell, J. B., *On the Prevention of Tuberculosis* (Glasgow, 1895), 59-61.

15 It is unclear why his report took so long to complete.

16 For a modern view of the mode of spread of pulmonary TB and a résumé of the work of Cornet, Flügge and others see Topley and Wilson, 1745-6.

17 Russell (1896), 40.

18 ibid. 25

19 By Flügge in 1899 and others.

20 Minutes of the Corporation of Glasgow, 20 Apr. 1909, 1377-8. SRA CI/3/41.

21 Russell (1896), 49.

22 ibid. 50.

23 One such scientific meeting of the Association was held in Edinburgh in 1910. From 1899 the Association published the journal *Tuberculosis,* see Anon., *National Association for the Prevention of Consumption, a Historical Sketch.* (1926).

24 *GH,* 23 Mar. 1901.

25 There were also some other sanatorium beds available for patients from Glasgow. There were beds for women at the Bridge of Weir Consumptive Homes and for advanced cases at Lanfine Home for Incurables. Both these institutions were supported by voluntary contributions.

26 Latham, A., (1907), 80 ff.

27 *GH,* 24 January 1905.

28 Minutes of the Parish of Glasgow, SRA D HEW 1 2 (15), 388.

29 Minute Book of House Committee, City Parish, SRA D HEW 1 3 (3), 34-6.

30 SRA D HEW 1 3 (7), 10.

31 SRA D HEW 1 3 (11), 424. There were no regular mortality returns published by poorhouses.

32 Pennington, C. I., 'Mortality, public health and medical improvements in Glasgow, 1855-1911', unpublished Ph.D. Thesis (1977), University of Stirling.

33 SRA D HEW 1 3 (12), 37-8.

34 SRA D HEW 1 3 (12), 78.

35 Reports to the LGB for Scotland (1911), *On the Administrative Control of Pulmonary Phthisis in Glasgow,* 37.

36 SRA D HEW 1 2 (16), 257. By 1911, Stobhill had 240 beds for pulmonary TB (including 60 in chalet shelters). The wards were always full and cases had to be treated elsewhere. Some 62 beds in the Eastern and Western District hospitals were set aside for phthisis and Govan had 147 beds at Merryflats. Rep. to LGB (1911), 168-9.

37 SRA D HEW 1 2 (16), 257. The Report gives the following figures of admissions of phthisis pulmonalis cases to institutions of Glasgow Parish Council 16 May 1904-15 May 1910: Stobhill hospital—3320; Barnhill poorhouse—3073; Eastern District hospital—534; Western District hospital—584. These figures include a certain number of transfers between hospitals.

38 National Association for the Prevention of Consumption and other forms of Tuberculosis (1911), *Transactions of Edinburgh Meeting and Conference on Tuberculosis* (July 1910), 99.

Table illustrating exclusion of phthisis from Glasgow general hospitals:

Period	Medical Admissions	Of which phthisis	Phthisis as % of medical admissions
1880-4	12 339	1848	15.0
1890-4	9 683	1115	11.5
1900-4	11 764	396	3.4
1907	2 556	74	2.7

39 Rep. to LGB (1911), 163-8.

40 ibid. 173.

41 Report of the Medical Officer of Health of the City of Glasgow (1905).

42 Nat. Assocn. Prev. Consump. (1911), 97-8. Whether the consumptive families studied had always lived in such economic circumstances is a debatable point.

43 ibid. 102

44 Mackenzie, W. L. 'The administrative aspects of tuberculosis' in *Studies in Pathology,* ed. by W. Bulloch (Aberdeen, 1906), 83-4.

45 5th AR L.G.B. 1899-1900 (Cd. 182) xli. 1.

46 8th AR L.G.B. 1902-1903 (Cd. 1521) xxvi. 1.

47 Nat. Assocn. Prev. Consump. (1911), 64.

48 MacKenzie, W. L., 1906, 91.

49 Minutes of the Corporation of Glasgow, (25 Feb. 1903), 530-1. Since 1900 a limited scheme of notification had been in operation whereby the voluntary hospitals, dispensaries, and the Poor Law authorities notified the medical officer of health of new cases of consumption so that the homes of fatal or advanced cases could be disinfected.

50 Report of the Medical Officer of Health of the City of Glasgow (1903), 80.

51 Minutes of the Corporation of Glasgow (1904).

52 ibid. (Apr. 1906).

53 Steps were also being taken to limit spitting in public places.

54 Minutes of the Corporation of Glasgow (1 Aug. 1906), 2718-9. SRA C1/3/35.

55 Nat. Assocn. Prev. Consump. (1911), 66-7. Existing legislation would have restricted notified cases from using public transport and so on.

56 Minutes of the Corporation of Glasgow (16 Mar. 1909), 1697. SRA C1/3/40.

57 Nat. Assocn. Prev. Consump. (1911), 157.

Chapter Seven   Medical radiology: its practical application 1895–1914

1 Kaye, G. W. C. (1914), 217-18.

2 Anon., 'The latest items about the new photography', *Photographic Review,* **1** (1896), 145-8.

3 Anon., 'Röntgen Rays', *British Journal of Photography,* **43** (1896), 179.

4 Anon., 'A Röntgen Ray Yarn', *Photographic Review,* 1 (1896), 301.

5 Anon., 'X-rays as a depilatory' *Lancet,* 1 (1896), 1296.

6 Sarton, G., 'The discovery of X-rays', *ISIS,* 26 (1937), 349-69.

7 Kelvin, Lord, Presidential Address, *Proceedings Royal Society,* 54 (1893), 376-89.

8 Röntgen, W. C., 'Ueber eine neue art von Strahlen', *Erste Mitt Sitzgsber Physik-Med Ges,* 137 (Wurzburg, 1895), 132-41.

9 Bottomley, J. T., Blythswood, Lord and Macintyre, J., 'On the Röntgen X-Rays or the new photography', *Proceedings Philosophical Society of Glasgow,* 27 (1896), 156-64.

10 Macintyre, J., *Practical Photography,* 7 (1896), 68-72.

11 Röntgen, W. C., 'On a new kind of rays', *Nature,* 53, 274-7.

12 Swinton, A. A. C., 'Professor Röntgen's discovery', *Nature,* 53, 277-9.

13 Anon., 'Professor Franz Exner's Work', *Photographic Review,* 1, 83-4, 100.

14 Macintyre, J., 'Application of Röntgen Rays to the soft tissues of the body', *Nature,* 54, 451-4.

15 Gray, A., 'Lord Blythswood FRS', *Nature,* 78, 301-2.

16 Blythswood, Lord and Scoble, W. A., 'Recent work on x-ray measurement', *PSG,* 38, 186-7.

17 Bell, J. and Paton, J. (1896), 273.

18 Macintyre, *GMJ,* 23 (1885), 17-24.

19 Macintyre, J. and Adams, J., *BMJ* (1896), 750.

20 Macintyre, J., *Lancet,* 1, 1876-7.

21 Macintyre, J., *GHR,* 1, 290-321.

22 Anon., 'The new method in hospital practice', *GMJ,* 1, 1412.

23 Macintyre, J., *Lancet,* 1 (1896), 1455.

24 Macintyre, J., *Lancet,* 2 (1896), 118.

25 Macintyre, J., *Archives of Skiagraphy,* 1 (1897), 37.

26 Ardian, G. M., *British Journal of Radiology,* 46 (1973), 885-8.

27 Macintyre, J., *GMJ,* 58 (1902), 161-70.

28 Macintyre, J., *Archives of the Röntgen Ray,* 7 (1902), 101-2.

29 Macintyre, J., *Lancet,* 2 (1896), 979-80.

30 Macintyre, J., *GMJ,* 82 (1914), 263-76.

31 Mackintosh, D. J. *Skiagraphic atlas of fractures and dislocations* (London 1899).

32 Ramsay, A. M., *GHR,* 3 (1900), 387-96.

33 Macintyre, J., *Archives of the Röntgen Ray,* 19 (1914), 255-8.

34 Macintyre, J., *GMJ,* 81 (1914), 321-32.

35 Macintyre, J., *GMJ,* 87 (1917), 257-82.

Chapter Eight *Maternal and Child Welfare*

1 MacLeary, G. (1905), 2.

2 McLeary, G. (1905), 12.

3 Mackenzie, W. L., *Scottish Mothers and children: being a report on the physical welfare of mothers and children.* Carnegie UK Trust, (Dunfermline, 1917), 17.

4 J. W. Ballantyne, 'The care of the expectant mother and her (unborn) infant: a problem in present-day public health', *in* Mackenzie, W. L. (1917), 28.

5 Russell, J. B. (1876).

6 Russell, J. B. (1876), 11.

7 MacLeary, G. (1905), 57.

8 MacLeary, G. (1905), 58.

9 The initial cost of the machinery and appliances in six of the British infants milk depots is set out as follows:

Battersea	£150
Dundee	200
Glasgow	650
Leith	150

Liverpool   £640
St Helens   235
McLeary, G. F., *Infantile Mortality and Infants' Milk Depots* (London, 1905), Appendix 129.
10 Mackenzie (1917), 190.
11 Mackenzie (1917), 28.
12 Reid, W. L., *GMJ* (1881), 438.
13 Croom, H., *EMJ* (1881), **xxvi**, part 2, 712ff.
14 Glasgow MOH AR (1907), 14.
15 Macgregor, A. (1967), 106.
16 MacLeary (1905), table opp. p. 22.
17 Macgregor (1967), 106.
18 Chalmers, A. K. (1930), 205.
19 Chalmers, A. K. (1930), 203.
20 MacLeary (1905), 27.
21 Chapin, H. D., 'Breast-feeding and the infants development', *Archives of Paediatrics* (New York, Aug. 1904).
22 MacLeary (1905), 44.
23 Mackenzie, W. L., 'The hygienics of milk', *EMJ* (1898).
24 Macgregor, A. (1967), 119.

Chapter Nine   *Women as doctors and nurses*

1 Hudson, K. *The place of Women in Society* (London, 1970), 46.
2 In her old age, Elizabeth Blackwell spent holidays on the Clyde. This connection with the west of Scotland resulted in Glasgow University's possession of her Diploma of Qualification from Geneva College, Upper New York State. GUA, Inventory number 36406.
3 Both these avenues of entry to the medical profession were deliberately closed to women once one member of the sex had slipped through.
4 C. R. Mackintosh designed Queen Margaret Medical College in 1894 see Howarth, T., *Charles Rennie Mackintosh and the modern movement,* (London, 1952), 64. The building is now incorporated into the BBC in Queen Margaret Drive.
5 Minutes of the Glasgow Southern Medical Society (4 Oct. 1877).
6 Records (Minutes) of the GRI (24 Mar. 1891), GHB 1/1/18.
7 The Universities Acts of 1889 cleared the way for the entry of women as full-time students, and by February 1892, the Scottish University Courts were empowered to make provision for the instruction of women. After lengthy discussions, the Council of Queen Margaret College agreed to make over its entire property to Glasgow University, and provide separate University education for women. From the session 1892-3, Queen Margaret students therefore were matriculated students of the University, though their classes were held in the College buildings. They could also be awarded degrees on completion of courses. The first female to graduate in medicine from GU was Marion Gilchrist in 1894.
8 In 1943, Dr Mary Moore was appointed extra Dispensary Physician for Diseases of the Skin (temporary).
9 Of these, 3 had the Triple Qualification (Licence of the RCPEd, RCSEd, and FPSG), 3 had a degree from GU, 2 had degrees from London University.
It is interesting to note that Jane Henderson took the Triple Qualification in 1890, and was therefore the longest-qualified woman practising in Glasgow at that time. Moreover, she had studied in London (at the Medical School for Women there) and in Paris, but she came to Scotland for a qualification. Subsequently she acquired a Certificate in Medical Psychology, and in 1891 took an MD in Brussels. She was serving in the Wynd Mission Dispensary in 1901.
10 Mrs Rona Mackie, MD, FRCP, was appointed to the Chair of Dermatology in 1978.
11 Florence Nightingale, letter to Sir Thomas Watson, Bart., London, dated 19 Jan. 1867. See Abel-Smith, B. (1960), 4.
12 Most charity hospitals disapproved of 'abusers' of their charity and tried through their system of requiring subscribers' recommendation lines, to exclude those who could pay. The

following examples indicate that boards of management, encouraged the pursuit of abusers of charity:

9 Oct. 1896. The Superintendent reported that a lady had been sent into the Infirmary for an injury to her head and had been an inpatient for 10 days. As her husband was in a position to pay for her treatment, he had rendered him an account for 3 guineas which he declined to pay. The Superintendent was instructed to write to him again and point out that the Infirmary was a charitable institution and only for those unable to provide for medical treatment. Failing a satisfactory reply, the Secretary was instructed to see him personally.

10 May 1897. The Superintendent reported on two cases which had been admitted to the Infirmary on subscribers' lines, whose parents, he thought, were quite able to pay for medical advice. It was remitted to the Convener and Sub-convener to see the subscriber who granted the lines.

Minutes of the GVI, HB 23/1/5.

13 For example, during the cholera scare of 1866, the Glasgow MOH, Dr W. T. Gairdner, appealed to the church congregations of the city to provide the names of women who would be willing to act as auxiliary nurses if the epidemic reached Glasgow. He received no names whatever, the danger of such work presumably deterring even the most Christian women.

14 City of Glasgow Fever Hospital, AR (25 Apr. 1865—30 Apr. 1866), 13-16. GGHB 23/1/2.

15 ibid. 18.

16 GH, 2 Jan. 1891.

17 The wage scales at the GRI in 1880 were as follows:
£12 p.a. for a probationer while in training;
£20 p.a. for a qualified nurse, rising in annual increments of £2 to a maximum of £30 p.a.
See GRI, 86th AR (1880).

18 Board of Supervision Rules and Regulations in Copy Minute dated 26 Mar. 1885. See Minutes of Barony Parochial Board House Committee, 1 May 1885, SRA D HEW 2/1.

19 Such advice was given in Sept. 1866 by Dr McGregor, in Nov. 1874 by Dr Strethill Wright and in Mar. 1878 by Dr Core.

20 Visit made on 5 Aug. 1885, report included in Minutes of Barony Parochial Board House Committee (30 Oct. 1885), SRA D HEW 2/1.

21 Some of the groups who applied to have their nurses trained at Barnhill were the Sunderland Nursing Institute (1890), the Nurses' Training Institute, Derby (1890), the Jubilee Institute (1891), the Burton-on-Trent Nursing Association (1894) and the Glasgow Sick Poor and Private Nursing Association (1894).

22 In the ten years following the first female medical graduate from GU, some 85 women successfully completed courses in medicine: not all of them stayed to work in Glasgow.

23 Male influence was dominant on Glasgow's hospital boards until almost the end of the century. Women were not involved in local government and therefore not in the management of local authority hospitals. In 1899, the GWI subscribers elected women directors and in the same year, the GRI Board of Management decided to allow women directors (though the first two appeared later, in 1905). Amongst Glasgow's Poor Law boards, Barony Parish elected the first women members—two in 1895—but there is no sign that they took an active part in running the Parish hospital.

Chapter Ten   *The National Health Service 1948–80*

Further Reading

Crawford, M. D. and Clayton, D. G., 'Lead in bones and drinking water in towns with hard and soft water', *BMJ*, **2** (1973), 21-3.

Crawford, M. D., Gardner, M. J. and Morris, J. N., 'Mortality and hardness of local water supplies', *Lancet*, **1** (1968), 827-31.

Elwood, P. C., Bainton, D., Moore, F., Davies, D. F., Wakley, E. J., Langman, M. and Sweetman, P. 'Cardiovascular surveys in areas with different water supplies', *BMJ*, **2** (1971), 362-3.

Shroeder, H. A., 'Municipal drinking water and cardiovascular death rates', *Journal of the American Medical Association*, **195** (1966), 81-5.

Stitt, F. W., Clayton, D. G., Crawford, M. D. and Morris, J. N., Clinical & bio-chemical indicators of cardiovascular disease amongst men living in hard and soft water areas. *Lancet,* **1** (1973), 122-6.

Howe, G. M., *National atlas of disease mortality in the United Kingdom* (London, 1970).

Howe, G. M., *Man environment and disease: a medical geography of Britain through the ages* (Newton Abbot, 1972).

'Directive on the quality of water for human consumption', 80/778, EEC. *Official Journal of the European Communities,* No L 229/11 (15 July 1980).

'The quality of water for human consumption directive', 80/778/EEC. An introductory note issued in Scotland by the SDD.

Beattie, A. D., Moore, M. R., Deveney, W. T., Miller, A. R. and Goldberg, A., 'Environmental lead pollution in an urban soft water area', *BMJ,* **2** (1972), 491.

Moore, M. R., 'Plumbo solvency of waters', *Nature,* **243** (1973), 222.

Addis, G. and Moore, M. R., 'Lead levels in the water of suburban Glasgow', *Nature,* **252** (1974), 120.

Moore, M. R., 'Lead in drinking water in soft water areas. Health hazards'. *Science of the Total Environment,* **7** (1977), 105.

Beavers, D. G., *et al.* (8 authors), 'Blood lead and hypertension', *Lancet,* **2** (1976), 123.

Moore, M. R., Meridith, P. A. and Goldberg, A., 'Retrospective analysis of blood lead in mentally retarded children', *Lancet,* **I** (1977), 717.

Lead duplicate diet study (MAFF, London, 1981).

Beattie, A. D., *et al.* (9 authors), 'The role of chronic low level lead exposure in the aetiology of mental retardation', *Lancet,* **I** (1975), 589.

Moore, M. R., Meridith, P. A., Campbell, B. C., Goldberg, A. and Pocock, S. J., 'Contribution of lead in drinking water to blood lead', *Lancet,* **2** (1977), 661.

Clyde River Purification Board 4th AR (Glasgow, 1979).

Health and Safety Executive. *Health and safety. Industrial air pollution, 1978* (London, HMSO, 1980).

Department of the Environment. Central Unit of Environmental Pollution. *Lead Pollution in Birmingham, a report of the Joint Working Party on Lead Pollution around Gravelly Hill* (London, HMSO, 1978). (Pollution Paper No. 14.)

World Health Organisation. Regional Officer for Europe. *Health and the Environment* (Copenhagen, WHO, 1977). (Public Health in Europe 8.)

Department of the Environment. *Lead in drinking water, a survey in Great Britain, 1975-1976,* report of an interdepartmental working group (HMSO, 1977). (Pollution Paper No. 12.)

Royal Commission on Environmental Pollution. Fourth report, pollution control, progress and problems (London, HMSO, 1974), Cmnd. 5780. (Chairman: Sir Brian Flowers.)

Department of the Environment. Central Unit on Environmental Pollution. *Lead in the environment and its significance to man, a report of an interdepartmental working group on heavy metals* London, HMSO, 1974). (Pollution Paper No. 2.)

Royal Commission on Environmental Pollution. Fifth report, air pollution control, an integrated approach (London, HMSO, 1976), Cmnd. 6371. (Chairman: Sir Brian Flowers.)

Department of Health and Social Security. *Lead and health, the report of a DHSS Working Party on Lead in the Environment* (London, HMSO, 1980). (Chairman: Professor P. J. Lawther.)

Statistical Tables, 1974-79. Greater Glasgow Health Board—Information Services Unit.

Ministry of Health. *Mortality and morbidity during the London fog of December,* (London, HMSO, 1954).

Logan, W. D., 'Mortality in the London fog incident, 1952', *Lancet* (14 February, 1953), 336-8.

World Health Organisation, Barker *et al., Air Pollution,* (Geneva, WHO, 1961). (Monograph Series No. 46.)

Report of Committee of Air Pollution (HMSO, 1954). (Chairman: Sir Hugh Beaver.)

Ministry of Housing and Local Government, the Secretary of State for Scotland and the Ministry of Fuel and Power. Committee on Air Pollution. Interim Report (London, HMSO, 1953 (Cmnd. 0911)). (Chairman: Sir Hugh Beaver.)

Ministry of Housing and Local Government, the Secretary of State for Scotland and the

Ministry of Fuel and Power. Committee on Air Pollution. Report (London, HMSO, 1954 (Cmnd. 9322)). (Chairman: Sir Hugh Beaver).

Wilson, T. S., *Health and the Environment,* vol. 3 of *Environment and Man* (Blackie, 1976), ch. 6, 'Clearing the air'.

Royal College of Physicians of London. Fluoride, teeth and health, summary of a report on fluoride and its effect on teeth and health. (Tunbridge Wells, Kent, Pitman Medical, 1976).

Ministry of Health, Scottish Office. Ministry of Housing and Local Government. *The conduct of the fluoridation studies in the United Kingdom and the results achieved after five years* (London, HMSO, 1962). (Reports on Public Health and Medical Subjects No. 105.)

Department of Health and Social Security, Scottish Office, Welsh Office and Ministry of Housing and Local Government. *The fluoridation studies in the United Kingdom and the results achieved after 11 years* (London, HMSO, 1969). (Reports on Public Health and Medical Subjects No. 122.)

Sexually transmitted diseases. GGHB. Various reports.

Scottish Road Safety Advisory Unit. *Trends in injury road accidents in Scotland during 1979* (Edinburgh, The Unit, 1980).

World Health Organisation. Regional Officer for Europe. *Summary report (of the) Technical Group on the Role of Health Services in the Prevention of Road Traffic Accidents,* London, 19-21 February 1980 (Copenhagen, WHO, 1980).

Department of Trade. *The Home Accident Surveillance System, the second twelve months' data* (Consumer Safety Unit, 1979).

Department of Trade. *The Home Accident Surveillance System, 1979—presentation of twelve months' data (the third twelve months)* (London, Consumer Safety Unit, 1980).

Department of Prices and Consumer Protection. *The home accident surveillance system, analysis of domestic accidents to children* (London, Consumer Safety Unit, 1979).

Scottish Accident Prevention Council. *Secretary's annual report 1977* (Edinburgh, The Council, 1978).

Department of Trade. *Personal factors in domestic accidents, prevention through product and environmental design* (London, Consumer Safety Unit, 1980).

Scottish Home and Health Department. *Scottish health authorities priorities for the eighties, a report by the Scottish Health Service Planning Council* (Edinburgh, HMSO, 1980). (Chairman: J. G. Wallace.)

Chapter Eleven   *The archives of the Greater Glasgow Health Board*

1 Temkin, O. 'An Essay on the Usefulness of Medical History for Medicine', in *Bulletin of the Institute of the History of Medicine,* **19** (1946), 21.

2 Greenock Infirmary, *Remarks of the Second Visiting Sub-Committee,* 1 November 1810 (AC/1/1/1).

3 *ibid.*

4 Buchanan, M. S., (1832), vii.

5 Buchanan, M. S., (1832), 33.

6 Comrie, J. D. (1932), vol. II, 616.

7 Guthrie, D., in *MH,* **1** (1957), 307-17.

8 Scottish Society of the History of Medicine, *Report of Proceedings* (1965-6), 4.

9 The formation of the Scottish Society of the History of Medicine in 1948 was the first tangible result of this north of the Border.

10 Rosenberg, C., 'The Medical Profession, Medical Practice and the History of Medicine', in E. Clarke (ed.), *Modern Methods in the History of Medicine* (London, 1971), 28, 35.

11 In Scotland, this was regulated in accordance with the Public Records (Scotland) Act, 1937.

12 British Records Association, *Catalogue of an Exhibition of Medical Records in the Library of the Royal College of Physicians of London* (London, 1958), 5-6.

13 Brotherston, J. H. F., 'Change and the National Health Service', in *SMJ,* **14** (1969), 134-5.

14 Gaffney, R. H., *The Development of Hospital Provision in Glasgow between 1867 and 1897* (Glasgow PhD, 1979), 10.

15 It should be noted that in normal circumstances administrative records are closed to the public for a period of 30 years, and clinical records for 100 years.

16 Buchanan, M. S., (1832), 19.

17 Christie (1888), 77.

18 Downie, J. W. (1923), 145.

19 Bridie, James (1939), 211-12

20 Absolute numbers do not reflect adequately the completeness of series. The earlier period saw fewer patients and less clinical data, and a single journal might suffice for several years. By the early twentieth century journals were filled within a few months.

21 Between 1814 and 1887, 14,765 insane patients were admitted to Gartnavel. Christie (1888), 129.

22 Henderson (1964), 14.

23 Christie (1888), 124.

24 Thomson, A. M. W. (1963), 78.

25 Rosenberg (1971), 27.

26 Hall, M. B., 'History of Science and History of Medicine', in Clarke (1971), 165.

27 McDaniel, W. B., 'The Place of the Amateur in the Writing of Medical History', *BIHM*, 7 (1939), 692.

28 Tait, A. C., 'History of Crichton Royal' in *MH,* 15 (1971), 178.

29 Buchanan, *op.cit.* 27.

30 Crossman, R. H. S., 'A Politician's View of Health Service Planning' (Maurice Bloch Lecture, Glasgow University, 1972).

31 Hutchison, I. G. C., *Politics and Society in Mid-Victorian Glasgow, 1846-1886* (Edinburgh PhD, 1975), 26.

32 *ibid.* 28.

33 Gaffney, *op.cit.* 55, 358-73.

34 *ibid.* 100 f.

35 Scotsman, 5 May 1893. Letter from 'Elder'.

36 Riddell, W. J. B., *The Glasgow Ophthalmic Institution, 1868-1968* (Glasgow, 1968), 18.

37 Dow, D. A., *Domestic Response and Reaction to the Foreign Missionary Enterprises of the Principal Scottish Presbyterian Churches, 1873-1929* (Edinburgh PhD, 1977), 268-80.

38 For Temperance organisations see B. Harrison, 'Drink and Society in England, 1815-1872. A Critical Bibliography', in *International Review of Social History,* 12 (1967), 209.

39 See General Assembly, Reports of, e.g., the Church of Scotland.

40 Gaffney, *op. cit.* 99.

41 Dow, *op. cit.* 26-9.

42 Gaffney, *op. cit.* 89-98.

43 Dow, *op. cit.* 259-67.

44 Blackden, S. M., *The Development of Public Health Administration in Glasgow, 1842-1872* (Edinburgh PhD, 1976), 435.

45 Robertson, E., *The Yorkhill Story* (Glasgow, 1972), 22-6.

46 Christie, *op. cit.* 96.

47 For a general discussion of this topic see Gomme A. and Walker D., *Architecture of Glasgow* (London, 1968), *passim.*

48 The *Glasgow Medical Journal* was one forum for such discussion. See articles by J. C. Steele (1853-4, 322-37) and J. McGhie (1860-1, 403-24). More recently, M. Millman has published an article on 'The Influence of the Social Science Association on Hospital Planning in Victorian England', in *MH,* 18 (1974), 122-37. Brief reference has also been made to the development of Poorhouse architecture in Glasgow by C. Harvey in *Social Welfare Archives in Britain and the USA,* an Occasional Paper published by the Museum of Social Work in January 1980, p. 3. Although it was a rare occurrence, former patients sometimes felt compelled to express their views on the subject. For criticism of wards in Gartnavel see J. Frame, *The Philosophy of Insanity* (Glasgow, 1860), republished (London, 1947), 53.

49 Bed complements, which both reflect and determine hospital building, are another worthwhile area of research. Used in conjunction with inpatient registers showing the

catchment areas from which patients were admitted, the results should prove interesting and illuminating. This aspect of health care provision remains a controversial one up to the present day.

50 See AC/1/1/1, 3 October 1810; H. J. C. Gibson, *Dundee Royal Infirmary, 1798-1948* (Dundee, 1948), 12.

51 Buchanan (1832), 43.

52 Pagan, J. M., 'Remarks on the Statistics of Glasgow University Lying-In Hospital, from 1st November 1852 till 1st January 1860', in *GMJ* (1860-1), 198.

53 Chalmers, A. K. (1930).

54 Glasgow Royal Infirmary statistics distinguish typhoid and enteric fevers from 1851, fourteen years before the Registrar-General's Office did likewise. Blackden, *op. cit.* 371.

55 Raffel, S. H., *Records as Phenomena: The Nature and Uses of Medical Records* (Edinburgh PhD, 1975) 6.

56 See Eaves-Walton, P. M., 'Hospital Archives', in *The Scottish Genealogist* (September 1978), 65-72 for an account of genealogical data from Edinburgh hospitals.

57 GGHB Archives, HB13/7/183.

58 As early as 1815 one man was admitted to the Glasgow Asylum for Lunatics 'deranged in consequence of attending the sacrament'. HB13/5/29, 156.

59 On 13 February 1877, for example, the Medical Committee of the Western Infirmary decided that patients suffering from *delirium tremens* should no longer be admitted or treated. HB6/1/3, 169.

60 See J. Ferrier, *The Greenock Infirmary, 1806-1968* (Greenock, 1968), 20, on the provision of wine for outpatients.

61 The extensive collections of Royal and Western Infirmary ward journals might furnish an interesting comparison of the policies of different doctors. W. T. Gairdner, 80 of whose journals for the years 1874-1900 are extant (HH66), is credited with being one of the first practitioners to regard alcohol as a poison and not as a medically-helpful stimulant. Downie, *op. cit.* 24.

62 See pamphlet by Dr. W. A. F. Browne (Superintendent of Crichton Royal), *Social Reform No. IV. Intemperance and Insanity.* (Issued under the Superintendence of the Scottish Association for the Suppression of Drunkenness, n.d.). Paradoxically, alcohol continued to be prescribed in significant quantities for asylum patients well into the latter part of the century. In 1873 one Woodilee patient received 4 oz whisky per diem for three weeks. HB30/4/1, fo. 129/2.

63 Pagan, J. M., *The Medical Jurisprudence of Insanity* (London, 1840), 102-18.

64 By the 1870s masturbation, euphemistically referred to by Pagan as 'a baneful solitary vice' (p. 43) had largely replaced drink in attracting moral censure of asylum attendants. See HB13/5/60 (1873), *passim.*

65 Browne, *op.cit.* Part II, 2, includes figures abstracted from Gartnavel reports.

66 Henderson, *op. cit.* 236.

67 See Francis, H. W. S., 'The Records of the Independent Contractors', in *The Preservation of Medical and Public Health Records* (Wellcome Unit for the History of Medicine, Oxford, 1979), 38-9.

68 Roberts, R. S., 'The Use of Literary and Documentary Evidence in the History of Medicine', in Clarke, *op. cit.* 50.

69 This theme was first voiced in the 1940s, since when the process has intensified greatly. See e.g., E. H. Ackerknecht, 'The Role of Medical History in Medical Education', in *BIHM,* **21** (1947), 141-2.

70 Roberts, *op. cit.* 37-46.

71 Temkin, *op. cit.* 43.

Chapter Twelve *British urban health in general and in a single city*

1 Two useful books are: Smith, F. B., *The People's Health, 1830-1910* (London, 1979). Youngson, A. J., *The Scientific Revolution in Victorian Medicine* (London, 1979).

2 For the challenge of infants and mothers in the 1930s see Winter, J. M., 'Infant mortality, maternal mortality and public health in Britain in the 1930s', *Journal of European Economic History* (1979), 450.

3 There is much useful information in Cunnison, J., and Gilfillan, J., *Third Statistical Account of Scotland* (Glasgow, 1958).

4 Webster, C., 'Healthy or hungry thirties?', forthcoming paper, 24.

5 Chave, S. P. W., 'The rise and fall of the Medical Officer of Health'. *Community Medicine* (1980).

6 Hamilton, D. N. H., *The healers: a history of medicine in Scotland* (Edinburgh, 1981).

7 Burnet, J., *History of the Water Supply of Glasgow.* (1869). McDonald, A. B. and Taylor, G. M., 'The main drainage of Glasgow', *Institution of Civil Engineers* (1912).

8 Allen, C. M., 'The genesis of British urban redevelopment, with special reference to Glasgow', *Economic History Review* (1965).

9 Bell, J. H., *The Sewermen at Work. Report of the Investigation into the Health and Conditions of Work in Glasgow Sewermen* (1952).

10 This passage derives from the work of Brenda White.

11 Paton, D. N. and Findlay, L., *Poverty, Nutrition and Growth. Studies of Child Life in the Cities and Rural Districts of Scotland.* Medical Research Council, Special Report Series, No. 101 (1926).

12 Lindsay, D. E., *Report upon a Study of the Diet of the Labouring Classes in the City of Glasgow* (Glasgow, 1913). Tully, A. M. T., 'Nutrition and economic conditions in Glasgow', *Lancet,* **ii** (1921); Tully, A. M. T. and Urie, E. M., 'A Study of the diets and economic conditions of labour-class families in Glasgow in June 1922', *GMJ* (December 1922). Tully, A. M. T., 'A study of the Diets and economic conditions of artisan families in Glasgow in May 1923'. *GMJ* (January 1924). Jacqueline Thorburn has provided these references.

13 Cockburn, F., 'The prospect for paediatrics', In *Report of the Proceedings at the Opening of the James Nicoll Lecture Theatre.* Department of Clinical Physics and Bio-Engineering, University of Glasgow (1980), 19.

14 Boyd-Orr, J., 'National food requirements', in Drummond, J. C. *et al., The Nation's Larder and the Housewife's Part Therein* (1940). Also: *Food, Health and Income; Report on a Survey of Diet in relation to Income* (London, 1936).

15 Hamilton, D., Chapter Five above.

16 Rice, F., Chapter Four above.

17 Lenihan, J., in *Proceedings, James Nicoll Lecture Theatre,* 24.

18 See Chapters Two and Nine above.

19 Hamilton, D., *op. cit.* (1981), 208.

20 Smith, F. B., *op. cit.* 414.

21 McKie, J., 'A hundred years on: clinical physics and paediatrics', in *Proceedings, James Nicoll Lecture Theatre* (1980), 27.

22 Cockburn, *op. cit.* 14.

23 Checkland, O., *Philanthropy in Victorian Scotland* (1980), ch. 22, section 4.

24 Luckin, B., 'Death and survival in the city', *Urban History Yearbook* (1980), 53.

25 McKeown, T., *The Modern Rise of Population* (London, 1976).

26 Webster, C., *op. cit.* 10.

27 Greenwood, M., *Epidemics and Crowd Diseases* (London, 1935).

Appendices

Appendix I

Life expectancy tables

TABLE 27

Crude death rates, Glasgow 1821–1931

Period	Rate	Census year	Rate
1821–4	24.8	1871	30.6
1825–9	26.8	1881	25.6
1830–4	31.5	1891	22.7
1835–9	33.0	1901	21.1
1840–4	31.0	1911	17.3
1845–9	39.9	1921	16.2
1850–4	38.2	1931	14.4
1855–9	29.6		
1860–6	30.5		

Source: Flinn, M. W., *Scottish Population History* (1977), 383.

TABLE 28

Crude death rates from selected causes, Western Lowlands region 1861–1939
(Annual means of deaths from specified causes per 1000 deaths from all causes)

Cause of death	1861 –70	1871 –80	1881 –90	1891 –1900	1901 –10	1911 –20	1921 –30	1931 –9
Whooping Cough	39	37	40	36	35	29	23	12
Diarrhoea and dysentery	27	29	26	29	19	36	22	23
Typhus and typhoid	57	25	15	13	7	3	—	—
Influenza	2	1	1	11	5	3	25	19
Respiratory diseases	164	195	110	205	188	205	190	151
Tuberculosis	186	184	157	132	132	109	83	68

Source: Flinn, M. W., *Scottish Population History* (1977), 392.

TABLE 29

Crude death rates from selected infectious diseases, Glasgow 1800–1865
(Deaths from specified diseases as percentages of all deaths in Glasgow)

Cause of death	1800–10	1836–42	1855–65
Fever	9.8	16.1	9.5
Whooping cough	6.8	5.3	5.6
Tuberculosis and bronchitis	22.8	16.8	29.6
Smallpox	6.6	5.0	1.9
Measles	7.5	6.6	3.1
Bowel diseases	8.9	12.1	11.4
Total	62.4	61.9	61.1

Source: Flinn, M. W., *Scottish population history* (1977), 39.

TABLE 30

Index of infant mortality rates in Scotland, Glasgow and England, 1926–1938
(Scotland 1926–9 = 100)

	1926–9	1930	1931	1932	1933	1934	1935	1936	1937	1938
Scotland	100	96	95	100	94	90	89	96	93	81
Glasgow	123	117	121	130	112	114	114	127	121	101
England	100	86	94	93	91	84	81	84	83	76

Source: Winter, J. M., Table VI in 'Infant mortality, maternal mortality, and public health in Britain in the 1930s', *Journal of European Economic History* (1979), 450.

TABLE 31

Glasgow: birth rates, child death rates and death rates, 1900–1980

Year	Birth rate per 1000 living	Illegitimate births (% of total births)	Deaths under 1 year per 1000 births	Neonatal death* per 1000 live births	Stillbirth rate per 1000 births (live and still)	Death rate per 1000 living (all causes)
1900	32.2	—	153	—	—	21.07
1905	30.8	—	131	—	—	17.9(RG)
1910	25.1(RG)	—	121(RG)	—	—	15.1(RG)
1915	26.0	—	143	—	—	18.76
1920	29.26	—	106	—	—	15.03
1925	23.15	5.8%	102	—	—	13.97
1930	21.43	6.5%	101	—	—	14.19
1935	19.67	5.9%	98	—	—	13.83
1940	19.08	5.4%	95	—	—	16.84
1945	19.33	8.3%	68	—	—	13.27
1950	18.21	5.5%	44	—	—	12.81
1955	19.37	4.7%	36	22.7	27	12.23
1960	21.69	5.3%	32	21.4	24	12.24
1965	20.8	7.7%	28	17.8	20	12.7
1970	17.9	11.8%	23	13	17	13.2
1975†	12.9	12.9%	19.1	12.3	12.3	12.9
1980†	13.2	15.3%	13.2	8.6	6.5	13.6

* Neonatal death—infant under one month of age. Spaces occur because relevant information was not then being reported.
† GGHB area figures (crude).
Source: AR MOHG; GGHB; RG.

Appendix II

Glasgow chronology, health and sanitation measures, 1800–1980

Scottish legislation	Glasgow legislation and initiatives	Incidence of epidemic disease	Deaths
	1800 First Police Act		
	1806 The Glasgow Waterworks Company. Works, Dalmarnock, Clyde Water		
	1807 Second Police Act		
	1808 The Cranstonhill Waterworks Company, Clyde Water	1818 Typhus epidemic	
	1821 Third Police Act		
	1830 Fourth Police Act		
1832 The Cholera Acts		1832 Typhus epidemic	2842
		First cholera epidemic— or 14 per 1000— deathrate, 46	
	1 8 Fifth Police Act	1837 Typhus epidemic —deathrate, 41	2180
	1838 Amalgamation of the two Water Companies		
	1843 Sixth Police Act	1843 Relapsing fever epidemic— deathrate, 32	1398
1846 Nuisance Removal Act	1846 Seventh Police and Extension Act		

Year	Legislation / Event		Epidemics	Deaths
1847			Typhus epidemic—deathrate, 56	4346
1848	Gravitation water introduced to Gorbals by private company (February)			
1848–9			Second cholera epidemic, in 1849, or 11 per 1000—deathrate, 35	3772
1851–2			Typhus epidemic	
1853–4			Third cholera epidemic, in 1854, or 12 per 1000—deathrate, 42	3883
1854	Scotch Registration Act			

Deaths from:		Typhus	Smallpox
1855	Corporation Water Works Act	460	203
1856	Amended Nuisance Removal Act	439	127
1857	'Committee on Nuisances' (March)	549	399
1858		504	113
1859	Parks and Galleries Act	381	201
1859	Loch Katrine water turned on (October)	408	347
1860			
1861		475	131
1862	Eighth Police Act	533	27
1862	'Sanitary Committee' (November)		
1863	First Medical Officer of Health (Jan.)	671	349
1863	Suppression of overcrowding by ticketing houses begun		
1864	Vaccination Act came into force (1 January)	1138	300
1864	First Municipal Disinfection and Washing-house (September)		
1864	First 'Sanitary Office' opened (Dec.)		
1865	First Municipal Fever Hospital	1177	26
1865	Market and Slaughter-houses Act		
1866	Cattle sheds in Burghs Act	596	104
1866	Ninth Police Act		
1866	City Improvements Act		
1866	Fourth and last cholera epidemic—only 68 deaths		

Scottish legislation	Glasgow legislation and initiatives	Incidence of epidemic disease			
		Deaths from:	Typhus	Smallpox	
1867 Scotch Public Health Act					
	1868 Cleansing assumed by City as a special department under a committee	1867	497	32	
		1868	367	3	
	1870 'Committee on Health' First Sanitary Inspector Sanitary Department organised Estate of Belvidere acquired for hospital purposes (November)	1869	970	2	
		1870	544	35	Epidemic of relapsing fever
	1870—7 14 intra-mural burial-grounds closed Improvement Trust demolitions and reconstructions				
	1871 New washing and disinfecting house at Belvidere	1871	284	184	
1872 Scotch Education Act	1872 Improvement Act Amendment Act First Reception House opened (June)	1872	182	149	
	1873 Permanent Vaccination Station opened (January) Streets Improvement Act	1873	68	228	Milk epidemic of enteric
	1874 System of Co-operation with School Board to prevent dissemination of infectious disease through schools (September)	1874	113	214	
		1875			Milk epidemic of enteric fever— Washington Street, Pollokshaws Road, and Kingston
	1876 Hospital treatment of infectious diseases wholly in the hands of municipality				

Year	Legislation	Year	Events	Year	Epidemics
1878	Public Parks Act	1871–79	District Model Lodging-House erected	1877–8	Milk epidemic of enteric fever— West End
		1877	Smallpox Hospital Belvidere, opened Streets Improvement Act		
		1878–84	5 district public baths and wash-houses erected		
		1879	Dairies and Milkshops Order Fulwood Moss leased		
		1880	Improvement Act Extension Act	1880	Milk epidemic of enteric fever— North and Central
		1881	First Refuse Despatch Work opened Arrangement made with registrars for returns of vaccination defaulters Resolution to admit all citizens free to hospitals (April)		
		1882	Systemic drain testing begun		
		1883	New Municipal Washing and Disinfecting Establishment opened at Belvidere		
		1884	Second Refuse Despatch Work opened	1884	Milk epidemic of enteric fever— hospitals
		1885	Glasgow Corporation Water Works Act (extension of Loch Katrine Works)		
		1887	Belvidere Fever Hospital completed	1888	Milk epidemic of scarlet fever— Garnethill
		1889	Improvement Trust resumes reconstruction Resolution of Committee on Health condemning the Privy System Tuberculosis meat case		
1890	The Housing of the Working Classes Act Infectious Disease (Notification) Act	1890	Glasgow Police (Amendment) Act Third Refuse Despatch Work opened		

Scottish legislation	Glasgow legislation and initiatives	Incidence of epidemic disease	Cases	Deaths
	1891 City of Glasgow Act (1 Nov.) extension			
	1892 Second Reception House opened; Site acquired for fever hospital, Ruchill; Building Regulations Act	1892 Milk epidemic of scarlet fever—Paisley Road		
	1894 First Sewage Purification Works opened (May); New Bye-laws—Cow-houses and Byres; Washing and disinfecting establishment for North and West, opened at Ruchill (Oct.)	1893–4 Milk epidemic of scarlet fever—(Kelvinside)		
1897 Public Health Act; Rabies Order	1900 MOH—Plague Report (last visitation in late seventeenth century)	1900 Plague	36	16
		Enteric fever	1013	158
		Typhus	72	17
		Whooping cough		323
		Smallpox	397	41
1901 Factories and Workshops Act; Importation of Dogs Order		1901 Enteric fever	1257	210
		Typhus	41	10
		Whooping cough		850
		Smallpox	1394	193
		1902 Enteric fever	698	110
		Typhus	36	9
		Smallpox	460	42
	1903 Visit by Sub-Committee on Health to Liverpool, St Helens and Bradford to study Municipal Infant Milk Depots prior to establishment of same in Glasgow	1903 Enteric fever	944	142
		Typhus	32	6
		Whooping cough		604
		Smallpox	292	24
		Measles	9161	346
		Puerperal fever	108	

Year	Legislation	Events	Year	Disease		
1904		First Infant Milk Depot—68 Osborne Street. Inquiry into conditions of neonates in districts with high infantile mortality—Dr W. Smith	1904	Enteric fever	628	84
				Smallpox	870	67
1905		Start of an early intimation of birth scheme from Maternity Hospital. 1s. fee paid to obtain early information under circular letter—November. Report of a Glasgow enquiry into pulmonary phthisis—reference to work in Edinburgh of Dr Philips. Dispensary for Pulmonary phthisis—23 Montrose Street	1905	Enteric fever	447	53
				Typhus	53	14
				Whooping cough		621
				Smallpox	4	1
				Measles	12 329	551
1906	Dog Order	Cerebro spinal fever made notifiable. Corporation approval in principle, for compulsory notification of phthisis. Baird Street Reception House opened. Bellfield Dispensary opened. Examination of children in Anderston (based at G. U. Settlement)—Dr Smillie. Similar examination in Cowcaddens—Dr Gallacher. Baby centre opened in Anderston.	1906	Typhus	10	2
				Smallpox	3	0
1907	Vaccination (Scotland) Act. Notification of Births Act (operative on 1.1.08)	140 rats examined for plague—one positive. Baby centre opened in Cowcaddens, Mile End, Garngad, Osborne Street, (Bridgeton) 'Visitors' there from COS or BWTA. Infant Milk Depots organised	1907	Enteric fever	470	92
				Typhus	5	2
				Smallpox	1	0
				Cerebro spinal fever	998	683
				Phthisis		1260
				Plague	2	1
1908	Children's Act. Education (Scotland) Act	1907–08 Inquiry into physical condition of children admitted to Belvidere. Significant incidence of rickets found: 31% males / 26.7% females } of 1357 2–10 yr olds / 4.25% of 329 6 mth–2 yr olds	1908	Enteric fever	594	72
				Whooping cough		526
				Smallpox	2	0
				Measles	14 690	824
				Phthisis		1135

Scottish legislation	Glasgow legislation and initiatives	Incidence of epidemic disease		Cases	Deaths
	1908	Administrative scheme for phthisis formulated. TB notifiable under 1889 Act			
		Glasgow Infant Health Visitors Association formed (as result of 1907 Notification Act)			
1909 Housing, Town Planning etc. Act.	1909	Medical inspection of school children begun	1909 Whooping cough		775
			Puerperal fever	108	18
			Phthisis		1128
	10 cases diphtheria associated with milk supply.	Diphtheria	1846	222
1910 Infectious Diseases (Notification) Act	1910-	Testing of milk for TB: 1.29% samples from county byres—TB+ 1.23% samples from town byres—TB+	1910 Enteric fever	340	56
			Typhus	15	2
			Whooping cough		232
		Infant Milk Depots discontinued—no obvious advantages	Smallpox	1	0
	5 TB dispensaries set up	Measles	14 579	527
1911 Rag Flock Act National Insurance Act	1911	Third International Congress on Infant Mortality (Berlin)	1911 Enteric fever	384	59
			Typhus	7	
	Full report to Corporation: a 'crusade' to be mounted in Glasgow to deal with the problem	Whooping cough		625
		Measles		294
		Plague (a lascar seaman on ship in dock)	1	
	1912	Report on effects of fog and low temperature—disastrous to health	1912 Smallpox	1 (seaman)	
	City boundaries extended to include	Pneumonia		1378

Year	Legislation	Notes	Disease statistics		
1913	Mental Deficiency and Lunacy (Scotland) Act	Govan, Partick, Pollokshaws, part of landward areas of Lanark, Renfrew and Dumbarton	1913		
		TB lung included under provisions of 1910 Notification Act	Enteric fever	239	37
		Examination of 528 samples of milk from cows with diseased udders: 14 were TB+	Whooping cough		753
		Wasserman Test available to City practitioners (for syphilis)	Measles	14 935	578
			TB	2534	1457
1914	Milk & Dairies (Scotland) Act	Note: There was only one Health Report covering the war years, 1914–19			
	Housing of the Working Classes Act				
	Public Health (TB) Regulations, Scotland				
1915	Midwives (Scotland) Act				
	Notification of Births (Extension) Act				
1916	Public Health (VD) Regulations, Scotland	Scheme submitted to Corporation re VD			
	Venereal Diseases Act				
1917					
1918	Public Health (Ophthalmia Neonatorium) Regulations		1918		
			Smallpox	1	
			Malaria	1428	
			Influenza		2015
1919	Public Health (Pneumonia Malaria, Dysentery, etc.) Regulations, Scotland	Housing Department created by Corporation to meet demand for houses	1919		
	Housing of the Working Classes Act (Addison Act)	(World pandemic, influenza, 1918–19)	Smallpox	3	
	Rats and Mice (Destruction) Act		Influenza		1919
1920	Blind Persons Act	Smallpox cases within 1¼ mile radius (197) of Belvidere Smallpox Hospital ∴ moved to Robroyston	1920		
	Census Act		Typhus	9	112
	National Health Insurance Act		Smallpox	533	20
			Acute encephalitis lethargica	61	

	Scottish legislation	Glasgow legislation and initiatives	Incidence of epidemic disease	Cases	Deaths
1920	Unemployment Act	Bridgeton Child Welfare Centre opened Corporation Milk Scheme—free, or at reduced prices to needy expectant and nursing mothers and to children under 5 years	Acute encephalitis Acute poliomyelitis	3 4	
1921	Housing (Scotland) Act Licensing Act	1% silver nitrate for Ophthalmia Neonatorum introduced	1921 Encephalitis lethargica	28	11
1922	Bread Acts Amendments Act Milk and Dairies (Amendment) Act. Sale of Tea Act	Outbreak of influenza	1922 Influenzal pneumonia Pneumonia Typhus Trachoma Non-pulmonary TB Encephalitis lethargica	767 5967 20 50 1050 20	605 2303 10
1923	Dangerous Drugs and Poisons (Amendment) Act Housing, etc. Act Workmens's Compensation Act	Health Visitors Circular—application for certification and registration of health visitors	1923 Typhus Encephalitis lethargica Puerperal fever	2 110 278	20 72
1924	National Health Insurance Act Housing (Finance) Act (for building 2½ million houses in UK in 15 yrs)	Whooping cough notifiable in Glasgow for 3 yrs from July 1924 Influenza epidemic Child Welfare centres to be built in Springburn and Maryhill Domestic help (Home Help) scheme inaugurated. 30–40 women joined	1924 Enteric fever Whooping cough Smallpox Pneumonia Influenzal pneumonia Ophthalmia neonatorum Encephalitis lethargica	82 10 048 2 6747 512 592 391	648 2198 412 46

Legislation

1925	Town Planning (Scotland) Act
	Housing (Scotland) Act
	Dangerous Drugs Act
	Widows, Orphans & Old Age Contributory Pensions Act
1926	Housing (Rural Workers) Act
	Lead Paints (Protection against Poisoning) Act
	Merchandise Marks Act
1927	Midwives and Maternity Homes (Scotland) Act
	Sale of Food and Drugs Act
1928	Food and Drugs (Adulteration) Act
	Rag Flock Act (1911) Amendment Act
1929	Local Government (Scotland) Act
1930	Education (Scotland) Act

Notes

1925	Areas to be cleared—housing
	Rose Street Area: 2.82 acres—534/acre
	Richard Street, Anderston:2.14 acres—946/acre
	Glasgow Boundaries Act
1926	Boundaries Act effective:
	10,328 acres added in SW, and N districts
	17,344 added to population
	Reason for extension—space for housing
	Infective jaundice (spirochaetosis) notifiable to December 1926
1928	First recorded outbreak of poliomyelitis in the city
1929	Mearnskirk Hospital opened
1930	Typhus absent since 1926

Disease statistics

Year	Disease		
1925	Whooping cough	12 194	587
	Measles	6507	118
	Scarlet fever	3472	68
	Encephalitis lethargica	73	48
1926	Enteric fever, i. e.		
	typhoid	68	
	paratyphoid B	32	1
	typhus	8	1
	smallpox	1	1
		(on a ship)	
	Encephalitis lethargica	20	
	Scarlet fever	4634	88
	Ophthalmia neonatorum	665	
	Puerperal fever	307	69
	Puerperal sepsis	309	64
	Diphtheria	2323	132
1927	Enteric fever (typhoid)	148	10
	Whooping cough	9993	364
	Measles	8983	307
	Scarlet fever	4117	44
	Diphtheria	3036	113
1928	Poliomyelitis	112	8
	Measles	10 098	376
1929	Smallpox	15	
		(from ship from India)	
	Cerebro-spinal fever	203	152
1930	Typhus	2	
	Trachoma	145	

	Scottish legislation		Glasgow legislation and initiatives		Incidence of epidemic disease		
						Cases	Deaths
1931	Foodstuffs (Prevention of Exploitation) Act	1931	Unification and co-ordination of Maternity, Child Welfare and Education Health Services in Glasgow, under 1929 Local Government Act, i.e. certain functions of Education Authority, including medical inspection—Health Dept. Parish Council functions taken over by Town and County Councils. Local Authority PH Dept. began work in field of general hospitals (previously concerned with infectious disease hospitals)	1931	Typhus	66	
					Scarlet fever	7020	69
					Paratyphoid B	46	
1932	Children and Young Persons (Scotland) Act	1932	Local cow herd connected with some cases of Scarlet fever. Chickenpox no longer notifiable	1932	Scarlet fever	9158	102
					Typhoid	47	8
					Paratyphoid B	27	1
1934	Unemployment Act			1933	Scarlet fever	8378	83
	Shops Act			1934	Scarlet fever	5953	77
1935	Housing (Scotland) Act National Health Insurance and Contributory Pension Act Restrictions on Ribbon Development Act Diseases of Animals Act	1935	Beginning of scheme to transfer outdoor poor law medical service from part-time to full time 14 whole time MOs employed Beginning of Corporation Outdoor Medical Service which related closely to the Corporation hospitals	1935	Typhoid Paratyphoid	85 } 100 }	15

Year		Disease	Cases	Deaths
1936		Typhoid	22	
		Paratyphoid	195	
		Puerperal fever	500	57
		Diphtheria	1958	54
		Poliomyelitis	26	
1937		Scarlet fever	5598	29
		Diphtheria	2330	116
1939		Diphtheria	3144	163
1940		Diphtheria	5910	226
1941		Diphtheria	4039	155
		Whooping cough	11 000	286
1942		Smallpox	36	8
		Typhoid	63	8
1946		Typhoid	29	
1947		Poliomyelitis	300	
		Polioencephalitis	19	29
1950		Smallpox	18	6
		Poliomyelitis	278	11
		(212 paralysed cases)		

1937	No smallpox since 1931
1938	City boundaries extended
1939	War declared, September
1940	Immunisation campaign (diphtheria) initiated in Glasgow

1936	Education (Scotland) Act
1937	Children and Young Persons (Scotland) Act
	Factories Act
1945	Public Health (Scotland) Act
1947	National Health Service (Scotland) Act
	Education (Scotland) Act
1948	Factories Act
	Nurseries, Child Minders Regulation Act
1949	Education (Scotland) Act
	Milk (Special Designation) Act
	Nurses (Scotland) Act
1951	Rivers (Prevention of Pollution) (Scotland) Act

Scottish legislation	Glasgow legislation and initiatives	Incidence of epidemic disease	Cases	Deaths
		1954 Poliomyelitis (32 paralysed cases)	51	
	1955 Salk vaccine produced in Britain	1955 Dysentery	6071	
		Poliomyelitis (172 paralysed cases)	245	
1956 Clean Air Act; Foods and Drugs (Scotland) Act	1956 Vaccination campaign (poliomyelitis) using Salk vaccine begun in Glasgow Nationwide introduction of Pertussis immunisation	1956 Dysentery	4628	
		Diphtheria (the last truly Glasgow case)	1	
	1957 Glasgow X-Ray campaign 715,000 people examined over 5 weeks	1957 Active pulmonary TB	2369	
		Influenza A (Asian) pandemic	161	
1958 Adoption Act; Children's Act	1958 Glasgow's First smoke control area declared: 201 acres in City centre Dobbie's Loan Child Welfare Centre closed—clinic transferred to Glenfarg Street Clinic, Glasgow	1958 Poliomyelitis (99 paralysed cases)	161	
	1959 From 1956 to end 1959 in Glasgow 266,348 persons had had 2 injections Salk vaccine 123,530 had had 3 injections	1959 Dysentery (Endemic since 1953: 30,000 cases 1953–9)	4751	10
		Asian influenza		117
1960 Mental Health (Scotland) Act; Noise Abatement Act	1960 Glasgow Corporation Order Confirmation Act, 1960. Glasgow Corporation Consolidation (General Powers) Order Confirmation Act			
1961 Factories Act		1961 Poliomyelitis (none since 1959)	8	

Year	Legislation	Year	Events	Data
1962	Commonwealth Immigrants Act Education (Scotland) Act Health Visiting and Social Work (Training) Act	1962	Sabin oral vaccine (poliomyelitis) introduced in the city	Poliomyelitis (42 paralysed cases) 100
1963	Office, Shops and Railway Premises Act			
1964	Adoption Act Housing Act	1964	Reappearance of rickets in the city Campaign begun on value of Vitamin D Balvicar Child Development Centre opened. 'Happy Shute' Dental Health Campaign launched in the city	Dysentery 2584
1965	Public Health (Notification of Births) Act Registration of Births, Deaths, Marriages (Scotland) Act	1965	Dental Health Campaign continued Pilot study in multiple screening of men over 45 yrs of age resident in Glasgow Dietary study (under auspices of Scottish Home and Health Department) of Glasgow children Social Paediatric Research Unit established (in conjunction with University of Glasgow) New syllabus of Council for Education and Training of Health Visitors	
1966	Housing (Scotland) Act	1966	Population fell below 1 million: average density of population—24 persons/acre	
1967	Abortion Act Dangerous Drugs Act Water (Scotland) Act	1967	Screening for cervical cancer begun 'Well Woman' Clinics opened in several maternity and child welfare centres in the city	Social Paediatric Research Unit reported rickets amongst some native Glaswegians Many anaemic children Evidence of rickets in 6 mth–2 yr age group

	Scottish legislation		Glasgow legislation and initiatives		Incidence of epidemic disease	Cases	Deaths
1968	Clean Air Act Commonwealth Immigrants Act Health Services and Public Health Act Social Work (Scotland) Act			1968	Salmonella (Source—pigs slaughtered in Glasgow)	472	3
1969	Education (Scotland) Act Housing (Scotland) Act	1969	Welfare Section of Health and Welfare Department absorbed into newly-created Glasgow Social Work Department				
		1971	Rubella vaccination for schoolgirls begun in city	1970	Whooping cough	1063	
1972	National Health Service Reorganisation Act The Local Government (Scotland) Act			1972	Dysentery	1287	
1975	Housing (Scotland) Act Health and Safety at Work etc. Act Control of Pollution Act Local Government (Scotland) Act	1974	Establishment of new integrated Health Service Abolition of office of MOH	1974	No ill-effects resulted from Glasgow sewage workers' strike (October–December)		
		1975	Municipal Authorities called for military assistance in March, to clear rubbish accumulated as result of resumed strike of Cleansing Department motor drivers (October 1974 and January–14 April 1975) City cleared by end of May	1975	No ill-effects resulted from the potential health hazard of street rubbish dumps		

1978	National Health Service (Scotland) Act Local Government (Scotland) Act	
1979	Nurses, Midwives and Health Visitors Act	
1980	Health Services Act Water (Scotland) Act	
1977	Whooping cough controversy	
1979	Special arrangements for distribution of Vitamin D supplement to Asiatic families in Glasgow	
1979	Rickets amongst Asiatic children and young people	

Source: J. B. Russell, *The evolution of the function of Public Health Administration* (Glasgow, 1895), ARMOHG and various tables and reports made available by courtesy of GGHB.

Appendix III

Suggested tariff of fees to be charged by doctors in Glasgow in 1809 and 1900

TARIFF OF FEES, 1809

The scale for the different charges of Medicine, Surgery and Attendance are presumed on the data of Income and the Faculty have therefore divided the inhabitants of the City and its neighbourhood into four classes.

	Class I Income over £500 per annum	Class II Income £300–£500 per annum	Class III Income £50–£300 per annum	Class IV Income under £50 per annum
Attendance				
Visit from 8 a.m. to 10 p.m.	£1 1s. 0d.	10s. 6d.	5s. 0d.	2s. 6d.
Visit in town during the night	£2 2s. 0d.	£1 11s. 6d.	£1 1s. 0d.	10s. 6d.
Visit a mile from town during the day	£2 2s. 0d.	£1 1s. 0d.	10s. 6d.	5s. 0d.
Every additional mile	10s. 6d.	7s. 6d.	5s. 0d.	2s. 6d.
Visit to Anderston, Bridgeton Port Dundas or such distance	£1 11s. 6d.	£1 1s. 0d.	15s. 0d.	7s. 6d.
Attendance with a midwife the same as an ordinary delivery				
Consultations				
Consultation with a Physician Surgeon or midwife	£2 2s. 0d.	£1 11s. 6d.	£1 1s. 0d.	15s. 0d.
Report of a case to Physician or surgeon the same as a consulation				
Advice at the shop	10s. 6d.	7s. 6d.	5s. 0d.	2s. 6d.
Surgery				
Blood vessels taking up or stitching wounds	£2 2s. 0d.	£1 11s. 6d.	£1 1s. 0d.	10s. 6d.
Bloodings	£1 1s. 0d.	10s. 6d.	5s. 0d.	2s. 6d.
Fracture reducing, Bandages etc.	£5 5s. 0d.	£3 3s. 0d.	£2 2s. 0d.	£1 1s. 0d.
Inoculation	£3 3s. 0d.	£2 2s. 0d.	£1 1s. 0d.	10s. 6d.
Leeches applying	10s. 6d.	7s. 6d.	5s. 0d.	2s. 6d.

Operations

Great: amputation of leg and arm				
aneurism of large arteries				
extirpation of mamma or testicle				
hydrocoele by incision	£31 10s. 0d.	£21 0s. 0d.	£10 10s. 0d.	£5 5s. 0d.
Lesser: amputation of toes or fingers				
cancerous lips				
harelip				
fistula in ano				
hydrocoele by injection				
tumours	£10 10s. 0d.	£5 5s. 0d.	£3 3s. 0d.	£2 2s. 0d.
Suspended animation from drowning or any similar cause when means are used for recovery	£10 10s. 0d.	£5 5s. 0d.	£3 3s. 0d.	£2 2s. 0d.
When dressed at the patient's house each time the charge as for a visit and a half				
Ditto at the shop, the charge as for a visit				
In all of the above surgical cases the charge is for the operation only—visits and dressings to be charged separately				

Midwifery

Delivery in ordinary cases	£10 10s. 0d.	£5 5s. 0d.	£3 3s. 0d.	£2 2s. 0d.
Delivery by crotchet, forceps or turning	£15 15s. 0d.	£10 10s. 0d.	£5 5s. 0d.	£3 3s. 0d.
Extracting placenta or Reducing inverted uterus	£5 5s. 0d.	£2 12s. 6d.	£1 11s. 6d.	£1 1s. 0d.

Medicines took the form of balsams, tinctures, elixirs, decoctions, linctuses: liniments and ointments: powders, pills and plasters, etc. Charges are generally given 'per ounce' or 'per dozen'. They range from 4s. (Class I) to 1s. 6d. (Class IV) for the most expensive item, to 1s. (Class I) to 6d. (Class IV) for the simplest and cheapest.

[It should be noted that these scales were drawn up by members of the FPSG and were guidelines rather than strict rules. It is probable that there was undercutting by the increasing numbers of non-members practising in later years.]

Source: Minutes, 4 June 1809, FPSG
See under 'Charges of Medicine, Surgery and attendance'.

TARIFF OF FEES, 1900

Adopted by the Glasgow Southern Medical Society, February 1880, with Amendments proposed and confirmed at a Meeting of the Society in April 1900.
Note—The attention of the Members of the Society is directed to the undernoted Tariff of Fees as amended during the Session 1899–1900.

Class I Income under £200 or Rent under £25	Class II Income £200 to £400 or Rent £25 to £40	Class III Income £400 to £800 or Rent £40 to £80	Class IV Income £800 and upwards or Rent £80 and upwards

(1) Ordinary
    Visit,   2s. 6d. to 3s. 6d   3s. 6d. to 5s.   5s. to 10s. 6d.   10s. 6d. to 21s.

(2) Special Visit. A fee and a half to double fee. A Special Visit is one made after 7 a.m. and before commencing the daily round, or one made after the usual visiting hours, or one in which immediate attendance is requested, or attendance at a fixed hour, or one which from any cause entails exceptional trouble or expense.

(3) Night Visit. Treble fee. A Night Visit is one made between 10 p.m. and 7 a.m. Charge for detention according to No. 9.

(4) Advice at Practitioner's Consulting Rooms. Fee as for ordinary visit. Charge for detention according to No. 9.

(5) Letters of Advice. Fee as for two visits.

(6) Consultations.
    (*a*) Consultant's fee in town. Two guineas to be paid by the patient to the consultant at time of visit.
    (*b*) When a general practitioner is himself called in consultation he is entitled to a consultant's fee.
    (*c*) When the ordinary attendant meets a consultant, or other medical man, he is entitled to a special fee of not less than three visits.
    (*d*) When a general practitioner is called to assist at a case of Midwifery or other emergency, the charge, to be paid by the patient at the time, should be arranged between himself and the practitioner calling him in.

(7) Attendance on Servants, 2s. 6d. to 5s. per visit.

(8) Two or more patients in one house. When these are paid by one person, half a visit is chargeable for each patient beyond the first. When this is not the case, the full charge should be made for each.

(9) Detention. When, at the desire of the patient or from the urgency of the case, the practitioner is detained more than twenty minutes, an ordinary visit is to be charged for each twenty minutes or part thereof.

(10) Visits beyond two miles from practitioner's residence should be charged at the rate of three visits per hour, travelling expenses being charged in addition; but coast or country visits, i.e., visits outside a radius of 10 miles from the Royal Exchange, Glasgow, according to time and distance, but not less than £2 2s.

(11) Midwifery and Premature Births.

Class I	Class II	Class III	Class IV
£1 1s. £2 2s.	£2 2s. £4 4s.	£4 4s. £7 7s.	£7 7s. upwards.

In normal confinements the fee for Classes I, II, III, and IV, shall cover the confinement and five after visits; any visits in excess of this number shall be charged according to the class.

In abnormal cases, e.g., when forceps, turning, chloroform, etc. are required, the practitioner is entitled to double fee.

(12) Vaccination, 2s. 6d. in addition to ordinary visit or consulting fee.

(13) Surgical operations to be charged according to their importance and the social condition of the patient. The Anaesthetist's fee shall be from £1 1s. to £5 5s.

(14) Ordinary Certificates of Health to be charged as for ordinary visits.

(15) Certificates of Lunacy, £1 1s. to £2 2s.

(16) For filling up Insurance Certificates, whether of Accident or of Death, a minimum fee of 10s. 6d. is to be charged, with an extra fee of 10s. 6d. for every additional £500.

Source: Appendix to *Historical sketch of Glasgow Southern Medical Society,* (Glasgow, 1900). RCPSG, 11 and 12.

Appendix IV

Greater Glasgow Health Board records

GUIDE TO THE RECORDS OF THE GGHB*

The GGHB records project was initiated in September 1975, largely as a response to the re-organisation of the National Health Service in 1974. The primary aim of the project was the location and listing of important historical, medical and administrative non-current records of the Board and associated institutions, and the secure preservation of such material. Catalogue entries now exceed 11,000, some 9000 of which relate to items held in a central repository under the direct control of the archivist. Access to the records is normally granted to scholars after the expiry of the statutory period of closure (currently thirty years for administrative records, 100 years for clinical). The index to the summaries of the records surveyed differentiates between those which have been transferred to the GGHB Archives and those which have been retained by individual districts or institutions. Records held in the Archives carry the prefix HB while those still in the care of individual hospitals are prefixed GHB. The series headed HH contains clinical records of the Glasgow Royal and Western Infirmaries and the Ophthalmic Institution, formerly deposited in the Scottish Record Office and now returned to the GGHB Archives. Holdings listed relate to both administrative and clinical records from the 1780s onwards, with the bulk of the material dating from the late nineteenth century to 1948. The summaries provided here are not a complete guide to the records held, a full inventory of which is contained in the surveys retained in Glasgow University Archives and the Scottish Record Office in Edinburgh. Lists of the records of the Argyll and Clyde, Ayrshire and Arran, and Lanarkshire Health Boards have also been compiled. In addition to material retained by the Health Boards, some records pertaining to local authority hospitals are deposited in Strathclyde Regional Archives.

All enquiries regarding the GGHB records should in the first instance be addressed to The Archivist (GGHB), The Archives, The University, Glasgow G12 8QQ, tel. 041–339 8855 ext. 7516.

INDEX

Abbreviations: BM—Board of Management
WRHB—Western Regional Hospital Board

* The copyright of these records is vested in the Greater Glasgow Health Board.

Barnhill Poorhouse: HB19, HB29, GHB24
Barony Parish, Parochial Board and Asylum: HB24, HB30, GHB6
Beatson Institute for Cancer Research, Glasgow: GHB31
Bellahouston Dispensary: HB23
Bellefield Sanatorium: HB23
Bellsdyke Mental Hospital BM: HB28
Belvidere Hospital: GHB1, GHB23
Birdston Hospital: HB33, HB39
Blind Asylum: GHB6
Blinkbonny Certified Institution: HB19, HB20
Brooksby Convalescent Home: HB23
Broomhill Home and Hospital: HB31, HB39
Bute and Cumbrae Hospitals BM: HB28
Caldwell House Institution and Hospital: HB20
Campbeltown and District Hospitals BM: HB28
Cancer Hospital: HB11, HB37
Cancer Registration Bureau, WRHB: HB17
Canniesburn Hospital: GHB1
Central Dispensary, Glasgow: HB6, GHB6
Central Lanarkshire Hospitals BM: HB28
Centre for Rheumatic Diseases: GHB1
Children's Home, Aberfoyle: HB12
Children's Home Hospital, Strathblane: HB2, HB12
City of Glasgow Fever Hospitals (Kennedy Street and Belvidere): GHB23
City of Glasgow Local Dental Committee: HB41
City Laboratory: GHB31
Clinical Physics and Bio-Engineering: GHB31
Coatbridge Airdrie and District Hospitals BM: HB28
Corporation of the City of Glasgow: HB19, HB20, HB30, HB31, HB38, GHB6,
    GHB13, GHB23, GHB31
Cowglen Hospital: HB16, HB17
Darleith House: HB13
Darnley Hospital: HB15
David Elder Infirmary: HB6, HB16, HB17, HB35, GHB21
Deaf and Dumb Institution: GHB6
Dental Hospital and School: GHB5, GHB31
Department of Clinical Physics and Bio-Engineering: GHB31
Department of Health for Scotland: HB40
Duke Street Hospital: HB19, GHB1, GHB10
Dumfries and Galloway Hospitals BM: HB28
Dumfries, Galloway and Crichton Royal Hospitals BM: HB28
Dunbartonshire Hospitals BM: HB28
Dunoon Hospitals BM: HB28
Dykebar and Associated Hospitals BM: HB28
Ear, Nose and Throat Hospital: HB8, HB37
East House and Hospital, Dundee: HB17
Eastern District Hospital, Duke Street: HB19, GHB1, GHB10
Eastern Medical Society: GHB33
Elder Cottage Hospital: HB16, HB18
Epileptic Colony, Stoneyetts: HB19, HB20
Executive Council for the City of Glasgow: HB41

Spencer Research Committee: HB3
Stirling and Clackmannan Hospitals BM: HB28
Stirling, Falkirk and Alloa Hospitals BM: HB28
Stobhill Hospital: HB19, HB32, GHB6, GHB22, GHB27, GHB31
Stoneyetts Certified Institution: HB19, HB20
Strathblane Children's Home Hospital: HB2, HB12
Town's Hospital, Glasgow: GHB6
University Lying-in Hospital and Dispensary: HB22
University of Glasgow: HB35, GHB6
Victoria Cottage Hospital, Kilsyth: HB39
Victoria Infirmary, Glasgow: HB23, GHB1, GHB6, GHB12, GHB17
Waverley Park Institution and Hospital: HB20
West Muckcroft Colony: HB20
West of Scotland Foot Hospital: HB23, GHB1
West of Scotland Neuro-Psychiatric Research Institute: HB21
Western District Hospital, Oakbank: HB2, HB19, HB32, HB44
Western Infirmary, Glasgow: HB6, HB37, GHB1, GHB6, GHB21, HH66
Western Joint Ophthalmic Services: HB41
Western Regional Hospital Board: HB20, HB28, GHB13, GHB23, GHB31
Woodilee Asylum and Hospital: HB1, HB6, HB19, HB30, GHB13
Woodside Health Centre: GHB31
Yorkhill and Associated Hospitals BM: HB2, HB28, GHB31
Yorkhill Children's and Maternity Hospitals BM: HB2, HB28

SUMMARY LISTS

HB1
Gartloch Hospital: Board of management for Glasgow north-eastern mental hospitals: minutes, 1948–73, including papers of chairman's, finance and planning committees, 1968–73; accounts, 1959–72; files relating to endowment fund, farms and gardens, 1949–74; pamphlet, *Gartloch Asylum and Hospital for Mental Diseases, c.*1898. 5 pages.

HB2
Royal Hospital for Sick Children: minutes, 1861–1948, including salary and wages committee, 1937–47; annual reports, 1883–1943; proceedings of staff association, 1929–45; ledgers, 1881–1924; wages' records, 1928–40; register of admissions, 1893–1914; general register, 1914–29; ward journals, 1883–1914; memorandum on teaching facilities, 1945; records of bequests, *c.*1899–1964; photographs of staff, patients, premises and equipment, n.d.; pamphlet, *The Dispensary of the Royal Hospital for Sick Children, Glasgow,* 1980. Board of management for Glasgow and district children's hospitals: minutes, 1948–63; annual reports, 1958–63. Board of management for Yorkhill children's and maternity hospitals: minutes, 1963–8; papers relating to rebuilding programme, 1965–71. Board of management for Yorkhill and associated hospitals: minutes, 1968–74. 17 pages.

HB3
Glasgow Eye Infirmary: directors' minutes, 1824–1948; minutes of joint consultative committee with Glasgow ophthalmic institution, 1918–20, Spencer research committee, 1946–54, and house, finance and building committees, 1874–1948; annual reports, 1824–1943; accounts, 1899–1948; salaries' records, 1929–42;

registers of members and directors, 1912–43; visitors' book, 1922–48; pathological journals, 1920–63; miscellaneous papers, 1922–73, including file marked 'civil defence', 1951–2. 8 pages.
HB4
Glasgow Homoeopathic Hospital: minutes, including house, finance and outpatients' department committees, 1911–48; annual reports, 1934–47; miscellaneous pamphlets, press cuttings, photographs and other papers relating to the hospital, 1930–74, including memorandum concerning future of the hospital under proposed National Health Service, 1947. Board of management for Glasgow homoeopathic hospitals: minutes, 1948–74. 5 pages.
HB5
Glasgow Homoeopathic Hospital for Children: minutes of management, 1920–44, and of house, 1920–44, committees; annual reports, 1932–43; hospital and dispensary expenses' analysis book, 1922–40; pamphlets appealing for funds, 1932–6. 4 pages.
HB6
Western Infirmary: minutes, 1874–1948, including staff association, 1920–38; annual reports, 1873–1947; letter books, 1911–31; register of deaths, 1874–1979; clinical surgery attendance register of students, 1875–87; printed pamphlets relating to the Western infirmary, 1883–1930; scrap books, 1893–1967; photographs of staff and buildings, 1903–*c*.1960; annual reports of various hospitals in Scotland, England and America, 1879–1907. 15 pages.
HB7
Hozier House: annual reports, 1894–1914. 2 pages.
HB8
Glasgow Ear, Nose and Throat Hospital: minutes, 1880–1941; annual reports, 1933–43; legacies and donations book, 1937–46; photographs of staff, premises and patients, *c*.1925–30 and n.d. 4 pages.
HB9
Glasgow Physiotherapy and Rehabilitation Clinic: minutes, 1934–48. 1 page.
HB10
Redlands Hospital for Women: minutes, 1902–74, including general, 1902–45, executives, 1903–23, finance, 1903–43, extension, 1927–48, house, 1929–45, diet, 1964–74; and other committees; extension fund accounts, 1919–37; register of patients, 1903–35; case notes, 1903–25; operations notes, 1925–6; visitors' books, 1909–66; MSS historical notes on Redlands hospital, 1903–40; photographs and paintings of staff, premises and persons connected with Redlands including the Mirrlees family, *c*.1870–1972. 6 pages.
HB11
Royal Beatson Memorial Hospital: minute, 1921–48, including house, medical advisory and research committees, with reference book to minutes, 1912–45; accounts, 1942–8. 5 pages.
HB12
Children's Home Hospital, Strathblane: minutes, 1904–44. Aberfoyle children's home: diary and press cuttings, 1903–13. 2 pages.
HB13
Gartnavel Royal Hospital: draft minutes, 1925–34; annual reports, 1815–1947; accounts, 1811–1955; wages' records, 1844–53; patients' ledgers, 1848–1946; registers of admissions, 1814–1964, patients, 1831–1963, sureties, 1857–1915, physical condition, 1872–1958, discharges, removals and deaths, 1873–1964, accidents, 1876–1949, and rates of board for service patients, 1918–48; asylum

registers of lunatics, 1858–1963; pathological registers, 1889–1935; admission documents, 1815–1962; case notes, 1814–1973, including medical reports, 1814–42, Dr Angus MacNiven's examinations of persons involved in criminal proceedings, 1933–65, and records of ECT treatment, 1943–73; visitors' books, 1865–1946; papers relating to occupational therapy, 1918–51, and to various aspects of psychiatric medicine, c.1925–52; letter book, 1846–8; letters from patients to physicians superintendent, 1892–1934; correspondence of physician superintendent (Dr MacNiven), 1931–47, correspondents include Drs R. D. Gillespie and D. K. Henderson on planned publications, 1931–9, MOH, Glasgow, 1931–47, Dr H. C. Marr on early treatment of the insane, 1935–6, Dr E. Glover on psychological effects of war on society, 1938–40, and Dr C. Watson on schizophrenia, 1946; correspondence and papers relating to cancer of Miss Brodie, lady superintendent, 1909–45, boarding charges, 1915–46, staffing policy, 1919–45, 'Talkie Picture Equipment' at Gartnavel, 1932–5, employment for Austrian and Czech refugee psychoanalysts, 1938–41, proposed nurses' strike, 1939, patients evacuated from Gartloch, 1939–45, electric shock therapy apparatus, 1939–46, and proposed acquisition of Garscube and Kelvindale Houses, 1946–7; pamphlets and press cuttings relating to Garnavel hospital, 1888–1960; plans of Gartnavel, 1841, and Kelvindale house, 1946; photographs of staff and premises, 1900 and n.d.; *Gartnavel Gazette,* 1903–25, and *Newsletter,* 1979–80; Revd Brodie's typescript *History of Glasgow Mental Hospital 1810–1948,* n.d., Darleith house: cash books, 1922–46; pamphlet, *Darleith House, c.*1930. Ex-service welfare society: conference proceedings, 1942–5. Board of management for Glasgow Royal mental hospital: minutes, 1947–65. 37 pages.
HB14
Glasgow Royal Infirmary: annual reports, 1874–1934; pamphlets and handbooks relating to Glasgow Royal history and staff. 5 pages.
HB15
Darnley Hospital: registers of patients, 1913–71, and of staff, 1913–66; case notes, 1935–57. 3 pages.
HB16
Board of Management for Glasgow South-Western Hospitals: minutes, including chairman's house, finance, medical and nurses' services committees, 1948–64, and planning and development committee, 1949–50; accounts, 1948–74; papers relating to endowments, 1948–56. 4 pages.
HB17
Southern General Hospital: superintendents reports, 1925–39; registers of admissions and discharges, 1923–69, including phthisis cases, 1923–41, and air raid casualties, 1939–48, deaths, 1932–61, and operations, 1954–70; asylum registers of lunatics, 1923–57, and of discharges and removals, 1923–61; maternity registers, 1923–66; mental wards visitors' 1922–48, and accident, 1923–70, books; papers relating to patients transferred from London hospitals, 1939–46; 'Flying Squad', 1954–63, and BCG, 1959–69, notebooks; statistical returns relating to patients, 1930–52, bed complements, 1966–70, and operations, 1969, including David Elder infirmary and Shieldhall hospital; diet sheets for various Scottish hospitals and poorhouses, 1920–8; pamphlets and articles relating to history of the Southern General, 1957–63. Govan poorhouse: reports of governors and medical officers, 1906–12; wages' book, 1909–18; registers of admissions and discharges, 1885–1922, including phthisis cases, 1914–22; asylum registers of lunatics, 1858–1922, restraint and seclusion, 1874–1900, and discharges and removals, 1887–1922; maternity register, 1896–1922; lunatic wards accident book, 1865–1922. Govan parochial board:

abstracts of accounts, 1868–86; details of accommodation at Merryflats, 1877; medical discharge certificates, 1882–1951. David Elder infirmary: registers of patients, 1928–57, and admissions and discharges, 1954–70, including road accident cases, 1961–7. Shieldhall hospital: register of patients, 1913–43, and admissions and discharges, 1946–69, including Cowglen hospital, 1961–2. Western regional hospital board: 7th annual report of the regional cancer committee, 1967. 15 pages.

HB18
Elder Cottage Hospital: accounts, 1946; admissions books, 1930–72; visitors' book, 1903–48; regulations, 1927; year-book, 1928–9; floor plans, n.d. 2 pages.

HB19
Parish Council and Corporation of Glasgow. Parish of Glasgow minutes, 1912–30, including Glasgow district board of control and individual districts and hospitals. Corporation of the City of Glasgow: minutes of hospitals and mental services, and health committees, 1942–7; health and welfare accounts, 1947–69; miscellaneous reports on medical and social matters, 1930–44. 4 pages.

HB20
Lennox Castle Hospital and Associated Institutions. Stoneyetts certified institution: registers of accidents, 1915–36, restraint and seclusion, 1925–36, and patients transferred to Lennox Castle, 1936; case notes, 1914–30, including treatment of epilepsy, 1926–30; correspondence of medical superintendent, 1913–36. Blinkbonny certified institution: registers of discharges and removals, 1922–35, deaths, 1922–36, accidents, 1922–36, and restraint and seclusion, 1925–36. Glasgow association for the care of defective and feeble-minded children: minutes, 1930–48; ledger, 1933–48. Lennox Castle certified institution: register of admissions, 1936–7; correspondence of medical superintendent, 1936–50; rules, 1930–60; miscellaneous papers relating to patients' diet, 1914–77, Stoneyetts and Lennox Castle boy scouts, 1930–54, wartime use of Lennox Castle, 1937–42, and medical subjects, 1927–c.1950; printed, *The Book of Lennox Castle,*1936. Board of management for Lennox Castle and associated institutions: minutes, 1948–74, including finance and other committees, 1948–62, and Lennox Castle, Caldwell House and Waverley Park sub-committees, 1955–62; correspondence files, 1951–75. 11 pages.

HB21
West of Scotland and Neuro-Psychiatric Research Institute: minutes, research memoranda and financial statements, 1931–48. 3 pages.

HB22
Glasgow University Lying-in Hospital and Dispensary: minutes, 1834–78; annual report, 1836–7. 4 pages.

HB23
Victoria Infirmary and Glasgow Victoria Hospitals. Victoria infirmary: minutes, 1881–1948; annual reports, 1881–1940, including ladies' auxiliary association, 1917–40; accounts, 1903–47; registers of patients, 1890–1918; ward journals, 1890–1922; printed, *The Victoria,* by James Bridie c.1947; framed caricatures of Glasgow medical men, by Dr O. H. Mavor, n.d. Board of management for Glasgow Victoria hospitals: minutes, 1948–68; accounts relating to endowments, 1948–57. 15 pages.

HB24
Leverndale and Hawkhead. Board of management for Leverndale hospital: minutes, 1948–68. Govan district lunacy board: minutes, 1889–95; legal, financial and other papers relating to Govan district asylum, 1878–1923, including food budgets, 1898–1923, staffing, 1901–8, and floor plans, 1893. 5 pages.

HB25
Royal Samaritan Hospital for Women: medical report, 1946; registers of patients, 1892–1968, including dispensary patients, 1927–67, and operations, 1956–72; ward journals, 1913–46; dispensary case notes, 1932–46; summaries of radium treatment, 1930–42; notes relating to early history of hospital, 1890; microfilm of press cuttings, 1925–48. 14 pages.

HB26
Lebanon Hospital for Mental and Nervous Disorders: minutes of general and executive committees, 1943–55; annual reports, 1941–52; correspondence of Dr Angus MacNiven relating to finances of hospital, 1943–55; pamphlet commemorating opening of Scottish house of hospital, 1933. 4 pages.

HB27
Lansdowne Clinic: annual reports, 1936–47; correspondence of Dr Angus MacNiven relating to founding of clinic, 1934–49. Board of management for Glasgow Royal mental hospital: annual reports, 1936–47. 4 pages.

HB28
Western Regional Hospital Board: statements of accounts and statistical data relating to finance, staffing, patients and other matters, 1948–73; annual accounts of boards of management, 1956–74; analysis of pharmacy department expenditure, 1963–4. 17 pages.

HB29
Foresthall Hospital: annual report, 1931; historical notes, c.1973. 3 pages.

HB30
Woodilee Hospital: Woodilee and Gartloch committee minutes, 1898–1923; annual reports, 1903–19; reports on Woodilee by HM commissioner of the general board of control, 1875–1948; business and administrative letter books, 1916–56, with register of business letters received, 1928–56; registers of admissions, discharges and deaths, 1875–1951, accidents, 1879–1951, escapes, 1879–1962, post mortems, 1881–1956, and staff, 1920–51; case notes, 1875–1956; social work department case files, 1957–74; visitors' books, 1877–1955; miscellaneous papers, bills, Acts of Parliament and pamphlets relating to health, welfare and lunacy in Glasgow and Scotland, 1857–1956. Glasgow district board of control: minutes, including Woodilee and Gartloch committees, 1898–1923. 20 pages.

HB31
Broomhill and Lanfine. Association for the relief of incurables in Glasgow and the west of Scotland: minutes, 1874–1948, including house, finance and medical committees, 1876–1948, and building sub-committee, 1894–5; annual reports, 1875–1947; accounts, 1874–1948, including expenditure analysis books, 1932–48; investments, 1937–48; registers of patients, including case notes, 1876–1948; Broomhill legal and estate papers and correspondence, 1879–1955, including some relating to flooding of river Kelvin, 1879–1938, and to application for exemption from provisions of NHS (Scotland) Act, 1947; letter books, 1874–1948; estate and hospital plans, 1892–1970; miscellaneous pamphlets and press cuttings, 1874–1947. Scottish national institute for incurables: directors' and committee minutes, 1874–8. Glasgow convalescent home, Lenzie: reports of visiting directors and medical officers, 1921–47. 18 pages.

HB32
Glasgow Northern Hospitals: bed complement returns, 1967–74, with correspondence on same, 1958–66; papers and correspondence of chairman's committee, 1957–67; papers and correspondence relating to endowment funds, 1949–50, voluntary help organisations, 1949–50, proposed new pharmacy and other building

developments at Stobhill, 1953–63, establishment of nurse training school at Stobhill, 1954–61, medical administration, 1955–69, hospital prescribing, 1961–6, and hospital catering, 1962–4; plan of the Glasgow convalescent home grounds, n.d.; legal and financial papers relating to Easter Auchinloch farm, Lenzie, 1948–51. 5 pages.
HB33
Birdston Hospital: plans of buildings and utilities, 1960–7. 2 pages.
HB34
Glasgow Hospitals Auxiliary Association: annual reports, 1949–78. 3 pages.
HB35
Papers of Sir Hector Hetherington: correspondence and papers concerning the relationship between Glasgow university and the NHS, psychiatric medicine in Glasgow, and other medical matters, 1934–50. 3 pages.
HB36
Robroyston Hospital: registers of tuberculosis, 1919–64, smallpox, 1919–54, puerperal fever, 1930–46, pneumonia, 1932–60, maternity, 1945–77, and gynaecology, 1946–60, patients, and of operations, 1939–77, vaccination, 1942–76, births, 1945–77, and mantoux tests, 1955–76; TB patients' case notes, 1925–7; details of TB patients sent to Switzerland, 1951–5; mortuary, 1920–77, and accident, 1962–76, books; patient and bed statistics, 1941–77. 5 pages.
HB37
Boards of Management for Glasgow Western Hospitals and for Glasgow Western and Gartnavel Hospitals: minutes of Glasgow western hospitals, 1948–68, and of Glasgow western and Gartnavel hospitals, 1968–74. 2 pages.
HB38
Corporation of the City of Glasgow: annual reports of the medical officer of health, 1901–62, medical inspection of schoolchildren, 1910–70, and education committee, 1922–39; printed, Scotch education department report, 1907; press cuttings relating to child welfare in Glasgow, 1909–73. Govan parish school board: map of the school board areas, 1904. 6 pages.
HB39
Kirkintilloch and Kilsyth Hospitals Board of Management: minutes, 1948–74, including liaison committee of the boards of the dental hospital, homoeopathic hospital, and Kirkintilloch and Kilsyth hospitals, 1949–66; register of seals, 1949–74. 3 pages.
HB40
Scottish Home and Health Department: miscellaneous publications and reports (to be listed).
HB41
Executive Council for the City of Glasgow: minutes, 1948–74, including special meetings, 1948–58, and western joint ophthalmic services committees, 1948–74; annual reports, 1952–73. City of Glasgow local dental committee: annual reports, 1952–79. Scottish medical practices committee: annual reports, 1949–75. 4 pages.
HB42
Ruchill Hospital: registers of patients, 1937–51, tuberculosis, 1943–53, infectious diseases, 1951–61, sanatorium, 1953–60, and deaths, 1956–66; unit register, 1961–2; indexes to registers of admissions, 1937–59; daily returns, 1934–55; Ruchill hospital opening brochure, 1900. 5 pages.
HB43
Killearn Hospital: registers of admissions and discharges, 1940–50. 2 pages.

HB44
Western District Hospital: registers of admissions, 1951–65, births, 1956–65, deaths, 1958–65, and operations, 1960–4; maternity, 1960–5, and casualty, 1963–5. 4 pages.

HB45
Glasgow Royal Maternity Hospital: Glasgow Royal maternity and women's hospital: minutes, 1911–47. 3 pages.

HB46
Scottish Association of Executive Councils: minutes of executive committee, with related correspondence, 1958–66; executive committee report, 1951; constitution and standing orders, n.d.; transactions of annual conference, 1948–73, with related papers, 1958–62; agenda of terminal meeting, 1974; memoranda drawn up by SAEC concerning Annis Gillie report, doctors' remuneration, and patients' expenses, 1958–65. 3 pages.

GHB1
Glasgow Royal Infirmary: minutes, 1787–1948, including finance committee, 1886–1909; annual reports, 1798–1947. Ophthalmic institution: minutes, 1881–91; annual reports, 1870–1940. Joint consultative committee of the Royal, Western and Victoria infirmaries and the Royal hospital for sick children: minutes, 1941–8. Board of management for Glasgow Royal Infirmary and associated hospitals: minutes, 1948–73; annual reports, 1948–73. 7 pages.

GHB4
Glasgow Royal Maternity Hospital: minutes, 1867–1948, including house, 1867–1916, students' residence, 1913–47, and stores, 1930–48, committees, and meetings of employees' representatives, 1913–47; annual, 1868–1947, ladies' auxiliary, 1927–34, and medical, 1929–51, reports; registers of patients, 1867–1961, including west end branch, 1888–96, fatal cases, 1916–52, operations, 1956–62, and admissions to labour ward, 1967–8; patients' monthly returns, 1916–38; case book, 1895; pathological, 1915–21, and ante-natal, 1942–6, journals; visitors' books, 1941–8; papers and plans relating to building work, 1899–1910; miscellaneous pamphlets, historical notes, press cuttings and photograph relating to maternity and Redlands hospitals, 1830–1974, including *The Chapbook of the Rottenrow,* 1913. Glasgow lying-in hospital: annual reports, 1858–67; registers of patients, 1834–67. Board of management for Glasgow maternity and women's hospitals: minutes, 1948–74, including diet committee, 1963–74, senior staff conference, 1964–8, and house committees of the maternity, 1966–74, and Redlands, 1966–70, hospitals; clinical reports of Glasgow Royal maternity and Ross hospitals, 1960–2. 12 pages.

GHB5
Glasgow Dental Hospital and School: minutes of management committee, 1885–1904, and boards of governors, 1904–48, and management, 1948–69; minutes of dental, 1885–1969, house, 1905–69, finance, 1932–70, and other committees; annual reports, 1885–1947; calendars, 1919–39; summaries of the work of the school, 1885–1924; student records, 1885–1927; visitors' book, 1905–46; correspondence relating to Dental Practitioners' Bill, 1878–9; miscellaneous pamphlets, programmes, press cuttings and plans, 1879–1970. 6 pages.

GHB6
Glasgow Royal Infirmary Historical Museum Collection. Glasgow Royal Infirmary: minutes of directors, 1840–1948, pathological museum committee, 1852–1902, senior residents, 1894–1914, and staff and executive association, 1911–75; annual reports, 1795–1973; printed copies of Royal charters, 1791–1932; regulations, 1867–1915; accounts, 1792–1921; legal and financial papers relating to subscribers and

bequests, 1781–1924, including printed minute of first meeting of subscribers' committee, 1788; superintendent's reports, 1840–3; weekly returns of admissions, dismissals and deaths, 1863–1930; ward journals, 1794–1869; professor Lister's operations book, 1864–90; visitors' books, 1903–43; correspondence and papers relating to fever wards, 1818–66, students, 1821–1908, lectures, 1824–1913, staff and premises, 1825–1918, St Mungo's burial ground, 1833–1903, chaplains, 1836–49, and other hospital business, 1795–1935; miscellaneous pamphlets and printed books relating to Glasgow hospitals, 1737–1972, including *A Short Account of the Town's Hospital in Glasgow,* 1737. St Mungo's college: correspondence and papers relating to administration and teaching, 1876–1914, including articles of association, 1889, and student certificates, 1908. Glasgow central dispensary: minutes, 1889–1940; annual reports, 1895–1914; list of subscribers. 1901–31; wages, 1919–40, and staff pensions, 1938–40, books. Glasgow ophthalmic institution: minutes, 1870–81; annual reports, 1887–1915; accounts, 1896–1910; subscribers' book, 1879–96; patients' books, 1871–91; visitors' book, 1858–1948. Schaw convalescent home: correspondence and papers, 1878–1931, including admissions book, 1909. 21 pages.

GHB7
Royal Hospital for Sick Children: private minute book (locked), n.d.; registers of nurses, 1882–1948; photographs of rebuilding at Yorkhill, 1969. 7 pages.

GHB10
Duke Street Hospital: registers of nurses, 1904–54, and midwifery staff, 1929–54; floor plans, 1929. 3 pages.

GHB13
Gartloch Hospital: annual reports, 1898–1916; registers of staff and patients, 1896–1968, admissions, discharges removals and deaths, 1896–1969, and establishment, 1897–1948; case notes, 1896–1955; visitors' books, 1897–1954, some containing reports by commissioners in lunacy and inspectors from the ministry of pensions; circulars and correspondence, 1897–1947; photographs of staff and premises, n.d. Board of management for Glasgow north-eastern mental hospitals: papers relating to endowments, 1948–72, building programme, 1949–56, reorganisation of health service, 1966–74, and general purposes committee, 1969–73; miscellaneous pamphlets and hospital magazines, 1925–73; plans, 1891–1925 and n.d. 14 pages.

GHB14
Gartnavel Royal Hospital: copy of letter to subscribers, 1812; regulations, 1899; plans of hospital at Gartnavel, *c.*1840; Gartnavel Christmas number, 1882. 2 pages.

GHB17
Victoria Infirmary: case notes, 1909–48. 17 pages.

GHB18
Leverndale Hospital: registers of admissions, discharges and deaths, 1895–1963, and establishment, 1910–48; case notes, 1895–1916; miscellaneous papers, 1895–1918, including plans of proposed Hawkhead asylum, 1893. 5 pages.

GHB21
Western Infirmary: registers of nurses, 1890–1930; pamphlets, photographs and press cuttings relating to staff and premises, 1898–1967. 5 pages.

GHB22
Glasgow Northern Hospitals Board of Management: minutes, 1948–74. 2 pages.

GHB23
Belvidere Hospital, Ruchill Hospital and Kennedy Street Hospital. Belvidere hospital: minutes of hospital medical society, 1890–2; annual, 1870–1914, and

physician superintendent's, 1927–41, reports; staff regulations, 1885; log book, 1889–97; registers of patients, 1870–4, staff, 1878–1964, and vaccination, 1920–48; operations' book, 1940–9; visitors' book, 1888–1942; medical and historical notes, press cuttings, and photographs of staff, premises and treatments used at Belvidere, c.1870–1971. Kennedy Street hospital: annual reports, 1865–1901; photograph of hospital, n.d. Ruchill hospital: annual reports, 1900–9; opening ceremony booklet, 1900; regulations for patients, n.d. Western Regional Hospital Board: annual reports on the work of the infectious diseases hospitals and their associated laboratory services, 1951–73. Papers relating to public health in Glasgow, 1866–1946, including: reports and lectures by Sir William Gairdner, 1866–90; sanitary department, annual and chief sanitary inspectors' reports, 1876–99; report on the air of Glasgow by E. M. Dixon, 1877; papers of Dr James Russell, 1879–86; annual reports of MOH for Dunbartonshire, 1891–7; Glasgow public health department medical appointments' book, 1926–46; meteorological notes by James Whitson, 1893–1902. 10 pages.
GHB24
Foresthall Hospital: register of children's admissions and dismissals, 1914–53; photographs of staff and premises, c.1920–70. Barnhill poorhouse: regulations, 1893–1905; wages' records, 1924–7. 2 pages.
GHB27
Stobhill Hospital: student nurses' duty books, 1919–64; photographs of staff and premises, 1931–c.1970. 3 pages.
GHB31
Greater Glasgow Health Board Library: Greater Glasgow Health Board: statements of accounts, 1975–7; bed-use statistics, 1974–current; annual reports of city of Glasgow MOH, 1965–72; miscellaneous pamphlets and reports concerning GGHB institutions, 1966–76. Western Regional Hospital Board: minutes, 1947–72; annual reports, 1966–72; statements of accounts, 1959–74. 8 pages.
GHB33
Glasgow Royal Infirmary: minutes of chairman's salaries' and other committees, 1920–47; annual reports, 1915–73; regulations, 1852–1915; accounts, 1914–45; papers relating to legacies and endowments, c.1860–1955; pamphlets, books and press cuttings mainly relating to history of Glasgow Royal, 1832–1971. Papers relating to Queen Victoria jubilee institute for nurses, 1888–1926, and to district nursing in Scotland, c.1925–c.1945. 7 pages.
GHB35
Glasgow Royal Infirmary: nursing class roll books, 1893–1918, and lecture notes, c.1895–9; experimental scheme for nurses' training, 1956–67; miscellaneous pamphlets, press cuttings, correspondence and photographs relating to Mrs Rebecca Strong, matron 1879–1907, nursing, and history of Glasgow Royal, 1893–1974. 3 pages.
HH66
Western Infirmary: ward journals, 1874–1942, with indexes, 1901–34. 83 pages.
HH67
Glasgow Royal Infirmary: registers of admissions and dismissals, 1794–1939, including army book 27A, 1915–6; indexes of patients, 1829–1939, including ophthalmic, 1921–39; ward journals, 1811–1943, including fever, 1815–55, ophthalmic, 1897–1939, wounded soldiers, 1914–7, and casualty, 1917–42; gynaecological department clinical abstracts, 1911–39. St Mungo's college: medical superintendent's reports, 1907–22, and letters, 1910–28; register of students, 1891–1920. 158 pages.

Bibliography

1.   Primary sources

Barony Parochial Board Minutes SRA D HEW 2/1
  House Committee Minutes SRA D HEW 2/1
Brodie, Revd J., typescript, A History of Glasgow Mental Hospital 1810–1948
Corporation of Glasgow Minute books SRA
Faculty of Medicine, University of Glasgow
Faculty of Physicians and Surgeons of Glasgow, Minute books 1790–1911
Faculty of Physicians and Surgeons of Glasgow, Regulations and Laws
General Register of patients admitted to Lunatic Asylums SRA MC 7/1, 1859
Glasgow Asylum for Lunatics AR, ML 1814–1900
Glasgow Asylum for Lunatics, patient case notes, 1830–1865
Glasgow City Parochial Board Minutes SRA D HEW 1/1
  House Committee Minutes SRA D HEW 1/1
  Finance Committee Minutes SRA D HEW 1/1
Glasgow Faculty of Medicine, Minute Books of, 1824
Glasgow Lying in Hospital Minute Book of, 1834 GUL Gen., Ms 76
Glasgow Medical Society Essays
Glasgow's parochial Boards, Minutes of, SRA
Glasgow Royal Infirmary, AR from 1800
Glasgow Royal Infirmary, Historical Museum Collection
Glasgow Royal Infirmary, Records of (Minutes) GGHB1/1/17 GGHB1/1/18
Glasgow University Lying in Hospital and Dispensary Minute Book GUA 191, 79
Letters written to William MacKenzie 1814–19, RCPSG
Local Government Board for Scotland AR
Medical Officer of Health for the city of Glasgow
Medical and Sanitary Committee of City Parish, 1847 SRA D HEW 1/5
Report of the General Committee appointed to carry into effect the proposals for a
    Lunatic Asylum in Glasgow, ML
Report of the Lord Provost, Magistrates and Council of Glasgow at the opening of
    the Lunatic Asylum, ML
Student notes of lectures by Harry Rainy and J. B. Cowan, RCPSG
University of Glasgow, Matriculation album of
University of Glasgow, Graduation Roll

2.   Newspapers and periodicals

Archives of Skiagraphy (from 1896) became Archives of the Röntgen Ray in 1897
Bulletin of the Institute of History of Medicine
British Journal of Photography (from 1860)
British Journal of Radiography
British Medical Journal
Edinburgh Medical Journal
Gartnavel Christmas number 1882
Gartnavel Gazette 1903–25
Glasgow Herald
Glasgow Medical Journal
Glasgow Philosophical Society, Proceedings of, after 1901 Royal, after 1960, the
    Philosophical Journal

Isis
Journal of the Royal Sanitary Institute
Lancet
Medical History
Nature
Photographic Review
Practical Photography
Royal Society, proceedings of
Sanitary Journal, vol. I called Sanitary Journal for Scotland Glasgow 1876–1902
Scottish Medical Journal
Scottish Society for the History of Medicine, report of Proceedings
Scotsman
Tuberculosis (from 1899)

3. Official reports

1842	Sanitary condition of the labouring population of Britain HL xxviii
1844	On the administration and practical operation of the Poor Laws (Scotland) RC including minutes of evidence (557) xx (563) xxvi (543)
1857	Report of the RC appointed to enquire into the state of lunatic asylums in Scotland and the existing law in reference to lunatics and lunatic asylums in Scotland (A. E. Monteith) (2148) v
1867–68	Police (Scotland) county and burgh police systems SC HL (Earl of Minto) report, minutes of evidence and appendix (486) ix
1868–69	On the poor laws, Scotland SC HC; proceedings, minutes of evidence, appendix and index (301) xi 1.
1871	SC on the protection of infant lives HC July 1871 (372)
1884	Housing of the working classes, RC (Sir C. W. Dilke) 2nd Report (Scotland) c.4409, xxxi, 1.
1889	On the blind, deaf and dumb of the United Kingdom, RC evidence and appendix c.5781, xix, xx
1895	Lunacy (Scotland), increasing prevalence of insanity, GBCL Supplement to 36th AR c.7610, liv
1903	Report of the RC on Physical Training (Scotland) vol. I Report and Appendix; Cd.1507, xxx, 1 vol. II Evidence and Index; Cd.1508, xxx, 123
1904	Report of the inter-departmental committee on Physical deterioration Vol. I Report and Appendix; Cd.2175, xxxii, 1 Vol. II List of Witnesses and Evidence; Cd.2210, xxxii, 145 Vol. III Appendices and Index; Cd.2186, xxxii, 655
1905	Report of the Inter-departmental committee on medical inspection and feeding of children attending public elementary schools Vol. I report and appendices 1905; Cd.2779
1909–10	On the poor laws and relief of distress RC Cd.4798 Vol. VI Minutes of evidence, with appendices relating to Scotland Report on Scotland Cd.4922 Vol. XXX Documents relating especially to Scotland; Cd.5440 liv, 595
1936	Committee on Scottish Health Services, Report, Edinburgh Cmd.5204, xi, 577

4. Other reports

Board of Supervision of relief of the poor in Scotland AR from 1847 SRA
General Board of Commissioners of Lunacy for Scotland AR from 1857
Glasgow Hospital Reports 1898–1900 vols 1, 2 and 3
Glasgow Municipal Commission on the housing of the poor Glasgow 1904
Local Government Board, Reports from 1894–1920 SRA
Maternity and Child welfare, Scheme for, Glasgow Committee on Health, 1926
Medical Officer of Health, Reports, Glasgow
  Dr Gairdner
    1863 Quarterly reports for April, July, October
    1864 January (the 960 district scheme)
    1865 October (the 54 district scheme)
    1869 March (the high mortality figures for first quarter of 1869)
    1870 AR
    1871 AR
  Dr Russell
    1872 AR
    1873–80 Remarks to accompany quarterly tables on mortality GUL
    1881 Decennial census, report on
    1891 Decennial census, report on
  The 1897 Public Health Act required the MOH to produce an annual report
1898–1972 AR of MOH, GUL
Scottish Board of Health, AR, 1919–29
Scottish Department of Health, AR, 1929–49
Transactions of the Edinburgh meeting and conference on Tuberculosis July 1910

5. Directories

Glasgow Post Office Directories 1800–1921
Medical Directory for Scotland 1852
Medical Directories 1860–1921

6. Books, pamphlets and articles

(A) *Before 1837*

Adams, A. M., *Sketches from Life* (Glasgow, 1835).
Anon., *A Short account of the Town's Hospital* (Glasgow, 1742).
  Prices fixed by the Physicians and Surgeons of Glasgow for medicines and attendance (Glasgow, 1799).
  Report of the Town's Hospital of Glasgow on the management of the city poor (Glasgow, 1818).
  Regulations for the Town's Hospital of Glasgow (Glasgow, 1830).
Battie, W., *A Treatise on Madness* (London, 1758).
Bell, B., *Treatise on Lues Venerea* (Edinburgh, 1793).
Bell, George Hamilton, *Treatise on the Cholera Asphyxia* (Edinburgh, 1831).

Bellers, J., *An Essay towards the improvement of Physick in 12 proposals: The Assigns of J. Sowle* (London, 1714).
Bentham, J., *Panopticon, or the Inspection House* (London, 1791). *Management of the Poor* (Dublin, 1796).
Buchanan, M. S., *History of the Glasgow Royal Infirmary* (Glasgow and London, 1832).
Cleland, James, *Abridgement of the Annals of Glasgow* (Glasgow, 1817).
	Enumeration of the Inhabitants of the City of Glasgow and its Connected Suburbs (Glasgow, 1820).
	Statistical Tables relative to the City of Glasgow. 3rd edn (Glasgow, 1823).
	Enumeration of the Inhabitants of Scotland . . . and Mortality Bills for the City of Glasgow from 1820 to 1828 (Glasgow, 1828*a*).
	Enumeration of the Inhabitants of Scotland and the Bills of Mortality for Glasgow, 1821–27 (Glasgow, 1828*b*).
	Enumeration of the Inhabitants of the City of Glasgow and County of Lanark, 1831 (Glasgow, 1832).
	Letter to His Grace the Duke of Hamilton and Brandon Respecting the Parochial Registers of Glasgow (Glasgow, 1834).
	A Historical Account of Bills of Mortality and the Probability of Human Life in Glasgow and other large Towns (Glasgow, 1836).
Denholm, James, *History of Glasgow* (Glasgow, 1804).
Duncan, A., *Observations on the operation and use of Mercury in the Venereal Disease* (Edinburgh, 1772).
	A proposal for establishing a lunatic asylum in the neighbourhood of the city (Edinburgh, 1792).
	Reports of the practice in the clinical wards during November and December, 1817, January, May, June, July, 1818 (Edinburgh, 1818).
	A letter to Sir William Fettes affording demonstrative evidence that much great benefit will arise from improving the Royal Infirmary by the establishment of a Lock Hospital and an hospital for incurables, than by beginning a new rival infirmary (Edinburgh, 1825).
Duncan, J. J., *Tables of the Probability and Expectation of Male and Female Life in Glasgow* (Glasgow, 1829).
Gourlay, J., *A Glasgow Miscellany, the Tobacco period in Glasgow 1707–1755.* Privately printed n.d.
Graham, R., *Practical Observations on Continued fever with some remarks on the most effective plans for its suppression* (Glasgow, 1818).
Halliday, Sir A., *A general view of the present state of lunatics and lunatic asylums in Great Britain and Ireland and in some other Kingdoms* (London, 1828).
Harrison, Edward, *An Address delivered to the Lincolnshire Benevolent Society* (London, 1810).
Henderson, W., *Address to the Inhabitants of Aberdeen respecting the Medical Attendance of the Poor at their own Houses* (Aberdeen, 1822).
Howard, J., *Account of Principal Lazarettos in Europe* (Warrington, 1789).
Lettsom, T. C., *Medical memoirs of the General Dispensary in London 1773–1774* (London, 1774).
	Hints designed to promote beneficence, temperance and medical science (London, 1801).
MacGill, S., *On Lunatic Asylums, A Discourse delivered August 2, 1810, previous*

to laying the foundation stone of the Glasgow Lunatic Asylum (Glasgow, 1810).

Morison, A., *Cases of Mental disease, with practical observations on the medical treatment* (1828).

Poole, R., *An Essay on Education applicable to Children in general: the defective, the criminal; the poor, the adult and aged* (Edinburgh, 1825).

Stark, W., *Remarks on public hospitals for the cure of mental derangement (Edinburgh, 1807).*

Remarks on the construction of Public Hospitals for the Cure of Mental Derangement (Glasgow, 1810).

(B) *1837–1901*

Adam, J. R., *Gartnavel Minstrel,* Consisting of original pieces in rhyme, both comic and sentimental, with notes and a brief biographical sketch of the author (Glasgow, 1845).

Alison, W. P., *Observations on the Management of the Poor in Scotland* (Edinburgh, 1840).

Remarks on the Report of Her Majesty's Commission on the Poor Laws of Scotland (Edinburgh, 1844).

Anon., *Report of the Managers of the Charity Work-house, on the Lunatic Asylum* (Edinburgh, 1842).

Lectures on Medical Missions (Edinburgh, 1849).

'How Scottish doctors live', *GMJ* (1864).

The Philosophy of Insanity, by a late inmate of Glasgow Royal Asylum for Lunatics at Gartnavel (Glasgow, 1865).

Voices from Gartnavel Asylum, Extracts from My Diary (Glasgow, 1865).

Joint Hospital, Abstract of Agreement . . . of Burghs of Partick, Hillhead, and Maryhill for the erection and Maintenance of a joint Hospital for the treatment of patients under the Public Health (Scotland) Act 1867 (Glasgow, 1874).

A District Nurse's Diary, *GMJ* (1878).

Edinburgh Health Society, Health lectures for the people (Edinburgh, 1882).

Discussion on antisepsis, *GMJ* (Glasgow, 1880).

The Lord Provosts of Glasgow 1833–83 (Glasgow, 1883).

(James Erskine, MB), *The Abuse of our Medical Charities* (Glasgow, 1886).

Report of proceedings at the official inspection by the Lord Provost, Magistrates and Council of Belvidere Hospital as finally completed 4 March 1887 (Glasgow, 1887).

Rules and Regulations of Glasgow Royal Infirmary (Glasgow, 1894).

Royal Hospital for Sick Children, 45 Scott Street (Glasgow, n.d.).

List of some of the contributions to surgical literature by William Macewen, lecturer on surgery, Glasgow Royal Infirmary School of medicine, and surgeon to the Royal Infirmary, Glasgow, with comments by the medical press and other published statements by surgeons on the ideas advanced and the work done by him. (n.p., n.d.) (GUL store G17-y-18).

Baird, C. R., *Report on the Sanitary regulation of Glasgow* (Glasgow, 1841).

Report on the general and sanitary condition of the working classes and the poor in the city of Glasgow (Glasgow, 1841).

Balfour, G. W., 'How the Royal Hospital for Sick Children was founded', *EHR,* **1,** 35–41 (Edinburgh, 1893).

Beattie, P., *Barony Parochial Law* (Glasgow, 1881).
Bell, J., 'The Surgical Side of the Royal Infirmary', *EHR*, 1 (Edinburgh, 1893).
Bell, J. and Paton, J., *Glasgow its municipal organisation and administration* (Glasgow, 1896).
Blackwell, E., *Pioneer Work in opening the Medical Profession to Women.* (Hastings 1895).
Bristowe, Dr and Homes, Mr, *The Hospitals of the United Kingdom* (HMSO, 1864).
British and Foreign Medical Review, 14 (1842).
Browne, W. A. F., *What Asylums were, are and ought to be, being the substance of Five Lectures delivered before the Managers of the Montrose Royal Lunatic Asylum* (Edinburgh, 1837).
Buchanan, G., *Clinical Surgery* (Glasgow, 1876).
    'Address at the opening of the Medico-Chirurgical Society', *GMJ* (1881).
    'Glasgow Royal Infirmary: reminiscences', *GMJ,* 42 (1894).
Buckie, F., *Vital and Economical Statistics of the Hospitals for the Year 1863* (London, 1865).
Burdett, Sir H. C., *Cottage Hospitals* (London, 1880).
    Burdett's Hospitals and Charities, 1899 (London, 1899).
    Hospitals and Asylums of the World (London, 1891–3).
Carmichael, J., 'The Edinburgh Royal Hospital for Sick Children', *EHR,* 4 (Edinburgh, 1896).
Chalmers, A. K., *A new life table for Glasgow based on the mortality of the ten years 1881–90* (Glasgow, 1894).
Chalmers, T., *Selected Works* (Edinburgh, 1854).
Charteris, A. H., *Address at the opening of the Deaconess Hospital* (Edinburgh 1894).
Christie, J., *The Medical Institutions of Glasgow* (Glasgow, 1888).
Christison, R., *The Life of Sir Robert Christison, Bart.* (Edinburgh, 1885).
Clark, H. E., 'On the changes in surgical theory and practice in the past twenty-five years', *GMJ* (1899).
Clouston, T. S., 'New Craig House, Royal Edinburgh Asylum', *EHR,* 3 (Edinburgh, 1895).
Clugston, B., *West of Scotland Convalescent Sea-side Homes, Dunoon, being a short account of their present position and capabilities of extension and use* (Glasgow, 1871).
    Homes of refuge for the stricken . . . a short account of a visit to Putney and other hospitals for incurables (Glasgow, 1874).
Collins, A. G., *Glasgow School Board* (1879).
Coats, J. and Gairdner, W. T., *Lectures to Practitioners* (London, 1886).
Corder, Susanna, *Life of Elizabeth Fry: compiled from her journal, as edited by her daughters* (London, 1853).
Cowan, Robert, *Statistics of Fever and Smallpox in Glasgow* (Glasgow, 1837).
    Vital Statistics of Glasgow (Glasgow, 1840).
Cox, Sir James, 'On the Condition of the Insane in Scotland, as influenced by Legislation', *TNASS*, Edinburgh meeting 1863 (London, 1864).
Dale, W., *The State of the Medical Profession in Great Britain and Ireland* (Dublin, 1875).
Dougall, J., *A historical sketch of the Glasgow Southern medical society* (Glasgow, 1888).
Drysdale, C. R., *On Treatment of syphilis, and other diseases without mercury:*

being a collection of evidence to prove that mercury is a cause of disease, not a remedy (London, 1863).

Duncan, Alexander, *Memorials of the Faculty of Physicians and Surgeons of Glasgow,* (Glasgow 1896).

Duncan, E., *A plea for an hospital on the south side of Glasgow* (Glasgow, 1878).

Finlayson, J., *Glasgow Hospital for Sick Children* (Glasgow, 1888).

Finlayson, James, *Life and Works of Dr Peter Lowe* (Glasgow, 1889).

Frazer, Daniel, *The Story of Buchanan Street* (Glasgow, 1840).

Freeman, R. G., *The Straus milk charity* (New York, 1895).
   Milk pasteurization (New York, 1897).

Gairdner, W. T., *On medicine and medical education,* 3 lectures (Edinburgh, 1858).
   Public Health in relation to air and water (Edinburgh, 1862).
   'The Edinburgh Royal Infirmary in the Fifties', *EHR,* **2** (Edinburgh, 1894).
   Clinical Medicine (Edinburgh, 1862).
   The Sanitary Visitation Movement (Glasgow, 1867).

Gibson, G. A., 'The Deaconess Hospital, Edinburgh', *EHR,* **3** (Edinburgh, 1895).

Glaister, J., 'Sanitary and Epidemic History of Glasgow 1783–1883', *PSG* (1886).

Gordon, J. E., 'Distinguished British Nurses of the past. Mrs Rebecca Strong—pioneer and centenarian, 1843–1944', *Midwife, Health Visitor and Community Nurse,* **II,** 396 (December 1975).

Grainger, S., 'Sketch of the history of the Royal Infirmary and of the development of clinical teaching', *EHR,* **1** (Edinburgh, 1893).

Ireland, W. W., *On Idiocy and Imbecility* (London, 1877).

Jex-Blake, S., *Medical Women* (Edinburgh, 1872).

Kelvin Lord, 'Presidential address', *Proc. Roy. Soc* (1893).

Klein, 'On Tuberculosis with regard to diseased meat and infectious disease', *Sanitary Journal,* **XIII** (1889).

Lamond, H., *The Constitution and Rules and Regulations of the Glasgow Royal Infirmary* (Glasgow, 1867).

Lister, J., 'The effects of the antiseptic system . . .', *Lancet* (1870).

Macgeorge, A., *The Royal Hospital for Sick Children and its dispensary* (Glasgow, 1889).

Macintyre, J., 'Some notes on the use of electric light in Medicine'. *GMJ* (1885).
   'Direct vision by means of Röntgen rays', *Lancet* (1896).
   'Action of the X-rays', *Lancet* (1896).
   'Application of Röntgen Rays to the soft tissues of the body,' *Nature* (1896).
   'The application of the Röntgen rays in the medical and surgical departments of the Royal Infirmary, Glasgow,' *GHR* (1898).
   'X-rays: Instantaneous photography and experiments upon the heart and other soft tissues,' *Lancet* (1896).
   'Photography of renal calculus; description of an adjustable modification in the focus tube', *Lancet* (1896).
   'X-ray records for the cinematograph', *Archives of Skiagraphy* (1897).

Mackenzie, W. Leslie, 'The Hygienics of Milk', *EMJ* (1898).

Macleod, Sir G. H. B., *Address on Surgery.* BMA meeting (Glasgow, 1888).

McLeod, K. M., *The City's Sanitary Organisation* (Glasgow, 1872).

Mapother, E., *The Medical Profession* (Dublin, 1868).

Moir, D. M., *A Modern Pythagorian* (Glasgow, 1838).

Morison, A., *Outlines of Lectures on the Nature, Causes and treatment of Insanity* (London, 1848).

Morton, J., 'Carbolic Acid', *Lancet* (1870).

Munro, Revd A., *Sore Nipples and Nursing* (Aberdeen, 1861–2).
Napper, A., *On the advantages derivable to the medical profession, and the public, from the village hospital* (London, 1866).
Newsholme, Dr, *Public Health* (1899).
Nightingale, F., *Introductory notes on Lying-in institutions* (London, 1871).
    Notes on Nursing: what it is and what it is not (London, n.d.)
    Notes on Nursing for the Labouring Classes (London, 1876).
Pagan, J. M., *The Medical Jurisprudence of Insanity* (London, 1840).
    'Remarks on the statistics of Glasgow University Lying-in Hospital from 1st November 1852 till 1st January 1860', *GMJ* (1860–1).
Perry, R., *Observations on the Sanitary State of Glasgow* (Glasgow, 1841).
Philip, R. W., 'The Victoria Hospital for Consumption, Edinburgh', *EHR, 3* (Edinburgh, 1895).
Pollock, C. Fred., 'Anderson's College'. *GMJ* (1888).
Poole, R., *Memoranda Regarding the Royal Lunatic Asylum, Infirmary and Dispensary of Montrose* (Montrose, 1841).
Rathbone, W., *The History and Progress of District Nursing* (London, 1890).
Richardson, B. W., *Vita Medica* (London, 1897).
Rivington, W., *The Medical Profession* (Dublin, 1879).
Röntgen, W. C., 'On a new kind of Ray', *Nature* (1896).
Russell, James Burn, 'Analysis of 300 cases of Typhus Fever,' *GMJ* (1864).
    'Suggestions for the Logical Use of Hospital Statistics', Hospital Report (1866).
    'A Clinical Study of Stimulation in Typhus Fever', *GMJ* (1867).
    'On the Distribution of Enteric Fever in Glasgow', *GMJ* (1869).
    'Note of Disinfection with Carbolic Acid Vapour', *GMJ* (1869).
    'Cases of Typhus Fever, fatal, with rare complications', *GMJ* (1869).
    'Cases of Typhus Fever, fatal, with Intestinal Haemorrhage', *GMJ* (1869).
    'On Excretion of Urea in Typhus Fever, in relation to Temperature' (in conjunction with the late Dr Joseph Coats), *GMJ* (1869).
    'Clinical Observations on Hydrate of Chloral as a Hypnotic in Typhus Fever', *GMJ* (1870).
    'Liebreich's theory on the action of Chloral', *GMJ* (1870).
    'Cases of Pyogenic Fever (Jenner)', *GMJ* (1871).
    'On Sub-Glottic Oedema of the Larynx and permanent Stricture following Typhus', *GMJ* (1871).
    'On revaccination', *GMJ* (1871).
    'Notes on the use of Xylol in Small-pox with reference to the fallacies incidental to the treatment of Small-pox', *GMJ* (1872).
    'A Study of 972 cases of Small-pox with reference to the modifying influence of vaccination', *GMJ* (1872).
    'Report of an outbreak of Enteric Fever connected with milk supply (Parkhead)', *GMJ* (1873).
    'The Air of Glasgow, a review', *GMJ* (1873).
    'Occasional Reports on local Outbreaks of Epidemic Disease', *GMJ* (1874).
    'On the immediate results of the operations of the Glasgow Improvement Trust as regards the inhabitants displaced', *PSG* (1874).
    Report on Construction of Small-pox Hospitals (Glasgow, 1874).
    Report on certain outbreaks of Enteric Fever in Glasgow (Glasgow 1875).
    'Further information on the immediate results of the Operations of the Glasgow Improvement Trust as regards the Inhabitants displaced.' *GMJ* (1876).
    'An address on the sanitary results of the Glasgow Improvement Act delivered

at the opening of the Section on Public Medicine at the Sheffield meeting of the British Medical Association', *Sanitary Journal for Scotland*, I (1876).

'Local Vices of Buildings, as affecting the Death-rate', *Sanitary Journal for Scotland*, I (1876).

Report upon uncertified deaths in Glasgow (Glasgow, 1876).

'On the influence of the Friendly Societies Act, 1875, upon the proportion of uncertifed deaths in Glasgow', *GMJ* (1876).

'On the comparative prevalence of Filth Diseases in town and country', *PSG* (1877).

'Illustrations of a high death-rate independently of Zymotic Diseases', *Sanitary Journal for Scotland* (1877).

Report on outbreak of Enteric Fever in the West-end of Glasgow and Hillhead, with Memorandum on the milk supply of Glasgow in relation to dissemination of disease by milk (Glasgow, 1878).

Report on the Air of Glasgow, chiefly relative to enclosed spaces and smoke, by William J. Dunnachie, in co-operation with the MOH (Glasgow, 1879).

Lectures on the theory and general prevention and control of infectious disease, and of air, water supply, sewage disposal, and food, by William Wallace, PhD, FCS, delivered under the auspices of the Lord Provost, Magistrates, and Town Council of the City of Glasgow, and published by them (Glasgow, 1879).

'First principles of cleanliness as regards earth, air, and water', *Sanitary Journal for Scotland*, II (1879).

'On the result of Inquiries after defaulters under the Vaccination (Scotland) Act, 1863', *Sanitary Journal for Scotland*, II (1879).

'On the conveyance of the contagion of Anthrax to Hair Factory Workers, as illustrative of the particulate theory of infection', *PSG* (1880). (See also report of certain cases of sickness and death occurring among the workers in Adelphi Hair Factory, Glasgow, 1878, in Appendix to the Report of the Medical Officer of the Local Government Board of England, 1878).

Ventilation, Local Authority of Glasgow *v.* Young, *Sanitary Journal for Scotland*, II (1880).

Itch. A memorandum on the duties of Local Authorities with regard to Itch (Glasgow, 1880).

Certain epidemic outbreaks of Enteric Fever in April, 1880, traced to contamination of milk (Glasgow, 1880).

Remarks by the Medical Officer to accompany Quarterly Tables on Mortality (1873–80).

A Sanitary retrospect, The Decade, 1871–81, *PSG* (1881).

The House, Glasgow Health Lectures (Glasgow, 1881).

Report on cases of infectious disease in Dairy Farms (Glasgow, 1881).

'On the existing sanitary regulations of the Milk Trade', *Sanitary Journal for Scotland*, Part I (1881).

'On the existing sanitary regulations of the Milk Trade', *Sanitary Journal for Scotland*, Part II (1881).

Adulterated Butterine, *Sanitary Journal for Scotland* (1881).

Report on an outbreak of Splenic-apoplexy, or Anthrax, at Elderslie, near Glasgow, *Sanitary Journal for Scotland* (1881).

Report on outbreak of Fever at Balfron, *Sanitary Journal for Scotland* (1882).

Memorandum on the Hospital accommodation for infectious diseases in Glasgow (Glasgow, 1882).

'On transgressions of jurisdiction in medical relief of sickness', *Sanitary Journal for Scotland* (1882).

'The policy and practice of Glasgow in the management of epidemic diseases, with results, 1881–2', *Epidemiological Society of London* (1883).

'Remarks upon night inspection for overcrowding during last 11 years in Glasgow', *Sanitary Journal for Scotland* (1883).

Sanitary reform in the rural districts of Scotland. A necessity in the interests of populous places, *Sanitary Journal for Scotland.*

On Disinfection, *GMJ* (1884).

Report on outbreak of Enteric Fever in Glasgow Royal and Western Infirmaries, and at the Fever Hospital of Belvidere in Glasgow.

The houses of the poor and the responsibility of landlords: an address, *Sanitary Journal for Scotland* (1884).

Public Health and Pauperism, *Sanitary Journal for Scotland* (1884).

Children of the City. What can we do for them? *Edinburgh Health Lectures* (1886).

The Vital Statistics of the City of Glasgow, Parts I, II and III, including a retrospect of the 15 years, 1871–85 (Glasgow, 1886).

'On some Sociological aspects of Sanitation', *PSG* (1887).

The house in relation to Public Health, Insurance and Actuarial Society of Glasgow, (Glasgow 1887).

Reports on the air of Glasgow with tables of wind, temperature, and rainfall, by S. M. Dickson, BSc, in co-operation with the MOH (7 in number) (Glasgow, 1887–8).

On the 'Ticketed Houses' of Glasgow, with an interrogation of the facts for guidance towards the amelioration of the lives of their occupants, *PSG* (1888).

The history and circumstances of a peculiar outbreak of febrile disease in St. Mary's Roman Catholic Industrial School for boys (Glasgow, 1888).

The City of Glasgow Fever and Smallpox Hospitals, Belvidere (Glasgow, 1888).

Life in one room: A lecture delivered to the Park Parish Literary Institute (Glasgow, 1888).

Sanitation and Social Economics, *PSG* (1889).

On Common Lodging-houses, *Social and Sanitary Society of Edinburgh* (1889).

Sanitary requirements of a Dairy Farm (Glasgow, 1889).

Errors in diagnosis of infectious disease (Glasgow, 1890).

Report on Greening Vegetables with Sulphate of Copper (1890).

On some relations of the business of the Dairy Farm to public health: An address to the Glasgow and West of Scotland Agricultural Society (Glasgow, 1890).

Memorandum on the proposed open space in Cowcaddens (1892).

Obituary of W. R. W. Smith (Glasgow, 1893).

On food preservatives in relation to the provisions of the Food and Drugs Acts (1894).

'Uninhabitable houses', A paper read at the Congress of the Sanitary Association of Scotland (1894).

The evolution of the function of Public Health Administration, as illustrated by the sanitary history of Glasgow, etc. (Glasgow, 1895).

On the Prevention of Tuberculosis (Glasgow, 1895).

'On the physical laws which govern the distribution of infection:' An Address as President of the Preventive Medicine Section, British Institute of Public Health, Glasgow Congress (1896).

'A history of meat inspection in Glasgow. The detective v. Clearing-house system'. An Address as President of the Sanitary Association of Scotland, Annual Congress (Dumfries, 1896).

'Public Health and social problems'. An Address to the Glasgow University Medico-Chirurgical Society (February, 1898).

Simpson, A. R., 'Sketch of the history of the Royal Maternity and Simpson Memorial Hospital'. *EHR*, 1 (Edinburgh, 1893).

Spens, W. C., *Should the Poor Law in all Cases Deny Relief to the Able-bodied Poor?* (Edinburgh, 1879).

Stark, James, *Contributions to the vital statistics of Scotland* (London, 1851).

Stewart, A. M., *Romish Nurses: with an appendix . . . containing letters to the managers of the Glasgow Royal Infirmary* (Glasgow, 1878).

Stewart, H. D., *Statistics of Insanity: Crichton Royal* (n.p.n.d.).

Strang, John, *Report on the Census of Glasgow and Suburbs for 1851* (Glasgow, 1851).

Report on the Census of the Parliamentary and Municipal City of Glasgow for 1861 (Glasgow, 1861).

Economic and Social Statistics of Glasgow and the West of Scotland for various Years from 1851 to 1861 (Glasgow, 1862).

Strange, W., *Health and sickness of towns population* (London, 1846).

Straus, N., *The influence of a pure milk supply on the death-rate of children* (New York, 1897).

Strong, R., *Education in Nursing* (Glasgow, 1893).

Swete, H., *Village hospitals and their position with regard to County Infirmaries, Unions and the professions* (London, 1866).

Swinton, A. A. C., 'Professor Röntgen's Discovery'. *Nature* (1896).

Thomas, M., *Suggestions to Improve the Nursing in the Glasgow Royal Infirmary* (Glasgow, 1877).

The Royal Infirmary and the Royal Infirmary School of Medicine (Glasgow, 1888).

Thomson, J., *Life, lectures and writings of William Cullen, MD* (Edinburgh, 1859).

Tiffany, F., *Dorothea Lynde Dix* (Boston, 1890).

Transactions, Epidemiological Society of London, *The Policy and practice of Glasgow in the management of epidemic diseases* (1881–2).

Tuke, H. D., *Chapters in the history of the insane of the British Isles* (London, 1882).

Reform in the Treatment of the Insane (London, 1892).

Early history of the Retreat, York (London, 1892).

Watt, Alexander, *Report on the Local Census of Lanarkshire* (Glasgow, 1841).

The Glasgow Bills of Mortality for 1841 and 1842 (Glasgow, 1844).

The Vital Statistics of Glasgow for 1843 and 1844 (Glasgow, 1846).

Waring, E. J., *Cottage Hospitals, their objects, advantages and management* (London, 1876).

Weir, W., *Address on the origin and early history of the Faculty of Physicians and Surgeons of Glasgow* (Glasgow, 1864).

Wilson, C., *On the Expediency of Founding an Hospital for the Diseases of Children, with notes on Continental Children's Hospitals* (Edinburgh, 1859).

Yellowlees, D., 'Glasgow Royal Asylum, Gartnavel' in J. Christie, *The Medical Institution of Glasgow* (Glasgow, 1888).

(C) *1902–1981*

Abel-Smith, B., *A History of the Nursing Profession* (London, 1960).
   The Hospitals, 1800–1948: a study of Social Administration in England and Wales (London, 1964).
Ackerknecht, E. H., 'The role of Medical History in Medical Education', in *BIHM* **21**, (1947).
   Short History of Psychiatry (London, 1959).
Alexander, F. and Selesrick, S. T., *The History of Psychiatry* (New York, 1967).
Anderson, J. B., MacKenzie, *Glasgow Royal Infirmary, Three great names on the Infirmary Roll* (Glasgow, 1930).
Anderson, J. Wallace, *Four Chiefs of the Glasgow Royal Infirmary* (Glasgow, 1916).
Anon., *National Association for the prevention of Consumption, an historical sketch* (London, 1926).
   Lister and the Lister Ward in the Royal Infirmary of Glasgow. A centenary contribution (Glasgow, 1927).
   'Mrs Rebecca Strong's Anniversary', *Nursing Mirror* (22 April 1939).
   Fortuna Domus (Glasgow, 1952).
   Administrative re-organisation of the Scottish Health Service. HMSO (1968).
Arthur, J. R., *Introduction to Social Psychiatry* (London, 1972).
Ashton, A. F. and Young, E. T., *British Social Work in the Nineteenth Century* (London, 1962).
Ayers, G. M., *England's first State Hospitals and the Metropolitan Asylums Board, 1867–1930* (London, 1971).
Bell, E. M., *The Story of Hospital Almoners* (n.p., 1961).
Best, G., *Mid-Victorian Britain 1851–75* (London, 1971).
Blackwell, E., *Essays in medical sociology* (London, 1902).
Blackwell, W., *Medicine and Society in America* (New York, 1972).
Blanco, R. L., 'The Attempted Control of Venereal Disease in the army in Mid-Victorian England', *Journal of the Society of Army Historical Research,* **45** (1967).
Bleich, A. R., *The Story of X-rays from Röntgen to Isotopes* (New York, 1960).
Blythswood, Lord and Scoble, W. A., 'Recent work on X-ray measurement', *PSG* (1907).
Boog Watson, W. N., *A short history of Chalmers Hospital* (Edinburgh, 1964).
Bowman, A. K., *The Life and Teaching of Sir William Macewen* (London, 1942).
Brand, Jeanne L., *Doctors and the State: the British medical profession and government action in public health 1870–1912* (Baltimore, 1965).
Brearley, Gibbons *et al., The Social Context of Health Care* (London, 1968).
Bridie, J., *One Way of Living* (London, 1939).
Briggs, A., 'Cholera and society in the nineteenth century', *Past and Present,* **XIX** (1960–1), 79–96.
British Medical Association, *The Book of Glasgow* (90th annual meeting) (Glasgow, 1922).
Brotherston, J. H. F., *Observations on the early public health movement in Scotland* (London, 1952).

'Change and the National Health Service' in *SMJ* **14**, 1969).

Bruce, M., *The Coming of the Welfare State* (London, 1968).

The rise of the Welfare State: English Social Policy 1601–1971 (London, 1973).

Buchanan, A., *Life of James Wallace Anderson, MD* (Glasgow, 1914).

Bynum, W., 'Rationales for therapy in British Psychiatry', *MH,* **18** (1974).

Cameron, Sir H. C., *Reminiscences of Lister* (Glasgow, 1927).

Carr-Saunders, A. M. and Wilson, P. A., *The Professions* (Oxford, 1933).

Cartwright, F. F., *Social History of Medicine* (London, 1977).

Chalmers, A. K. (ed.), *Public Health administration in Glasgow: a memorial volume of the writings of J. B. Russell (Glasgow, 1905).*

The Health of Glasgow 1818–1925: an outline (Glasgow, 1930).

Chambers, W. D., *A History of Murray Royal* (Perth, 1927).

Chapin, H. D., *The Theory and Practice of Infant Feeding* (London, New York, 1903), and Pisik, G. R., *Diseases of Infants and Children* (London, 1911).

Checkland, E. O. A., *Queen Margaret Union, 1890–1980* (Glasgow, 1980).

Philanthropy in Victorian Scotland (Edinburgh, 1980).

Cheney, C. O., 'Dorothea Lynde Dix' *American Journal of Psychiatry,* **100** (1944).

Cherry, S., 'The role of a provincial hospital; the Norfolk and Norwich Hospital 1771–1880', *Population Studies,* **26** (1972).

Chesler, P., *Women and Madness* (London, 1974).

Ciba Foundation Symposium 43 (n.s.), *Health Care in a Changing setting the U.K. experience* (Amsterdam, 1976).

Clarke, E., ed., *Modern Methods in the History of Medicine* (London, 1971).

Clarke, J. J., *Social Administration, including the Poor Laws* (London, 1973).

Cockburn, F., 'The prospect for paediatrics' in *Report of the Proceedings at the Opening of the James Nicoll Lecture Theatre, Department of Clinical Physics and Bio-Engineering* (University of Glasgow, 1980).

Cole, G. D. M. and Bourdillon, A. F. C., *Voluntary Social Services* (London, 1945).

Collins, E. T., *The History and Traditions of the Moorfields Eye Hospital* (London, 1929).

Comrie, J. D., *History of Scottish Medicine,* 2 vols (Edinburgh, 1927, 1932).

Cooper, D., *Psychiatry and anti-psychiatry* (London, 1967).

The death of the family (London, 1971).

Cormack, A. A., *District nursing in Scotland; Peterculter, Aberdeenshire* (n.p., 1965).

Susan Carnegie, 1744–1821, her life of service (Aberdeen, 1966).

Coutts, J., *A History of the University of Glasgow, 1451–1909* (Glasgow, 1909).

Cowan, J. M., *Some Yesterdays* (Glasgow, 1949).

Craig, Archibald (ed.), *The statue of Mrs John Elder, Govan . . . together with some account of the Elder Free Library, the Elder Cottage Hospital, and the Cottage Nurses' Training Home and an obituary notice of Mrs Elder* (Govan, 1912).

Craig, W. S., *Child and Adolescent life in Health and Disease* (Edinburgh 1946).

John Thomson: pioneer and father of Scottish paediatrics 1856–1926 (Edinburgh, 1968).

Craig, W. S., *The History of the Royal College of Physicians of Edinburgh* (Edinburgh, 1976).

Crathorne, N., *Tennants' Stalk* (London, 1973).

Creighton, C., *A History of Epidemics in Britain* (2nd edn), 2 vols (London, 1965).

Creswell, C. H., *The Royal College of Surgeons of Edinburgh* (Edinburgh, 1925).

Crossman, R. H. S., 'A Politician's View of Health Service Planning' (Maurice Bloch lecture, the University of Glasgow, 1972).

Cunnison, J. and Gilfillan, J. B. S. (ed.), *Third Statistical Account of Scotland: Glasgow* (Glasgow, 1958).

Curie, E., *Madame Curie* (London, 1938).

Davie, G. E., *The Democratic Intellect—Scotland and her Universities in the Nineteenth Century* (Edinburgh, 1961).

Deane, P., and Cole, W., *British Economic Growth 1688–1959* (Cambridge, 1967).

Devine, T. M., *The Tobacco Lords* (Edinburgh, 1975).

Dicey, A. V., *The Relationship between Law and Public Opinion in England* (London, 1905).

Dock, L., *A History of the nursing profession* (London, 1912).

Donnison, J., *Midwives and Medical Men* (London, 1977).

Downie, J. W., *The Early Physicians and Surgeons of the Western Infirmary Glasgow* (Glasgow, 1923).

Drummond, A. L. and Bulloch, J., *The Church in Victorian Scotland* (Edinburgh, 1975).

Drummond, J. C., *The English man's food; a history of five centuries of English diet* (London, 1939).

Dunlop, J. C., 'Misstatement of Age in the Returns of the Census of Scotland'. *JRSS,* **86** (1923).

Easterbrook, C. C., *Chronicle of Crichton Royal 1833–1936* (Dumfries, 1940).

Eaves-Walton, P. M., *The Royal Infirmary of Edinburgh, 1729–1900* (Edinburgh, 1968).

'Hospital Archives', *The Scottish Genealogist* (September, 1978).

Erskine, J., *Old Glasgow Hospitals* (Glasgow, 1905).

Evans, E. J., *Social Policy 1830–1914: Individualism, Collectivism and the origins of the Welfare State* (London, 1978).

Ewan, James, *The School Health Service* (Glasgow, n.d. but 1957).

Fergus, A. F., *The origin and development of the Glasgow School of Medicine* (Glasgow, 1911).

Ferguson, T., *The dawn of Scottish Social Welfare* (Edinburgh, 1948).

Scottish Social Welfare (1864–1914) (Edinburgh, 1958).

Ferrier, J., *The Greenock Infirmary 1806–1968* (Greenock, 1968).

Finzi, J., King, C., and Boover, D. (eds.), *Volunteers in Hospital* (London, 1971).

Fish, F., 'David Skae, MD, FRCS, founder of the Edinburgh School of Psychiatry', *MH,* **IX** (1965), 1.

Fish, F. J., *Outlines of psychiatry* (2nd edn) (Bristol, 1968).

Fisher, R. B., *Joseph Lister 1827–1912* (London, 1977).

Flinn, M. W. (ed.), *Report on the Sanitary Condition of the labouring population of Great Britain by Edwin Chadwick 1842* (Edinburgh, 1965).

Public health reform in Britain (London, 1968).

ed. *Scottish Population History* (Cambridge, 1977).

Foucault, M., *Madness and Civilisation* (New York, 1965).

Francis, H. W. S., 'The Records of Independent Contractors' in *The preservation of Medical and Public Health Records.* Wellcome Unit for the History of Medicine (Oxford, 1979).

Fraser, D., (ed.), *The New Poor Law in the Nineteenth Century* (London, 1976).

Friedson, E., *The Hospital in modern society* (New York, 1963).

Profession of Medicine (New York, 1970).

Gibson, G. A., *Life of Sir William Tennant Gairdner* (Glasgow, 1912).

Gibson, H. J. C., *The history of Dundee Royal Infirmary 1789–1948* (Dundee, 1948).

Glasser, O., *Wilhelm Conrad Röntgen and the early history of X-Rays* (London, 1933).

Godlee, R. J., *Lord Lister* (London, 1917).

Goffman, E., *Asylums: essays on the social situations of mental patients and other inmates* (London, 1961).

Gomme, A. and Walker, D., *The Architecture of Glasgow* (London, 1968).

Goodall, A. L., 'The Royal Faculty of Physicians and Surgeons of Glasgow.' *J. History of Medicine and Allied Sciences* (1955).

Gourvish, T. R., 'The cost of living in Glasgow in the early nineteenth century', *ECHR*, **XXVI** (1972).

Gray, A., 'Lord Blythswood FRS', *Nature* (1908).

Guthrie, D., 'Whither Medical History?', *MH1*, (1957).

Hamilton, B., 'The Medical Professions in the eighteenth century', *Economic History Review* (1951).

Hamilton, D. N. H., *The Healers. A history of Medicine in Scotland* (Edinburgh, 1981).

Handley, J. E., *The Irish in Scotland, 1798–1845* (2nd edn) (Cork, 1945). *The Irish in Modern Scotland* (Cork, 1947).

Heasman, K., *Evangelicals in Action* (London, 1962).

Henderson, D. and Gillespie, G., *Textbook of Psychiatry*. Rev. by I. Batchelor (10th edn) (Oxford, 1969).

Henderson, D. K., *The evolution of psychiatry in Scotland* (Edinburgh, 1964).

Henderson, T. B., *The History of Glasgow Dental Hospital and School 1879–1959* (Glasgow, 1960).

Hodgkinson, R. G., *The Origins of the National Health Service: the medical services of the New Poor Law, 1834–1871* (London, 1967).

Hollinshead, B. and Redlich, F., *Social Class and Mental Illness* (New York, 1958).

Horn, D. B., *Short History of Edinburgh University* (Edinburgh, 1967).

Horrobin, D., 'A singular solution for schizophrenia'. *New Scientist*, **85**, no. 1196 (1980).

Houghton, W. E., *The Victorian Frame of Mind* (London, 1957).

Howells, J. W. (ed.), *World History of Psychiatry* (London, 1975).

Huxley, E., *Florence Nightingale* (London, 1975).

Illich Ivan, *Limits to medicine: medical nemesis* (London, 1977).

Illingworth, Sir Charles, *Royal College of Physicians and Surgeons of Glasgow* (Glasgow, 1976).

Irving, G., *Dumfries and Galloway Royal Infirmary, the First Two Hundred Years 1776–1975* (Dumfries, 1975).

Jardine, M. B., *The Chapbook of the Rottenrow* (Glasgow, 1913).

Jefferson, G., *Sir William Macewen's contribution to Neuro-Surgery and its sequels* (Glasgow, 1950).

Jennett, B., 'Sir William Macewen, 1848–1924, pioneer Scottish neuro-surgeon', *Surgical Neurology*. **6**, no. **2** (August 1976), 57–60.

Jones, K., *Lunacy, Law and Conscience 1744–1845* (London, 1955). *History of the Mental Health Service* (London, 1972).

Kay, H. D., *John Boyd Orr: Baron Boyd Orr of Brechin Mearns 1880–1971*. Royal Society (London, 1972).

Kaye, G. W. C. in *X-Rays: an introduction to the study of Röntgen Rays* (London, 1914).

Kendall, R. E., 'The concept of disease and its implications for psychiatry'. *British Journal of Psychiatry,* **127** (1975).

Kennedy, Ian, *The Unmasking of Medicine* (London, 1981).

King, A. G., *Kelvin the Man* (London, 1925).

Laidlaw, S., *Glasgow Common Lodging Houses* (Glasgow 1956).

Laing, R. D., *The Divided Self* (London, 1959).

The Politics of Experience and The Bird of Paradise (Harmondsworth, 1967).

Laing, R. D. and Cooper, D., *Reason and Violence* (London, 1964).

Society, Madness and the family (London, 1972).

Larrabee, E., *The Benevolent and Necessary Institution, The New York Hospital 1771–1971* (New York, 1971).

Latham, A., *Pulmonary Consumption* (London, 1907).

Lee, A. and Sclare, A. B., *Psychiatry* (London, 1971).

Lefanu, W. R., *A list of the original writings of Joseph, Lord Lister OM,* (London, 1965).

Lewis, A., 'The Psychoses' in Beeson, P. and McDermott, W., *Cecil Loeg Textbook of Medicine* (London, 1963).

Lindsay, D. E., *Report upon a study of the diet of the labouring classes in the City of Glasgow carried out during 1911–1912, under the auspices of the Corporation of the City* (Glasgow, 1913).

Lindsay, J., *The Scottish Poor Law: Its Operation in the North East from 1745–1845* (Ilfracombe, 1975).

Lin, T. Y. and Standley, C. C., 'Scope of epidemiology in psychiatry', *Public Health papers No. 16, World Health Organisation* (1960).

Lister, J., *The collected papers of Joseph, Baron Lister* (London, 1909).

Lister centenary celebrations in Glasgow (Glasgow, 1927).

Longmate, N., *King Cholera: the biography of a disease* (London, 1966).

Alive and well (London, 1970).

Lythe, S. G. C. and Butt, J., *An economic history of Scotland* (Glasgow, 1975).

McAlpine, I. and Hunter, R., *Three Hundred Years of Psychiatry 1535–1860* (Oxford, 1962).

McDaniel, W. B., 'The place of the amateur in the writing of Medical History', *BIHM* (1939). 7.

McDonald, J. C. M., 'History of Dr Gray's Hospital, Elgin', *MH* (April, 1976).

Macewen, W., *The growth of bone* (Glasgow, 1912).

Macgregor, Sir A., *Public Health in Glasgow 1905–1946* (Edinburgh, 1967).

Macintyre, J., 'The new electrical pavilion of the Glasgow Royal Infirmary', *GMJ* (1902).

'The electrical pavilion, Glasgow Royal Infirmary'. *Archives of the Röntgen Ray* (1902).

'The new Medical Electrical Department of the Glasgow Royal Infirmary', *GMJ* (1914).

'The comparative value of X-rays and radium in the treatment of malignant growths', *Archives of the Röntgen Ray* (1914).

'Radium: question of a supply for Glasgow, collected opinions from workers at home and abroad', *GMJ* (1914).

'The modern developments of radium and X-ray therapeutics', *GMJ* (1917).

Mackay, G. A., *The Management and Construction of Poorhouses and Almshouses* (Edinburgh, 1908).

Mackenzie, W. L., 'The Administrative aspects of tuberculosis' in *Studies in Pathology*, ed. Bulloch, W. (Aberdeen, 1906)

Scottish Mothers and Children: being a report on the physical welfare of mothers and children. Carnegie UK Trust (Dunfermline, 1917).

McKeown, T., *Medicine in Modern Society* (London, 1965).

McKeown, T. and Brown, R. G., 'Medical evidence related to English population change in the eighteenth century'. *Population Studies,* **9** (1955).

McKeown, T. and Lowe, C. R., *An introduction to social medicine* (Oxford, 1966).

McKeown, T. and Record, R. G., 'Reasons for the decline of mortality in England and Wales during the nineteenth century', *Population Studies,* **16** (1962).

Mackie, J. D., *The University of Glasgow* (Glasgow 1954).

Mackie, W. A., 'A Sketch of Sir William Macewen'. *British Journal of Surgery,* **54** (1967).

Mackintosh, D. J., *Skiagraphic atlas of fractures and dislocations* (London, 1899).

McLachlan, G. (ed), *Medical Education and Medical Care: a Scottish American Symposium* (London, 1977).

McLeary, G. F., *Infantile Mortality and Infants' Milk depots* (London, 1905).
  Early history of the infant Welfare Movement (London, 1933).
  The Maternity and Child Welfare Movement (London, 1935).

McQueen, L. and Kerr, A. B., *The Western Infirmary, 1874–1974.* (Glasgow, 1974).

McVail, J. C., 'Dr John Borland', *GMJ* (Glasgow, 1923).

Manton, J. G., *Sister Dora. The Life of Dorothy Pattison* (London, 1971).

Massey, Arthur, *Modern Trends in Public Health* (New York, 1949).

Maylard, A. E., *Memories and Musings of a Hospital Surgeon* (Glasgow, 1920).
  Glasgow Infirmaries (Glasgow, 1933).

Mechie, S., *The Church and Scottish Social Development, 1780–1870* (Oxford, 1960).

Miller, J. D., 'William Macewen, master of surgery', *Virginia Medical,* **109** (1979).

Milne, G. P., 'History of Midwifery in Aberdeen', *MH* (April, 1978).

Mitchison, R., 'The Making of the Old Scottish Poor Law', *Past & Present* (1974).

Monro, J., 'Remarks on Dr Battie's treatise on Madness, 1758', reprinted in *Psychiatric Monographs,* series no. **3** (1962).

Morris, R. J., *Cholera 1832; the social response to an epidemic* (London, 1976).

Morton, R. S., 'Some aspects of the early history of Syphilis in Scotland', *British Journal of Venereal Disease* (1962).
  'The Sibbens of Scotland', *MH* (1967).
  Venereal Disease (London, 1972).

Mowat, C. L., 'The Approach to the Welfare State in Great Britain', *American Historical Review* (1952).
  The Charity Organisation Society (London, 1961).

Muir, James, *John Anderson . . . and the College he founded* (ed. James Macaulay) (Glasgow, 1950).

Murray, D., *Memories of the old College of Glasgow* (Glasgow, 1927).

Murray, I., *The Victoria Infirmary of Glasgow* (Glasgow, 1947).

Murray, N., *The Scottish handloom weavers* (Edinburgh, 1978).

Newman, C., *The Evolution of Medical Education in the Nineteenth Century* (Oxford, 1957).

Newsholme, Sir A., *International Studies on the Relation between the Private and Official Practice of Medicine* vol. III. *England and Wales, Scotland and Ireland* (London, 1931).

Oddy, D., and Miller D. (eds), *The making of the modern British diet* (London, 1976).

O'Neil, J. E., 'Finding a policy for the sick poor', *Victorian Studies* (1964).
Orr, J. B., *Food, Health and Income: Report on a survey of adequacy of diet in relation to Income* (London, 1936).
   Infant mortality in Scotland (HMSO, Edinburgh, 1943).
   As I recall (London, 1966).
Owen, D., *English Philanthropy, 1660–1960* (London, 1965).
Parry, N. and J., *The Rise of the Medical Profession* (London, 1976).
Parry-Jones, W., *The Trade in Lunacy* (London, 1972).
Paton, D. N. and Findlay, L., *Poverty nutrition and growth: Studies in child life in the cities and rural districts of Scotland.* Medical Research Council Special Report Series no. 101 (1926).
Patrick, J., *A short history of the Glasgow Royal Infirmary* (Glasgow, 1940).
Pattison, F. M. L., 'The Pattison-Miller quarrel', *SMJ,* **25,** 234–40 (1980).
Pavey, A., *The Story of the growth of Nursing* (London, 1938).
Pelling, M., *Cholera, Fever and English medicine 1825–1865* (Oxford, 1978).
Pennington, C. I., 'Mortality and medical care in nineteenth century Glasgow', *MH* (1979).
Peterson, M. Jeanne, *The Medical Profession in mid-Victorian London* (California, 1978).
Porter, I. A., *Alexander Gordon, MD of Aberdeen, 1752–1799* (Edinburgh, 1958).
Poynter, F. N. L. (ed), *The Evolution of Medical Practice in Britain* (London, 1961).
   The Evolution of Hospitals in Britain (London, 1964).
   Medicine and Science in the 1860s (London, 1968).
Poynter, F. N. L. and Keele, K. D., *A Short History of Medicine* (London, 1961).
Pryde, G., *Central and Local Government in Scotland* (London, 1960).
Reader, W. J., *Professional Men* (London, 1966).
Reid, J. M., *Glasgow* (London, 1956).
Reid, R., *Observations on the structure of Hospitals for the treatment of lunatics* (new edn) (London, 1964). Hunter, R. and Macalpine, E. (eds).
Riddell, W. J. B., *The Ophthalmic Institution 1868–1968* (Glasgow, 1968).
Robertson, D. J., 'Population Past and Present', in Cunnison, J. and Gilfillan, J. B. S. (eds), *Glasgow* (Third Statistical Account) (Glasgow, 1958).
Robertson, E., *The Yorkhill Story* (Glasgow, 1972).
Robertson, P. L., 'The finances of the University of Glasgow before 1914' in *History of Education Quarterly* (Winter, 1976).
Rose, M., *The relief of poverty* (London, 1972).
Rosen, G., *Madness in Society* (New York, 1968).
   From Medical Police to Social Medicine (New York, 1974).
Rosenberg, C., 'The Medical Profession, Medical Practice and the History of Medicine' in E. Clarke (ed), *Modern Methods in the History of Medicine* (London, 1971).
Rothman, D., *The discovery of the asylum* (Boston, 1971).
Rothstein, W. G., *American Physicians in the Nineteenth Century* (Baltimore, 1972).
Russell, J. B., Public Health Administration in Glasgow (ed. A. K. Chalmers) (Glasgow, 1905).
Sarton, G., 'The discovery of X-rays', *Isis* (1937).
Saunders, L. J., *Scottish Democracy* (Edinburgh, 1950).
Scrole, L., 'Urbanization and Mental health; some reformulations', *American Scientist,* **60,** 5 (1972).

Scull, A., *Museums of Madness* (London, 1979).

Shakespeare, W., *King Lear* (Oxford, 1975).

Sheman, J., *Voluntary Service in Seven Hospitals in Scotland* (Edinburgh, 1969).

Shepherd, M., 'Lunacy and labour', *Bulletin for the study of Labour History,* **34** (1977).

Shryock, R. H., 'Nineteenth Century Medicine', *Journal World History* (1957).

Sigerist, H. E., *History of Medicine* (London, 1951).

Sigsworth, E. M., 'Medicine, Hospitals and Mortality 1700–1850' in *Science and Society 1600–1900* (ed. Mathias, P.) (Cambridge, 1970).

Skultans, V., *Madness and morals: ideas on insanity in the nineteenth century* (London, 1975).

    English madness: ideas on insanity, 1580–1890 (London, 1979).

Slaven, A., *The development of the West of Scotland* (London, 1975).

Smith, F. B., *The People's Health 1830–1910* (London, 1979).

Smout, T. C., *A History of the Scottish people 1550–1830* (London, 1969).

Sorsby, A., 'Defunct London Eye Hospitals', *British Journal of Ophthalmology* (1936).

    'Nineteenth Century Provincial Eye Hospitals', *British Journal of Ophthalmology* (1946).

Spencer, J. A., *Management in Hospitals* (London, 1967).

Stalker, H., *Murthly Hospital 1864–1964: a Centenary History* (Perth, 1964).

Stansky, P., *The Victorian Revolution: Government and Society in Victoria's Britain* (New York, 1973).

Stocks, M., *A Hundred Years of District Nursing* (London, 1960).

Strong, R., *Reminiscences* (Edinburgh, 1935).

Szasz, T., *The Manufacture of Madness* (London, 1971).

    The Myth of Mental Illness (London, 1971).

Tait, A. C., 'History of Crichton Royal', *MH, XV* (1971).

Tait, H. P., *A Doctor and Two Policemen, the history of the Edinburgh health department, 1862–1974* (Edinburgh, 1974).

Talbott, J., 'Radical psychiatry', *American Journal of Psychiatry,* **131,** 2 (1974).

Temkin, O., 'An essay on the usefulness of Medical History for Medicine' in *BIHM* (London, 1946).

Thompson, E. P., *The making of the English working class* (London, 1968).

Thompson, J. D. and Goldin, G., *The Hospital: a Social and Architectural History* (New Haven, 1975).

Thomson, A. M. W., *The History of the Glasgow Eye Infirmary 1824–1962* (Glasgow, 1963).

    The life and times of Dr. William McKenzie, founder of Glasgow Eye Infirmary (Glasgow, 1973).

Tobias, J. J., *Crime and industrial society in the Nineteenth Century* (London, 1972).

Todd, M., *Sophia Jex-Blake* (London, 1918).

Treble, J. H., *Urban poverty in Britain 1830–1914* (London, 1979).

Tuke, S., *Description of the Retreat* (new edn), London 1964 (ed. Hunter, R. and Macalpine, I.).

Tully, A. M. T., 'Nutrition and economic conditions in Glasgow', *Lancet,* ii (1921).

    'A study of the diets and economic conditions of artisan families in Glasgow in May 1923', *GMJ* (January, 1924).

Tully, A. M. T. and Urie, E. M., 'A study of the diets and economic conditions of labour-class families in Glasgow in June 1922', *GMJ* (December, 1922).

Turner, A. L., (ed.), *Joseph, Baron Lister* (Edinburgh, 1927).
Turner, A. Logan, *Story of a Great Hospital, the Royal Infirmary of Edinburgh, 1729–1929* (Edinburgh, 1937).
Turner, G. G., *The Macewen outlook in Surgery* (Glasgow, 1939).
Underwood, E. A., *Boerhaave's Men at Leyden and After* (Edinburgh, 1977).
Waddington, Ivan, 'The development of medical ethics: a sociological analysis'. *MH* (1973).
    'The role of the hospital in the development of modern medicine: a sociological analysis', *Sociology* (1973).
Walsh, M. R., *Doctors wanted: no women need apply* (London, 1977).
Walton, J. K., 'Lunacy in the Industrial Revolution 1848–1850', *Journal of Social History* (Fall, 1979).
Watt, O. M., *Stobhill Hospital, the first seventy years* (Glasgow, 1971).
Webb, S. and B., *The State and the Doctor* (London, 1910).
Weeks, J., *Coming Out* (London, 1977).
Wilson, G. S. and Miles, A. (eds), *Topley and Wilson's Principles of Bacteriology, Virology and Immunity* (London, 1975).
Winter, J. M., 'Infant mortality, maternal mortality and public health in Britain in the 1930s', *Journal of European Economic History,* **8** (1979).
Wintrobe, T., *'Harrison' principles of internal medicine* (New York, 1974).
Wing, J. K., *Reasoning about madness* (Oxford, 1978).
Woodham Smith, C., *Florence Nightingale* (London, 1951).
Woodroofe, K., *From Charity to Social Work in England and the USA* (London, 1962).
Woodward, J., *To do the sick no harm: a study of the British Voluntary Hospital System to 1875* (London, 1974).
Woodward J. and Richards, D., *Health Care and Popular Medicine in England in the Nineteenth Century* (London, 1977).
Worsdall, F., *The tenement* (Edinburgh, 1979).
Young, A., *Sir William Macewen* (Glasgow, 1926).
    'Sir William Macewen and the Glasgow School of Surgery' *Surgery, Gynaecology and Obstetrics* (December, 1926).
Youngson, A. J., *The Scientific Revolution in Victorian Medicine* (London, 1979).
Zilboong and Henry, G. W., *A history of medical psychology* (New York, 1941).

Theses

Barclay, R. S., Some aspects of Fertility and Mortality in Scotland from 1855 to 1943 with special reference to Urban and Rural Environment (Edinburgh PhD, 1947).
Blackden, S. M., The Development of Public Health Administration in Glasgow 1842–1872 (Edinburgh PhD, 1976).
Cage, R. A., The Scottish Poor Law 1745–1845 (Glasgow PhD, 1974).
Dow, D. A., Domestic Response and Reaction to the Foreign Missionary Enterprises of the Principal Scottish Presbyterian Churches 1873–1929 (Edinburgh PhD, 1977).
Gaffney, R. H., The Development of Hospital Provision in Glasgow between 1867 and 1897 (Glasgow PhD, 1979).
Macdonald, H., Public Health Legislation and Problems in Victorian Edinburgh with special reference to Dr Littlejohn as Medical Officer of Health (Edinburgh PhD, 1971).

Paterson, A., A Study of Poor Relief Administration in Edinburgh City Parish between 1845–94 (Edinburgh PhD, 1974).

Pennington, C. I., Mortality, Public Health and Medical Improvements in Glasgow 1855–1911 (Stirling PhD, 1977).

Raffel, S. H., Records as Phenomena: The Nature and Uses of Medical Records (Edinburgh PhD, 1975).

Rice, F. J., Madness and Industrial Society: a study of the origin and early growth of the organisation of insanity in nineteenth century Scotland. (Strathclyde PhD, 1981).

Index

Figures in bold type indicate whole chapters or sections.
Alphabetical order: word-by-word, to first comma or colon.
Collected entries: INSTITUTIONS, SOCIETIES, STATUTES.
'bis' means twice; *'p'* means passim; *'n'* means note.